This is the most comprehensive anthology in English of 'Oulipo' writing, bringing together 100 pieces that celebrate the literary group who revelled in maths problems, puzzles, trickery, wordplay and conundrums. Featuring writers including Georges Perec, Raymond Queneau and Italo Calvino, it includes poems, short stories, word games and even recipes. Alongside these famous Oulipians are 'anticipatory' wordsmiths who crafted language with unusual constraints and literary tricks, from Jonathan Swift to Lewis Carroll. Philip Terry's playful selection is for all lovers of word games, puzzles and literary delights.

The Penguin Book of Oulipo

THE
PENGUIN BOOK
of

OULIPO

———

Edited by
PIIILIP TERRY

PENGUIN CLASSICS

UK | USA | Canada | Ireland | Australia
India | New Zealand | South Africa

Penguin Classics is part of the Penguin Random House group of companies
whose addresses can be found at global.penguinrandomhouse.com.

This collection first published 2019

001

Introduction and selection copyright © Philip Terry, 2019

The moral right of the introducer has been asserted

The acknowledgements on pp. 523–532 constitute an extension of this copyright page

Set in 11.25/14.75 pt Adobe Caslon Pro
Typeset by Jouve (UK), Milton Keynes
Printed and bound in Great Britain by Clays Ltd, Elcograf S.p.A.

A CIP catalogue record for this book is available from the British Library

ISBN: 978–0–241–37842–7

In memory of Harry Mathews and Stanley Chapman

Contents

Introduction by Philip Terry   xvii

1. HARRY MATHEWS
   35 Variations on a Theme from Shakespeare   1

2. JONATHAN SWIFT
   from *Gulliver's Travels*   5

3. RAYMOND QUENEAU
   A Hundred Thousand Billion Poems
   (translated by Stanley Chapman)   8

4. HENRY VASSALL-FOX, LORD HALLAND
   Eve's Legend   18

5. FRANÇOIS LE LIONNAIS
   Lipo: First Manifesto (translated by Warren Motte)   20

6. RAYMOND QUENEAU
   from *Exercises in Style (translated by Philip Terry)*   23

7. JOE BRAINARD
   from *I Remember*   29

8. ITALO CALVINO
   The Waverer's Tale (translated by William Weaver)   31

9. PAUL FOURNEL
   from *Suburbia (translated by Harry Mathews)*   39

10. JACQUES ROUBAUD
    from *The Form of a City Changes Faster, Alas,*
    Than the Human Heart
    (translated by Keith and Rosmarie Waldrop)   52

11. MICHÈLE MÉTAIL
    Cross-Examination   68

12. GEORGES PEREC
    from *A Void (translated by Gilbert Adair)*   70

13. STEFAN THEMERSON
    from *Bayamus*   75

14. LEWIS CARROLL
    from *Alice's Adventures in Wonderland*   80

15. MICHELLE GRANGAUD
    from *Poets' Calendar (translated by Cole Swensen)*   88

16. GEORGE PEREC
    81 Easy-Cook Recipes for Beginners
    (translated by David Bellos)   97

17. JORGE LUIS BORGES
    The Garden of Forking Paths
    (translated by Andrew Hurley)   112

18. THIERI FOULC
    New Observations on Harry Mathews's Face   122

19. FRANÇOIS RABELAIS
    from *Gargantua and Pantagruel*
    (translated by Sir Thomas Urquhart)   123

20. ITALO CALVINO
    The Burning of the Abominable House
    (translated by Tim Parks)   129

21. RAYMOND QUENEAU
    Redundancy in Phane Armé
    (translated by Philip Terry)   141

22. JACQUES JOUET
    from *The Great-Ape Love-Song*
    (translated by Iain White)   146

23. CHRISTIAN BÖK
    from *Eunoia*   155

24. ANNE GARRÉTA
    from *Sphinx (translated by Emma Ramadan)*   158

25. RAYMOND QUENEAU
    from *The Foundations of Literature (After
    David Hilbert) (translated by Harry Mathews)*   164

26. MICHÈLE AUDIN
    from *One Hundred Twenty-One Days
    (translated by Christiana Hills)*   170

27. ROBERT DESNOS
    from *Rrose Sélavy (translated by Timothy Adès)*   174

28. GEORGES PEREC
    Think / Classify (translated by John Sturrock)   176

29. MARCEL BÉNABOU
    from *One Aphorism Can Hide Another
    (translated by Philip Terry)*   193

30. HARRY MATHEWS
    from *Trial Impressions*   196

31. LUCRETIUS
    from *The Poem On Nature
    (translated by C. H. Sisson)*   205

32. OSCAR PASTIOR
    from *A Small Artistic Machine (translated by
    Harry Mathews and Christopher Middleton)*   207

33. MICHELLE GRANGAUD
    from *Forms of the Anagram
    (translated by Paul and Rosemary Lloyd)*   215

34. ALFRED JARRY
    from *Exploits and Opinions of Dr Faustroll,
    Pataphysician (translated by Simon Watson Taylor)*   217

35. from *The Psalms*
    (translated by Mary Herbert and Gordon Jackson) 221

36. GEORGES PEREC
    from *Life A User's Manual Chapter Fifty-one*
    (translated by David Bellos) 224

37. HERVÉ LE TELLIER
    from *Atlas Inutilis (translated by Cole Swensen)* 232

38. GEORGES PEREC
    from *I Remember (translated by Philip Terry)* 243

39. MATT MADDEN
    from *99 Ways To Tell A Story* 247

40. PHILIPPE MOUCHÈS
    The Reapers + seven seconds 251

41. HARRYETTE MULLEN
    Variation on a Theme Park 252

42. FRANÇOIS LE LIONNAIS
    Second Manifesto (translated by Warren Motte) 253

43. IAN MONK
    Spies in Newquay 257

44. HARRY MATHEWS
    Their Words, For You 260

45. DAN RHODES
    from *Anthropology* 279

46. ITALO CALVINO
    from *Invisible Cities*
    (translated by William Weaver) 282

47. HARRY MATHEWS
    from *The Orchard* 287

48. CHRISTOPHER SMART
    from *Jubilate Agno* 290

49. YIN ZHONGKAN
    Reversible Inscription
    (translated by Jody Gladding)   292

50. RAYMOND QUENEAU
    from *Elementary Morality*
    (translated by Philip Terry)   294

51. VALÉRIE BEAUDOUIN
    Body/Machine (translated by Philip Terry)   298

52. JACQUES ROUBAUD
    from *Exchanges On Light*
    (translated by Eleni Sikelianos)   300

53. JACKSON MAC LOW
    from *The Complete Light Poems*   309

54. FRÉDÉRIC FORTE
    from *Minute-Operas (translated by Ian Monk
    and Daniel Levin Becker)*   311

55. CHRISTOPHER MIDDLETON
    from *Pataxanadu*   323

56. GEORGES PEREC
    A Winter Journey (translated by John Sturrock)   326

57. FRANÇOIS CARADEC
    The Worm's Journey (translated by Ian Monk)   332

58. HUGO VERNIER
    Hell's Journey (translated by Ian Monk)   345

59. LEE ANN BROWN
    from *Polyverse*   352

60. BERNADETTE MAYER
    Before Sextet   356

61. JEREMY OVER
    from *Deceiving Wild Creatures*   358

62. RENÉ VAN VALCKENBORCH
from *Roomstanzas: Quennets for Floor,
4 Walls and Ceiling* 360

63. PAUL FOURNEL
American Terines (translated by Rachel Galvin) 362

64. JACQUES ROUBAUD
Is Le Pen French? (translated by Guy Bennett) 365

65. HERVÉ LE TELLIER
from *A Thousand Pearls (For A Thousand
Pennies) (translated by Ian Monk)* 366

66. MICHÈLE MÉTAIL
from *Toponym: Berlin (translated by Susan Wicks)* 369

67. ÉTIENNE LÉCROART
from *Vanity (translated by Philip Terry)* 376

68. JACQUES ROUBAUD
from *Mathematics (translated by Ian Monk)* 384

69. GEORGES PEREC
from *Life A User's Manual Chapter Sixty
(translated by David Bellos)* 387

70. JULIANA SPAHR
from *HR 4881 is a Joke* 394

71. LILY ROBERT-FOLEY
from *Graphemachine* 397

72. PHILIP TERRY
Exercises in Translation 400

73. GEORGES PEREC
*Memory of a Trip to Thouars
(translated by Philip Terry)* 406

74. GEORGE HERBERT
Eaſter Wings 410

75. RICHARD BEARD
    from *Lazarus is Dead*   412

76. ITALO CALVINO
    The Name, The Nose
    (translated by William Weaver)   414

77. M. NOURBESE PHILIP
    from *Zong!*   425

78. JACQUES ROUBAUD
    from *Saying Poetry*
    (translated by Matthew B. Smith)   428

79. ITALO CALVINO
    from *If on a Winter's Night a Traveller*
    (translated by William Weaver)   432

80. GEORGES PEREC
    from *W or The Memory of Childhood*
    (translated by David Bellos)   435

81. LYN HEJINIAN
    from *My Life*   442

82. HOMER
    from *The Iliad (translated by Robert Fagles)*   444

83. RAYMOND QUENEAU
    from *Elementary Morality*
    (translated by Philip Terry)   447

84. ALICE OSWALD
    from *Memorial*   451

85. ALINE GAGNAIRE
    Orgy   453

86. RICHARD LONG
    from *Dartmoor*   454

87. RAYMOND QUENEAU
   A Tale for Your Shaping
   (translated by Harry Gilonis) 455

88. ANNE GARRÉTA
   from *Not One Day (translated by*
   Emma Ramadan and Anne Garréta) 458

89. GILBERT ADAIR
   from *Memories* 463

90. TOM JENKS
   from *The Tome of Commencement* 465

91. OLIVIER SALON
   from *Fugues (translated by Philip Terry)* 469

92. ÉDOUARD LEVÉ
   from *Works (translated by Jan Steyn)* 472

93. JACQUES CARELMAN
   from *Exercises in Style* 475

94. RAYMOND ROUSSEL
   from *How I Wrote Some Of My Books*
   (translated by Philip Terry) 476

95. GEORGES PEREC
   A Little Illustrated ABC
   (translated by Philip Terry) 479

96 INGER CRISTENSEN
   from *alphabet (translated by Susanna Nied)* 486

97. PAUL GRIFFITHS
   let me tell you 492

98. GEORGES PEREC
   Sentimental Tales
   (translated by Harry Mathews) 495

99. FRÉDÉRIC FORTE
   from *Flat Sonnets*
   (translated by Emma Ramadan)   497

100. CHRISTINE BROOKE-ROSE
   from *Next*   505

Notes   509

Index of Constraints   515

Acknowledgements   521

Permission Credits   523

Introduction

Anticipatory Plagiarism

The *Ouvroir de littérature potentielle* (Workshop of Potential Literature or, in Stanley Chapman's words, Knitting Circle of Potential Literature) was founded in 1960 by Raymond Queneau and François Le Lionnais, with the aim of exploring the benefits of mathematics and rule-based constraints for the writing of literature. One of Oulipo's distinctions, as David Bellos has argued,[1] is its long history – in its over five decades it has already endured far longer than any other structured group in the history of French literature. Yet, long before Oulipo came into existence, its methods were already being used by writers and artists across the globe. One well-known constraint associated with Oulipo, the lipogram, where a text is written without the use of certain predetermined letters, has a long history, stretching back to the *grands rhétoriqueurs* of sixteenth-century France, and even further back, to rhetorical games played by the Romans and the Greeks. In China, from as early as the third century, a tradition of reversible poems flourished, which reached its apotheosis in the work of Su Hui, who embroidered a grid of 840 characters on silk that could be read in an estimated 12,000 ways. There are the sonnets of Petrarch and Dante, acrostics concealed in the Psalms, the formally complex sestinas of Arnaut Daniel, structured around the permutation of six end-words, and a host of other formal devices and rhetorical structures from the accumulative lists of Homer and Rabelais, to the calligrams of George Herbert and the alphabetical verses of Christopher Smart's *Jubilate Agno*. Part of Oulipo's project, from its inception, which they called 'anoulipism', was to study the literature of the past to discover formal constraints which could be used in the present, and writers who used such methods they called, not without a sense of humour, 'anticipatory plagiarists'. One perhaps unexpected example of anticipatory plagiarism, of English origin, is to be found in the call changes used by bellringers, whose permutational scores echo the patternings found in the sestina and related forms so beloved of Oulipo. Other important anticipatory plagiarists include Leibniz, for his work on combinatorial mathematics, and, among those included here, Jorge Luis Borges, whose bifurcating narratives anticipate Oulipo's own storytelling experiments (bifurcation is key to the structure of Roubaud's *Mathematics*, for example), Lewis Carroll, and Jonathan Swift, who in *Gulliver's Travels* imagined one of the first writing machines.

Bourbaki

Oulipo, when it was founded, didn't come out of the blue. Queneau had long been interested in structure and mathematics, and he had been an active member of the surrealists, with whom he shared an interest in the unconscious and dreams, though he gradually moved away from this group and its argumentative founder, André Breton. On one level, Oulipo was Queneau's riposte to the surrealists, for if surrealism maintains that writing can be released by the access given to the unconscious in 'automatic writing', Queneau quickly saw that the products of such a process were often the same. By replacing the unconscious with constraint and structure, and thereby enacting a return to neoclassicism, Queneau was proposing that rules are required to facilitate the expression of the truly individual self. Another key influence on Oulipo, often overlooked in accounts in English, is the avant-garde group of mathematicians Bourbaki. For Jacques Roubaud, it is the link to Bourbaki and mathematics that accounts for much of Oulipo's radical originality, by providing it with a counter-model to the surrealist group. As Roubaud writes: 'There can be no doubt that, when they founded Oulipo, Queneau and Le Lionnais, amateur mathematicians as they were, had this group in mind.'[2] Bourbaki, a secretive group, aimed to rewrite mathematics and provide it with solid foundations using a single source, Set Theory, and a rigorous system, the Axiomatic Method. For Roubaud, the Oulipo 'translates' Bourbaki into the domain of arts and language, while maintaining that its methods should not be taken to exclude the validity of other approaches. So the members of Oulipo include: (i) writers; (ii) mathematicians; (iii) writer-mathematicians; and (iv) mathematician-writers. When Oulipo began, like Bourbaki it was a semi-clandestine group, though under the influence of Queneau and some younger members it gradually threw off this restriction; it is also, like Bourbaki (and like surrealism) given to collaborative work.

Constraint

The most common description of Oulipo is that it explores constraint-based writing methods. Thus Roubaud writes: 'The aim of Oulipo is to invent (or reinvent) constraints of a formal nature (*contraintes*) and propose them to enthusiasts interested in composing literature.' The word 'constraint', however, while it is hard to find a better single-word substitute, is arguably inadequate to bear the weight of the variety of techniques and approaches explored by Oulipo. So Ian Monk writes: 'personally I dislike the word "constraint" which to me sounds too negative given that the general aim of the group's writers is to find ways to extend their artistic possibilities, not just to pull off extraordinary verbal stunts, which is more the domain of various loose groups who orbit around us.'[3] Monk prefers to use terms like 'structure', 'form' or 'technique', words which are echoed in some of the earliest documents relating to Oulipo. One should certainly add to this the term 'translation', for many Oulipian texts, like translations, transform already existing texts, and Oulipo can be credited with inventing the term 'homolinguistic translation' to describe translation from, say, French into French. Hidden behind the word 'constraint' three principal methods stand out: (i) strict constraints, such as writing without the letter 'e', as in Perec's novel *La disparition* (*A Void*), or the constraints of form involved in fixed-form poetries; (ii) what Oulipo refer to as 'combinatorial literature', as in Raymond Queneau's *Cent mille milliards de poèmes* (*A Hundred Thousand Billion Poems*); and (iii) techniques of transforming or 'translating' existing texts, such as their famous N+7 method, where all nouns are changed by going on seven places in a dictionary: 'To be, or not to be, that is the quiche.'

Dossier 17 of the College of 'Pataphysics

When Oulipo was first set up it became a sub-commission of the College of 'Pataphysics at the request of Raymond Queneau, and its first collective publication, *Exercices de Littérature Potentielle* (*Exercises in Potential Literature*), was published as Dossier 17 of the College. Here, in the 'First Manifesto', François Le Lionnais argues that all literature is subject to 'constraints' and 'procedures' – the three unities of classical tragedies for example – and he announces the goal of Oulipo as being to explore and discover new possibilities for writing in this domain with the aid of computers and mathematics. 'Anoulipism', as we've seen, denotes the analytical tendency in Oulipo, analysing the literature of the past to discover already-existing constraints; 'synthoulipism' describes the 'essential vocation' of Oulipo, the invention of new constraints. The rest of the collection contains Oulipo's first experiments: examples of the N+7 method (a particular case of the W±N method, where 'W' stands for any word, 'N' for any number); Queneau's 'Redundancy in Phanc Armé', where he removes all but a handful of words at the end of the lines in sonnets by Mallarmé to create new poems (a technique which has much in common with that of 'erasure' practised in, for example, Tom Phillips' treated Victorian text *A Humument*); Le Lionnais's 'Attempts at the Limit', where he reduces a poem to a single word ('Fenouil' or 'Fennel'), a single letter ('T.'), and writes a poem based on punctuation (ideas which would later influence other Oulipians of minimalist persuasion, like Michèle Métail); and Bourbaki-inspired excursions based on set theory such as the idea of the 'intersective novel', a genre which takes its vocabulary from the shared lexicons of two different novels. Today, Oulipo is completely independent from the College of 'Pataphysics, and some members of Oulipo have little or no connection to the College, but it continues to have a subliminal influence on the work of the group. One thing which profoundly links the two groups together is the symbol of the spiral or *gidouille* – it is not only the symbol *par excellence* of 'Pataphysics, appearing as it does on Ubu's chest, but it is the central symbol of Italo Calvino's *Cosmicomics*, and its circling motion describes the Fibonacci sequence and suggests the intricate patternings of the sestina, a form of central importance to the thinkings of Oulipo. And if you want to relinquish membership the bizarre ritual is nothing if not pataphysical: suicide in the presence of an officer of the court who must ascertain that in the Oulipian's last wishes they were committing suicide to be released from Oulipo.

Elementary Morality

Among the examples of 'synthoulipism' that stand out is the poetic form which has come to be known as the 'elementary morality' after Queneau's 1975 volume of the same title. David Bellos describes the form as follows:

> Three two-line stanzas, line 1 of each consisting of three phrases
> and line 2 of one phrase, each formed by a noun-adjective pair
> <u>followed by</u>
> Seven lines of at least two and not more than seven syllables
> <u>followed by</u>
> One two-line stanza conforming to the same constraint as at the start[4]

Queneau created the form out of the least Oulipian of all poetic sources – inspiration – but he noted in his diary that the form could be used to 'do Oulipo'. Queneau first named the form *lipolepse* (from the Greek for 'leaving out' and 'taking in'), but Oulipo have come to refer to the form more familiarly as the 'elementary morality' or, on occasions, the 'quennet', as it has one more line than the sonnet. While it has not yet become the canonical form that the sonnet is, it has been used and adapted by many writers both inside and outside Oulipo, including the present author, and several examples of the form are included here, from those of Queneau, Valérie Beaudouin and Frédéric Forte to English versions by Robert Sheppard, writing as René Van Valckenborch.

Foulipo

See under *Noulipo*.

Georges Perec

'One of the most singular literary personalities in the world', is how the Italian fabulist and fellow-Oulipian Italo Calvino once described Georges Perec. And while Perec was already an accomplished writer before he was co-opted by the Oulipo in March 1967 – his novel *Things* had won the Prix Renaudot in 1965 – his encounter with the Oulipo was explosive and played a major part in launching Oulipo onto the world stage. Perec's e-less novel, *La disparition* (*A Void*), appeared in 1969; and his monumental *Life A User's Manual*, where an invented Parisian apartment block is divided into squares like a chess board, and the order of chapters determined by the moves of a knight across the board (which is only to scratch the surface of the constraints Perec employed here) appeared in 1978, winning the Prix Médicis.

Heteromorphism

Oulipo, however, cuts across genres, and much of Perec's brilliance is not to be found in the novels he became famous for, but in his almost uncanny versatility: before his early death from lung cancer in 1982, Perec had composed uniquely dazzling essays on topics from spectacles to meditations on place, voluminous collections of poems based on constraints of his own devising, plays and film scripts, the longest palindrome in the French language (or any other language, for that matter), which gained him an entry in the *Guinness Book of Records*, memoirs such as *W or The Memory of Childhood* and *I Remember* (a uniquely French take on Joe Brainard's book of the same title), and many beguiling shorter texts, such as the brief story *The Winter Journey*, a parable of 'anticipatory plagiarism'. If Oulipo is an exploration of 'potential literature' – in the sense of creating new possibilities for literature – it is fair to say that this potential was realized nowhere more so than in the figure of Georges Perec. Yet Perec was as aware as anybody that Oulipian methods in themselves were no guarantee of artistic success. In *Life A User's Manual* the painter Hutting devises an elaborate formula for his portraits, where colour is dictated by the date and time of the painting's 'birth' and the phase of the moon at the painting's 'conception': 'The system's impersonality,' Perec writes, 'was the kind of thing to captivate Hutting. But perhaps because he applied it too rigidly, he obtained results more disconcerting than captivating.'

Italo Calvino

Co-opted by Oulipo in 1973, though his awarenesss of Oulipo dates to somewhat earlier, Calvino brought a wealth of experience as a writer to Oulipo, and his own writing took on a new turn as he increasingly experimented with potential literature, with the production of a number of books of an explicitly Oulipian nature, including *The Castle of Crossed Destinies*, which conjures stories of high adventure out of combinations of tarot cards, and *If on a Winter's Night a Traveller*, which gently satirises Oulipo in its invented New York collective the OEPHLW (Organization for the Electronic Production of Homogenized Literary Works).[5] In his 1967 lecture 'Cybernetics and Ghosts' Calvino states that: 'writing is purely and simply a process of combination among given elements.' This approach to storytelling, where story elements are combined and recombined to generate all the possible outcomes of a narrative, is present in many of Calvino's stories, from his computer-driven combinatorial detective story 'The Burning of the Abominable House', which Calvino presented to the Oulipo in November 1972, to his meta-story 'The Count of Monte Cristo', but it perhaps has its origins in his work on the traditional tales he collected in his monumental volume *Italian Folktales*. Here Calvino learnt how tellers of folktales could recombine a set of given elements in an almost infinite variety of ways to create the warp and woof of the world's stories. The storyteller's instinct to rearrange and improvise on a given theme is echoed in Le Lionnais's 'Second Manifesto', where he notes: 'Who has not felt, in reading a text . . . the need to improve it through a little judicious retouching?' From this perspective, Oulipo's interest in reframing, retelling, and translating stories – whether by the N+7 method or otherwise – appears less as a new and avant-garde departure for literature, but rather as a return to its roots, and it suggests too why the idea of the 'knitting circle', suggested in the word 'ouvroir', should have such importance for Oulipo, reminding us as it does of the domestic scenes which formed the backdrop to the recounting of so many folk tales.

Jeux de Mots

Wordplay can hardly be claimed as an invention of Oulipo, but many of Oulipo's anticipatory plagiarists, such as Lewis Carroll and Raymond Roussel, stand out for their exuberant and audacious wordplay. Perec's *I Remember* (and this is one of the things which makes translation difficult) is full of memories of jokes involving multiple puns, such as: 'Why do musicians get up late?' 'Because of the Partita 4 in D Flat.' (In French: 'Pourquoi les filles du Nord sont-elles précoces?' 'Parce que le concerto en sol mineur.') It's not hard to see how Oulipo's concept of 'homophonic translation' – where sound remains constant as sense changes – developed out of this interest, though here as elsewhere there are numerous anticipatory plagiarisms, notably Louis Zukovsky's homophonic translation of Catullus. Perec was one of the great and obsessive masters of this form, and in his homophonic texts such as 'A Little Illustrated ABC' he pushed it to the limit, using homophonic translation to create miniature story machines.

Kick-Starts

Another Oulipian method which functions as a text generator, as well as a gentle constraint, is the *'texte à démarreur'* or 'kick-start'. Perec's *I Remember*, where each numbered memory begins with the phrase 'I remember . . .', is the best-known example of this. Perec borrowed the form from New York artist Joe Brainard, and he was not the only writer to pick up on it: Ted Berrigan wrote a poem with the same title for his collection *Easter Monday* beginning 'I remember painting "I HATE TED BERRIGAN" in big black letters all over my white wall.' Other New York School writers like Kenneth Koch had also experimented with similar repetitive forms,[6] but Oulipo have made this form their own over the years. Anyone can write 'I remembers', and so Perec, in the first edition of his book, left a number of pages blank for the reader to write their own memories. Since its publication many others have tried their hand at the form, both inside and outside Oulipo, including Harry Mathews, who wrote *The Orchard* on the occasion of Perec's death. And Oulipo have rung the changes on the idea, with other kick-starts like 'I forget . . .', 'Where did I read . . .', 'Perhaps you're one of those who . . .', and 'I was thinking . . .', which Hervé Le Tellier turned into his book-length sequence *A Thousand Pearls (for a Thousand Pennies)*, while Étienne Lécroart has adopted the form in his strip-cartoon sequence *Vanity*.

Lucretius

Lucretius' *De Rerum Natura* (*The Poem on Nature*) supplied Oulipo with one of its key concepts in the 'clinamen', Lucretius' Latin for the Greek *klesis*, 'a bending'. The term was rescued from obscurity by Alfred Jarry, who used it for the name of his Painting Machine in his novel *Life and Opinions of Dr Faustroll, Pataphysician*. For Oulipo, it represents a moment when a particular constraint is broken, usually for aesthetic reasons – but it is something which should only be used when it is also possible to complete the writing task without breaking the constraint, and it is something which should be used sparingly. In Perec's *Life A User's Manual* each chapter describes one of the visible spaces in a building with 100 such spaces, but the novel contains only 99 chapters. Perec's missing chapter is the clinamen. For Lucretius, the term has a specific sense, referring to the spontaneous deviation that allows atoms falling in otherwise parallel lines through the void to collide with one another and thus create matter. Without the clinamen, in other words, there is no creation. Elsewhere in his argument, Lucretius likens atoms and letters, arguing that just as small changes in atomic structure can alter the nature of matter, so small changes in words can alter sense, as in the words 'fir' and 'fire'. All of a sudden, Lucretius' description of the creation of matter starts to sound uncannily like a description of Oulipian wordplay, and from this perspective clinamen can be seen to describe not just creative deviation from a rule, but the creative swerve involved in any textual manipulation, such as the N+7 method or homophonic translation.

Some recent, and some not so recent, work from Oulipo reveals a growing tendency to push the use of clinamen to the limit. Forte's *Minute-Operas* explores a variety of fixed forms, but each constraint is disrupted and set in motion by a vertical line separating 'stage' and 'wings'; Anne Garréta's *Not One Day* carefully sets its constraints in its opening (reproduced here), only to serially abandon them as her book progresses, as if desire itself was something always in flight from constraint; while in *Saying Poetry* Jacques Roubaud, usually the strictest of Oulipians, appears to abandon constraint altogether, giving himself over to chance (there is even a nod to John Cage) and an open field poetics reminiscent of Charles Olson.

Mathematics

Remaining ever open to new possibilities in verbal art, Oulipo have on the whole resisted attempts to systematically categorize constraints. Yet mathematics, while it does not underpin every constraint – the lipogram, for example, is not mathematical – has played a key role in their thinking. It is a mathematical discovery, the creation of a 10 × 10 Græco-Latin bi-square, which underpins the machinery of *Life A User's Manual*, and mathematics also plays a role in the N+7 method as it does in the combinatorial art of Queneau's *A Hundred Thousand Billion Poems*, and the novel *One Hundred Twenty-One Days* by mathematician-writer Michèle Audin, Chapter IX of which is structured entirely around numbers. Mathematics, too, underpins those Oulipian constraints which either shrink or expand existing texts, such as 'haikuization' or 'slenderizing', and *'tireur à la ligne'* or 'larding', where the scale of the text is altered, techniques which in turn take us back to the games with scale practised by some of Oulipo's most important anticipatory plagiarists, such as Jonathan Swift, in 'A Voyage to Lilliput' and 'A Voyage to Brobdingnag', and François Rabelais, in *Gargantua and Pantagruel*. And it is mathematics which, above all, has led Oulipo to create and develop new forms.

*

Oulipo's collective work on the sestina is one of the clearest examples of this. From Arnaut Daniel, its inventor, to John Ashbery in the twentieth century, the sestina has remained a constant and enduring form, and the structure of the end-words of its six stanzas has been governed by the following pattern: 1-2-3-4-5-6, 6-1-5-2-4-3, 3-6-4-1-2-5, and so on up to the final stanza, 2-4-6-5-3-2. It took Queneau to make the imaginative leap that conceived of sestina-like poems with stanzas of different lengths, which he named queninas. In the sestina, no end-words occupy the same position twice, and Queneau noted that this only remained the case with a select group of numbers, the first few being: 1, 2, 3, 5, 6, 9, 11, 14 and 18. As Ian Monk writes: 'Arnaut Daniel's experiment with poetic form had thus led to the discovery of a new sequence of numbers, now known as "Queneau numbers", one of whose main characteristics is that they obey the following formula: $2q + 1 = p$ (any Queneau number multiplied by 2, plus 1, always produces a prime number . . . thus, if there really is an infinite number of primes, there is also an infinite number of Queneau numbers). Queneau observed that a vast field of research had been opened up.'[7]

New York School

Asked in interview what the connection was between Oulipo and the New York School, Harry Mathews replied: 'There is no connection, except for me.'[8] Mathews knew of at least one other connection, in Joe Brainard's *I Remember*, which he had described to Perec, but beyond that there are other connections, in the work of John Ashbery, for example, who had revealed to Mathews the method of antonymic translation which became associated with Oulipo,[9] and in the work of Ron Padgett, who had experimented with games involving noun substitution long before he became acquainted with Oulipo. This synchronicity between the interests of the New York School poets and those of Oulipo can best be explained by their shared interests in the work of Duchamp and the French surrealists, and in the work of Oulipian anticipatory plagiarists such as Robert Desnos and Raymond Roussel. This was enough to ensure that as Oulipian ideas reached the US, often via Harry Mathews, they got a warm reception, even if sometimes, too, there was an accompanying sense of déjà vu. New York School poet Bernadette Mayer, who had taught poetry workshops at St Mark's, was one of the significant figures besides Mathews to actively disseminate Oulipian ideas across the US poetry community, teaching Charles Bernstein and Bruce Andrews among the Language poets, who in turn talked about Oulipo to Harryette Mullen among others.

Noulipo

A watershed in the Oulipian influence on the US took place at the California Institute of the Arts Noulipo conference in 2005, the purpose of which was to examine the legacy of Oulipian constraint-based writing among Anglophone writers, including Bernadette Mayer, Harryette Mullen, Juliana Spahr and Christian Bök, the central figure in a cluster of Canadian conceptualists given to Oulipian experiment. The idea of Noulipo, and its specifically feminist off-shoot, Foulipo, stood for a particular North American concept of Oulipo, which unlike Oulipo itself, proposed a more politically engaged use of constraint writing, exemplified in Juliana Spahr's 'HR 4811 is a joke', which attacks US anti-abortion legislation. At the conference, some Oulipian eyebrows were raised, but if Oulipo's purpose is to propose constraints that writers outside Oulipo are free to use in any way they want, then the possibility that writers will use constraints in ways that Oulipo themselves might not remains a constant possibility. And yet, if Oulipo itself remains unaffiliated politically as a group, individual members of Oulipo, including Jacques Roubaud and Georges Perec, have produced highly charged writings that are, in the broadest sense, nothing if not political.

Ou-x-pos

Working with Oulipo, as we have seen, Perec was able to produce not only a vast body of work, but a body of work in vastly different areas, stretching from novels to films and theatre, to cooking and music. Perec, without doubt, was a uniquely versatile writer, but his successes in writing recipes in his '81 Easy-Cook Recipes for Beginners', and in writing experimental music in his 'Memory of a Trip to Thouars' (to write 'musique aléatoire', Perec had joked, 'il faut aller à Thouars'), demonstrates that Oulipian methods can be applied to other fields beyond the literary. Perec's one excursion into music is interesting on several accounts. For one thing, if constraint is one possible way among many to go about writing, with musical composition it is something that it is almost impossible to do without, and many of the great advances in twentieth-century music, such as serialism, were effectively experiments with constraint. It is also interesting because Queneau explicitly argued that Oulipo was not an 'aleatory' movement. And yet, music that is composed using chance procedures, such as the music of John Cage, remains curiously close to Oulipo at times – perhaps because 'chance', viewed from another perspective, is not chance at all, but the exploration of a possible series of permutations, and it is notable here that both Queneau (in the prose poems in *Elementary Morality*) and Cage (in *Music of Changes*, as elsewhere) used the *I Ching*.

This insight concerning the wider applications of Oulipo was formalized by François Le Lionnais, who invented the acronym Ou-x-po to designate the generality of possible groups, where 'x' designates the field in question, and since the foundation of Oulipo these new groups, both official and unofficial, long- and short-lived, have continued to proliferate, and include: Ouarchipo (architecture), Oubapo (*bandes déssinées* or strip cartoons), Oucarpo (cartography), Oucuipo (cuisine), Ouhispo (history), Oulipopo (*romans policiers* or crime fiction), Oumumpo (music), Oupeinpo (*peinture* or painting), Ouphopo (photography), Oupolpot (politics), Ousonmupo (*son et musique* or sound and music), Outranspo (translation), Outrapo (tragicomedy), and Ouvipo (video). Each group goes its own way with Oulipian ideas: in Oupeinpo, for example, Philippe Mouchès adapts the N+7 method by moving the action of famous paintings forward by seven seconds, while in the Oubapo Étienne Lécroart and Jean-Christophe Menu have adapted the Oulipian method of *tireur à la ligne* or larding by progressively expanding a cartoon by the systematic insertion of new frames. Many of the Ou-x-pos are represented here, some by members of the Ou-x-po in question, some by Oulipians or outsiders with parallel interests, including: Oubapo (in the work of Étienne

Lécroart and Matt Madden); Oucuipo (in the work of Perec); Oulipopo (in 'The Burning of the Abominable House', in the work of Ian Monk, whose story 'Spies in Newquay' takes the form of a tale of espionage, and in Christine Brooke-Rose's *Next*, involving murder in the homeless community); Oumupo (in the work of Perec, and in the libretto by Paul Griffiths for music by Hans Abrahamsen); Oupeinpo (in the work of Jacques Carelman, Philippe Mouchès, Thieri Foulc, Aline Gagnaire and Édouard Levé); Ouphopo (in the work of Richard Long, whose *Dartmoor* echoes the form of Queneau's *A Hundred Thousand Billion Poems*); Outranspo (in the work of Lily Robert-Foley, and in the selection of translations of Queneau's *Exercises in Style* using the methods of Outranspo); and Ouvipo (in Valérie Beaudouin's *Body/Machine*). And perhaps Borges's 'The Garden of Forking Paths', as well as exploring infinitely bifurcating narrative possibilities, also gives a taste of what Ouhispo might look like in the alternative account it offers of events recorded in B. H. Liddell Hart's *History of World War I*. Any readers still left wanting more could do worse than turn to Umberto Eco's *The Name of the Rose*, the idea for which was obliquely suggested by Oulipopo's researches, which found that a book in which the murderer is the reader was yet to be written.

Potentielle

We have seen some of the important connotations of the word '*ouvroir*' in *Ouvroir de littérature potentielle*. The word '*potentielle*' is no less carefully chosen. There are at least four important and related senses here. Firstly, and most simply, 'potential literature' can be distinguished from literature in that, fundamentally, Oulipo invents or rediscovers constraints rather than writes literature. And these constraints, in the hands of Oulipians or those outside Oulipo, can *potentially* give rise to literature, even creating new possibilities for literature. A constraint, or a simple illustration of a constraint, is therefore not literature, but 'potential literature', whose real existence is virtual, in the future. This relates to a second sense, which Jacques Roubaud refers to as Oulipo's 'potential universality'. For Roubaud, this is something Oulipo shares with its two cousins, surrealism and Bourbaki, and put simply it refers to the fact that the practice of writing by constraints is conceivable in all languages. This constitutes a powerful 'attractive force' which has been recognized in the US and in the UK by a variety of writers and artists, and it is one of the chief reasons why 'oulipism' now extends beyond Oulipo and across languages. A third sense can be glimpsed in Queneau's *A Hundred Thousand Billion Poems*, the first Oulipian work consciously conceived. This is, certainly, a work of literature, but it is also a work whose horizon remains a potentiality, for its vertiginous unleashing of 10^{14} sonnets could not in actuality be read by any single reader in a lifetime. The final sense, also hinted at in Queneau's book, but rarely discussed in English or in French, is the mathematical sense of 'potentielle' in French, which refers to 'puissance' or power, as in raising a number to the power of 14. This exponential sense of multiplication, expressed in concrete form in Queneau's book, is there in all Oulipian literature and all Oulipian procedures, and it represents a hidden explosive force whose ramifications – potentially – are endless, as can be seen in the ever-increasing fields explored by the Ou-x-pos.

Queneau Numbers

See under *Mathematics*.

Research

Part of Oulipo's work, from its beginnings, has involved research into its antecedent anticipatory plagiarists. What has only come to light more recently, particularly in Michèle Métail's research into the interpretation and reading of early Chinese palindromic poetry in her book *Wild Geese Returning: Chinese Reversible Poems*, is that Oulipian methods might themselves be the research tools necessary to read the poetry of the past. Here, it was Métail's Oulipian background in forms such as the palindrome, which actually enabled her to read and decipher the multiple poems concealed in these Chinese pictograms. The book offers us a unique insight into another 'potential' hidden in Oulipian work, the potential of Oulipian methodology to unlock works which for a long time have been closed. It is early days, but her book potentially opens up a new field of Oulipian-related research which could be used to crack the hidden code of other ancient texts, such as runes, Arabic talismanic texts, and even the Ice Age signs found in caves such as Lascaux, Chauvet and Altamira, which currently remain illegible.

Selection

Existing anthologies on the work of Oulipo, both in English and in French, fall into three broad categories: the academic, consisting mostly of essays on Oulipo, such as *Oulipo: A Primer of Potential Literature*; the anthology of constraints, usually accompanied by short illustrative texts, such as *OULIPO: L'abécédaire provisoirement définitif* and *The Oulipo Compendium*; and anthologies which give priority to the writing itself, such as the *Anthologie de l'OuLiPo* and *The State of Constraint*. This anthology is along the lines of Gallimard's 2009 *Anthologie de l'OuLiPo*. In his preface to this book, Paul Fournel, the President of Oulipo, writes: 'This anthology has no intention of being a catalogue of constraints, rather it is a collection of texts . . . . For once, the reader is not in the kitchen . . . [but] seated at the table.' The Gallimard anthology is devoted exclusively to writings by members of Oulipo, and while such writings must necessarily form the core of any Oulipian anthology, there are strong reasons for spreading the net wider, and not just to include the Ou-x-pos. A defining characteristic of Oulipo from its inception, as we have seen, has been to propose constraints for writers outside Oulipo to use, in other words a primary function of Oulipo is to propose rather than to write – and the brief illustrative texts which usually accompany new ideas from Oulipo are not always intended to be more than illustrations, even if, in practice, they frequently transcend this provisional status. As well as containing work by Oulipians, this collection represents the work of writers outside Oulipo who have blazed the same trail, sometimes intentionally (as with Christian Bök's monovocalisms in *Eunoia*, and Christine Brooke-Rose's novel of homelessnes excluding the verb 'to have', *Next*), sometimes unintentionally, or with little or no direct influence from Oulipo (as in Alice Oswald's reduction of Homer, *Memorial*, which is a perfect illustration of Oulipo's concept of slenderizing, and Inger Christensen's *alphabet*, a meditation on nature both alphabetical and underpinned by the Fibonacci Sequence). One advantage of this approach is that it has enabled the inclusion of many pieces *written* in English, so that the problem of translating constraints which renders some Oulipian work in French close to untranslatable, is sidestepped. Similary, as we have seen, an important aspect of Oulipo's research has been to discover writers from the past who anticipate their methods, Oulipo's anticipatory plagiarists, and it is impossible to give a full picture of Oulipism without including some of these writers. This sheds unexpected light on Oulipo. It is a surprise to find in *Alice's Adventures in Wonderland* a poem created by changing another poem into its opposite, thereby anticipating the method of 'antonymic translation'; and George Herbert's calligram 'Eafter Wings', which shrinks and grows as we read, in turn illuminates the Oulipian form of the snowball, and a novel such as Richard Beard's *Lazarus is Dead*, the chapters of which shrink then grow again as Lazarus is reborn. (Beard's shortest chapter, where Lazarus lies dead, is reproduced here). To date, such writers have rarely featured in Oulipian anthologies, though Oulipo themselves have long cherished the as yet unrealized idea of an anthology dedicated exclusively to such anticipatory plagiarisms.

Translation

Given that so much writing by Oulipo is in French, and that even some English-speaking members of Oulipo, like Ian Monk, write principally in French, the problem of translation arises. Robert Frost famously claimed that what gets lost in translation is poetry, and it is immediately tempting in this context to say that what gets lost in translation is Oulipo. Georges Perec's e-less novel *La disparition* is a case in point. The correct translation of the title would be *The Disappearance*, but already the constraint has been broken three times. The first sentence of Chapter 1 in the novel reads: 'Anton Voyl n'arrivait pas à dormir'. This could be translated as 'Anton Voyl couldn't manage to get to sleep', or more colloquially 'Anton Voyl was having trouble getting to sleep'. Either way, the e's creep in. Translators, then, are faced with a decision: either translate the text before you or translate the constraint, allowing the inevitable departures from strict sense that this entails. Fortunately, we have been blessed with some very creative translators when it comes to Oulipo, among them David Bellos and Gilbert Adair. So Adair, throwing caution to the wind, and choosing to inhabit the constraint, translates the opening of Perec's first chapter like this: 'Incurably insomniac, Anton Voyl turns on a light.'

Untranslatability

I would tend to agree with David Bellos that nothing is untranslatable. However, with Oulipo, the harder the constraint, the further apart the literal and the constraint-based translation become, to the point where, in the latter case, the translation is close to becoming a new work. To date, the books by Perec that nobody has translated into English are the poems, simply because the constraints here are so strict. The poems have, though, been translated into German. Jürgen Ritte, commenting on Oskar Pastior's translations, which use the same constraints as Perec, notes: 'this makes completely different poems, but the "translation" is faithful in its own way.'[10] Translating a text like Perec's 'A Little Illustrated ABC' presents similar problems. When Perec homophonically translates 'Ta-Te-Ti-To-Tu', he gets 'Tâté, Tito tut' (literally 'Sounded out, Tito is silent'), but a translator with an eye on the constraint – and here constraint is everything – has to come up with something which may have quite a different sense, even if 'Tito' here is easy to hang on to, such as 'Tatty Tito too' or 'Tati, Tito: O'Toole', which when expanded into a miniature narrative in Perec's manner is likely to give a completely different result. Literally, such texts are untranslatable, but a sensitive translation of the constraint can give the work 'continued life', in Walter Benjamin's phrase.

Variations

First published in 1947, thirteen years before the foundation of Oulipo, Queneau's *Exercises in Style*, where he retells in 99 variations a single story about an incident on a crowded bus, proved to be a text of lasting and unforseeable importance for Oulipo. The idea came to Queneau in the 1930s after he and his friend Michel Leiris had attended a concert at the Salle Pleyel where Bach's *The Art of the Fugue* had been performed. What struck Queneau was that, although based on a slight theme, the variations proliferated endlessly, almost infinitely, and Queneau wondered if a similar exercise could be performed with written texts. *Exercises in Style* is his resounding answer to this, and its endless proliferations have continued to unfold in the work of Oulipo, making it a key work of 'potential literature'. Seeing this, Queneau revised the work in 1973, removing six variations that he considered unsatisfactory, and replacing them with overtly Oulipian variations – 'Set Theory' (inspired by Bourbaki), 'Definitional', 'Tanka', 'Translation' (using the method N+6), 'Lipogram', and 'Geometric' – all of which are here translated for the first time in English. Taking their cue from Queneau, other Oulipians have turned their hands to the variation, among them Harry Mathews, both in his '35 Variations on a Theme from Shakespeare' and his *Trial Impressions*. Other Oulipians have ploughed the same furrow, with variations and responses to Queneau: Jacques Carelman, of Oupeinpo, added 33 visual interpretations of Queneau for an edition of *Exercises in Style* published in 1963, and in 2006 Matt Madden, of Oubapo, responded with his strip cartoon variations in *99 Ways To Tell A Story*. Perhaps less well recognized is the impact that Queneau's variations have had on some of the major works of the Oulipo: for in this context many of Calvino's works can be seen to be of this type, such as *The Castle of Crossed Destinies*, which offers intricate variations on classic stories and myths, and his masterpiece *Invisible Cities*, which, in essence, is a series of variations on descriptions of Venice presented by Marco Polo to Kublai Khan. Perhaps the most remarkable of all Oulipian variations is the sequence of narratives collected under the title . . .

Winter Journeys

Perec's *The Winter Journey* appeared for the first time in 1980, almost secretly, in a publicity bulletin put out by Hachette. The hero, Vincent Degraël – to cut a short story even shorter – comes across a slim volume of poetry entitled *The Winter Journey* by an unknown author, Hugo Vernier. The volume is full of echoes of many of the great poets of nineteenth-century France, and at first Degraël takes it for a work of plagiarism, until he notices the date of publication, which falls way before the dates of the writers it appears to copy. It is not, it turns out, a work of plagiarism, but a work of anticipatory plagiarism: Degraël has discovered the unacknowledged wellspring of nineteenth-century French poetry, or so it would appear – but at this point the story is interrupted by the Second World War, and when Degraël returns to France in 1945 his attempts to trace the volume again prove fruitless, and he ends his days in the psychiatric hospital in Verrières. Perec's slim volume is a remarkable work in itself, a deft and playful parable condensing many of the ideas he had learnt as an active member of Oulipo. What Perec couldn't have predicted, though, was the way in which other members of Oulipo, beginning with Roubaud, would respond to his work, ringing the changes on its themes in a still-growing series of variations, which in their seemingly endless proliferations, turn Perec's text into one of Oulipo's definitive works of 'potential literature'. To date, there are twenty-one variations on this story, and counting, which have appeared in French in the *Bibliothèque Oulipienne* (the Oulipo Library). They are represented here by Perec's inaugural tale, by François Caradec's 'The Worm's Journey', and by the story by Valérie Beaudouin (writing as Hugo Vernier), 'Hell's Journey'.

X takes Y for Z

A fitting conclusion to this alphabetical introduction to Oulipo is the constraint, devised by Queneau, of X takes Y for Z. Illustrated in the form of a multiplication table, it describes fictional cases of mistaken identity. In a normal situation, each character knows who they are and who the others are:

	x	y	z
x	x	y	z
y	x	y	z
z	x	y	z

Yet in other cases, such as y and z being identical twins, confusions arise:

	x	y	z
x	x	z	y
y	x	y	z
z	x	y	z

In Perec's 'Sentimental Tales', included here, the method is adapted to describe who characters are – or appear to be – in love with.

Philip Terry

Notes

1. David Bellos, 'Introduction: *The Book of Bachelors* by Philip Terry', *The Review of Contemporary Fiction*, Vol. XIX, no. 2, Summer 1999, p. 8.
2. Jacques Roubaud, 'The Oulipo and Combinative Art', transl. Harry Mathews, *New Observations* #99, January/February 1994, p. 6.
3. Ian Monk, 'My Life with the Oulipians', *The noulipian Analects* (Los Angeles: Les Figues Press, 2007), p. 141.
4. David Bellos, 'Introduction', Raymond Queneau, *Elementary Morality*, transl. Philip Terry (Manchester: Carcanet, 2007), p. ix.
5. The Italian, '*Organizzazione per la Produzione Elettronica d'Opere Letterarie Omogeneizzate*', which gives us the acronym OPEOLO, or OLOEPO if you run it backwards, takes us closer still to OULIPO.
6. See for example Kenneth Koch, 'Taking a Walk With You', in Padgett and Shapiro (eds.) *An Anthology of New York Poets* (New York: Vintage, 1970), pp. 141–145.
7. Ian Monk, 'From the Sestina to the Quenina to the Monquenina', *The noulipian Analects*, pp. 189–90.
8. Barbara Henning, 'An Interview with Harry Mathews', www.belladonnaseries.org/images/reviews/harry_mathews_interview.pdf//, accessed 27 December 2018.
9. See Harry Mathews, 'In Quest of the Oulipo', *The Case of the Persevering Maltese* (Normal: Dalkey Archive, 2003), p. 87.
10. Camille Bloomfield 'Traduire la littérature à contraintes', in Bloomfield and Lesage (eds.) *Oulipo* (Paris: Gallimard, 2014), p. 160.

I.

Harry Mathews
35 VARIATIONS ON A THEME
FROM SHAKESPEARE
(Source text: To be or not to be: that is the question)
{Oulipo}

01 *Alphabetically*
A BB EEEE HH II NN OOOOO Q R SS TTTTTTT U

02 *Anagram*
Note at his behest: bet on toot or quit

03 *Lipogram in* c, d, f, g, j, k, l, m, p, v, w, x, y, z
To be or not to be: that is the question

04 *Lipogram in* a
To be or not to be: this is the question

05 *Lipogram in* i
To be or not to be: that's the problem

06 *Lipogram in* e
Almost nothing, or nothing: but which?

07 *Transposition (W + 7)*
To beckon or not beckon: that is the quinsy

08 *Strict palindrome*
No, it's (eu) qeht sit. Ah! te botton roebot

09 *Missing letter*
To be or not to be hat is the question

10 *Two missing letters*
To be or not to be at is the question

11 *One letter added*
To bed or not to be: that is the question

12 *Negation*
To be or not to be: that is not the question

13 *Emphasis*
To be, if you see what I mean, to *be*, be alive, exist, not just keep hanging around; *or* (and that means one or the other, no getting away from it)
not to be, *not* be alive, *not* exist, to – putting it bluntly – check out, cash
in your chips, head west: *that* (do you read me? not 'maybe this' or 'maybe
something else') *that* is, really *is*, irrevocably *is*, *the* one and only inescap-
able, overwhelming, and totally preoccupying ultimate *question*

14 *Curtailing*
Not to be: that is the question

15 *Curtailing (different)*
To be or not to be, that is

16 *Double curtailing*
Not to be, that is

17 *Triple contradiction*
You call this life? And everything's happening all the time? Who's asking?

18 *Another point of view*
Hamlet, quit stalling!

19 *Minimal variations*
To see or not to see
To flee or not to flee
To pee or not to pee

20 *Antonymy*
Nothing *and* something: this was an answer

21 *Amplification*
To live forever or never to have been born is a concern that has perplexed humanity from time immemorial and still does

22 *Reductive*
One or the other – who knows?

23 *Permutation*
That is the question: to be or not to be

24 *Interference*
a) Tomorrow and tomorrow and tomorrow: That is the question
b) To be or not to be
      Creeps in this petty pace from day to day
      To the last syllable of recorded time
      And all our yesterdays have lighted fools
      The way to dusty death

25 *Isomorphisms*
Speaking while singing: this defines *recitativo*
Getting and spending we lay waste our powers

26 *Synonymous*
Choosing between life and death confuses me

27 *Subtle insight*
Shakespeare knew the answer

28 *Another interference*
Put out the light, and then? That is the question

29 *Homoconsonantism*
At a bier, a nutty boy, too, heats the queasy tone

30 *Homovocalism*
Lode of gold ore affirms evening's crown

31 *Homophony*
Two-beer naughty beat shatters equation

32 *Snowball with an irregularity*
    I
    am
    all
    mute
    after
    seeing
    Hamlet's
    annoying
    emergency
    yourstruly
    Shakespeare

33 *Heterosyntaxism*
I ask myself: is it worth it, or isn't it?

34 *In another metre*
So should I be, or should I not?
This question keeps me on the trot

35 *Interrogative mode*
Do I really care whether I exist or not?
(We leave the reader saddled with this painful question.)

2.

Jonathan Swift
FROM *GULLIVER'S TRAVELS*
{Anticipatory Plagiarism}

We crossed a Walk to the other part of the Academy, where, as I have already said, the Projector in speculative Learning resided.

The first Professor I saw was in a very large Room, with forty Pupils about him. After Salutation, observing me to look earnestly upon a Frame, which took up the greatest part of both the Length and Breadth of the Room, he said perhaps I might wonder to see him employed in a Project for improving speculative Knowledge by practical and mechanical Operations. But the World would soon be sensible of its Usefulness, and he flattered himself that a more noble exalted Thought never sprung in any other Man's Head. Everyone knew how laborious the usual Method is of attaining to Arts and Sciences; whereas by his Contrivance, the most ignorant Person at a reasonable Charge, and with a little bodily Labour, may write Books in Philosophy, Poetry, Politics, Law, Mathematics and Theology, without the least Assistance from Genius or Study. He then led me to the Frame, about the sides whereof all his Pupils stood in Ranks. It was twenty Foot Square, placed in the middle of the Room. The Superficies was composed of several bits of Wood, about the bigness of a Die, but some larger than others. They were all linked together by slender Wires. These bits of Wood were covered on every Square with Paper pasted on them, and on these Papers were written all the Words of their Language in their several Moods, Tenses, and Declensions, but without any Order. The Professor then desired me to observe, for he was going to set his Engine at Work. The Pupils at his Command took each of them hold of an Iron Handle, whereof there were forty fixed round the Edges of the Frame, and giving them a sudden turn, the whole Disposition of the Words was entirely changed. He then commanded six and thirty of the Lads to read the several Lines softly as they appeared upon the Frame; and where they found three or four Words together that might make part of a Sentence, they dictated to the four remaining Boys who were Scribes. This Work was repeated three or four times, and at every turn the Engine was so contrived, that the Words shifted into new places, as the square bits of Wood moved upside down.

Six Hours a day the young Students were employed in this Labour, and the Professor showed me several Volumes in large Folio already collected, of broken Sentences, which he intended to piece together, and out of those rich Materials to give the World a complete Body of all Arts and Sciences; which however might be still improved, and much expedited, if the Public would raise a Fund for making and employing five hundred such Frames in *Lagado*, and oblige the Managers to contribute in common their several Collections.

He assured me, that this Invention had employed all his Thoughts from his Youth, that he had emptied the whole Vocabulary into his Frame, and made the strictest Computation of the general Proportion there is in the Book between the Numbers of Particles, Nouns, and Verbs, and other Parts of Speech.

I made my humblest Acknowledgement to this illustrious Person for his great Communicativeness, and promised if ever I had the good Fortune to return to my Native Country, that I would do him Justice, as the sole Inventer of this wonderful Machine; the Form and Contrivance of which I desired leave to delineate upon Paper as in the Figure here annexed. I told him, although it were the Custom of our Learned in *Europe* to steal Inventions from each other, who had thereby at least this advantage, that it became a Controversy which was the right Owner, yet I would take such Caution, that he should have the Honour entire without a Rival.

Plate.V.Part.III.

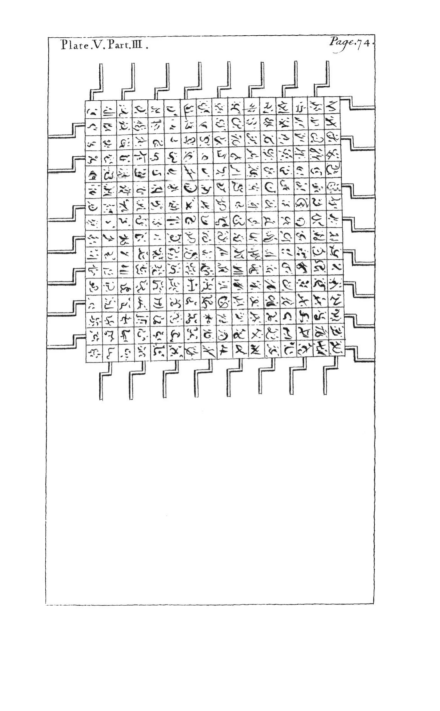

3.

Raymond Queneau
A HUNDRED THOUSAND BILLION POEMS
translated by Stanley Chapman
{Oulipo}

Don Pedro from his shirt has washed the fleas

the bull's horns ought to dry it like a bone

old corned-beef's rusty armour spreads disease

that suede ferments is not at all well-known

to one sweet hour of bliss my memory clings

signalling gauchos very rarely shave

an icicle of frozen marrow pings

as sleeping-bags the silent landscape pave

staunch pilgrims longest journeys can't depress

what things we did we went the whole darned hog

and played their mountain croquet jungle chess

southern baroque's seductive dialogue

suits lisping Spanish tongues for whom say some

the bell tolls fee-less fi-less fo-less fum

The wild horse champs the Parthenon's top frieze

✂

since Elgin left his nostrils in the stone

✂

the Turks said just take anything you please

✂

and loudly sang off-key without a tone

✂

O Parthenon you hold the charger's strings

✂

the North Wind bites into his architrave

✂

th'outrageous Thames a troubled arrow slings

✂

to break a rule Britannia's might might waive

✂

Platonic Greece was not so talentless

✂

a piercing wit would sprightliest horses flog

✂

Socrates watched his hemlock effervesce

✂

their sculptors did *our* best our hulks they clog

✂

with marble souvenirs then fill a slum

✂

for Europe's glory while Fate's harpies strum

At snuff no Cornish sailorman would sneeze

✂···

his nasal ecstasy beats best Cologne

✂···

upon his old oak chest he cuts his cheese

✂···

with cherry-pips his cottage floor is sown

✂···

the Frisian Isles my friends are cherished things

✂···

whose ocean stillborn herrings madly brave

✂···

such merchandise a melancholy brings

✂···

for burning bushes never fish forgave

✂···

when dried the terrapin can naught express

✂···

shallots and sharks' fins face the smould'ring log

✂···

while homeward thirsts to each quenched glass say yes

✂···

lobsters for sale must be our apologue

✂···

on fish-slab whale nor seal has never swum

✂···

they're kings we're mammal-cousins hi ho hum

At five precisely out went La Marquise

for tea cucumber sandwiches a scone

her native chauffeur waited in the breeze

which neither time nor tide can long postpone

how it surprised us pale grey underlings

when flame a form to wrath ancestral gave

a daring baron pockets precious Mings

till firemen come with hose-piped tidal wave

the fasting fakir doesn't smell the less

in Indian summers Englishmen drink grog

the colonel's still escutcheoned in undress

no need to cart such treasures from the fog

the Taj Mahal has trinkets spice and gum

and lessor's dates have all too short a sum

From playboy Chance the nymph no longer flees

though snobbish growing round her hemline zone

his toga rumpled high above his kness

one gathers rosebuds or grows old alone

old Galileo's Pisan offerings

were pots graffiti'd over by a slave

the leaning linguist cameramaniac sings

Etruscan words which Greece and Rome engrave

emboggled minds may puff and blow and guess

with gravity at gravity's great cog

on wheels the tourist follows his hostess

with breaking voice across the Alps they slog

do bank-clerks rule their abacus by thumb?

in cognac brandy is bacardi rum?

He bent right down to pick up his valise

that hordes of crooks felt they'd more right to own

he bent right down and well what did he seize

the thumb and finger-prints of Al Capone

oh how oh how he hates such pilferings

filching the lolly country thrift helped save

he's gone to London how the echo rings

through homestead hillside woodland rock and cave

the peasant's skirts on rainy days she'd tress

and starve the snivelling baby like a dog

watching manure and compost coalesce

one misses cricket hearth and croaking frog

where no-one bothered how one warmed one's bum

Childe Zazie to the Metro has not come

When one with t'other straightaway agrees

✂ ....

the answer is they could be twins full-grown

✂ ....

replies like this the dumstruck brain may tease

✂ ....

normal one aims to be *and* share the throne

✂ ....

and yet 'twas he the beggar Fate just flings

✂ ....

rejecting ermine to become a knave

✂ ....

the fertile mother changelings drops like kings

✂ ....

in purest cradles that's how they behave

✂ ....

the genealogist with field and fess

✂ ....

with quill white-collared through his life will jog

✂ ....

to prove mamma an adult with a tress

✂ ....

but *I* can understand you Brother Gog

✂ ....

and let you off from your opinions glum

✂ ....

a wise loaf always knows its humblest crumb

Prose took the minstrel's verse without a squeeze

his exaltation shocked both youth and crone

the understanding critic firstly sees

'ere meanings new to ancient tribes are thrown

they both are right not untamed mutterings

that metred rhyme alone can souls enslave

they both are right not unformed smatterings

that every verbal shock aims to deprave

poetic licence needs no strain or stress

one tongue will do to keep the verse agog

from cool Parnassus down to wild Loch Ness

bard I adore your endless monologue

ventriloquists be blowed *you* strike me dumb

soliloquies predict great things old chum

The acid tongue with gourmet's expertise

✂ ··

licks round carved marble chops on snails full-blown

✂ ··

the showman gargles fire and sword with ease

✂ ··

while sharks to let's say potted shrimps are prone

✂ ··

the roundabout eats profits made on swings

✂ ··

nought can the mouse's timid nibbling stave

✂ ··

in salads all chew grubs before they've wings

✂ ··

the nicest kids for stickiest toffees crave

✂ ··

the wolf devours both sheep and shepherdess

✂ ··

a bird-brain banquet melts bold Mistress Mog

✂ ··

the country lane just thrives on farmyard mess

✂ ··

whiskey will always wake an Irish bog

✂ ··

though bretzels take the dols from boardroom drum

✂ ··

fried grilled black pudding's still the world's best yum

The marble tomb gapes wide with jangling keys

when masons clutch the breath we held on loan

forms shadowy with indecision wheeze

and empty cages show life's bird has flown

it's one of many horrid happenings

with sombre thoughts they grimly line the nave

proud death quite il-le-gi-ti-mate-ly stings

victorious worms grind all into the grave

it's no good rich men crying Heaven Bless

or grinning like a pale-faced golliwog

poor Yorick comes to bury not address

we'll suffocate before the epilogue

poor reader smile before your lips go numb

the best of all things to an end must come

4.

Henry Vassall-Fox,
Lord Halland
EVE'S LEGEND
{Anticipatory Plagiarism}

Men were never perfect; yet the three brethren Veres were ever esteemed, respected, revered, even when the rest, whether the select few, whether the mere herd, were left neglected.

The eldest's vessels seek the deep, stem the element, get pence; the keen Peter, when free, wedded Hester Green,–the slender, stern, severe, erect Hester Green. The next, clever Ned, less dependent, wedded sweet Ellen Heber. Stephen, ere he met the gentle Eve, never felt tenderness; he kept kennels, bred steeds, rested where the deer fed, went where green trees, where fresh breezes greeted sleep. There he met the meek, the gentle Eve; she tended her sheep, she ever neglected self; she never heeded pelf, yet she heeded the shepherds even less. Nevertheless, her cheek reddened when she met Stephen; yet decent reserve, meek respect, tempered her speech, even when she shewed tenderness. Stephen felt the sweet effect: he felt he erred when he fled the sex, yet felt he defenceless when Eve seemed tender. She, he reflects, never deserved neglect; she never vented spleen; he esteems her gentleness, her endless deserts; he reverences her steps; he greets her:

'Tell me whence these meek, these gentle sheep,–whence the yet meeker, the gentler shepherdess?'

'Well bred, we were eke better fed, ere we went where reckless men seek fleeces. There we were fleeced. Need then rendered me shepherdess, need renders me sempstress. See me tend the sheep, see me sew the wretched shreds. Eve's need preserves the steers, preserves the sheep; Eve's needle mends her dresses, hems her sheets; Eve feeds the geese; Eve preserves the cheese.'

Her speech melted Stephen, yet he nevertheless esteems, reveres her. He bent the knee where her feet pressed the green; he blessed, he begged, he pressed her.

'Sweet, sweet Eve, let me wed thee; be led where Hester Green, where Ellen Heber, where the brethren Vere dwell. Free cheer greets thee there; Ellen's glees sweeten the refreshment; there severer Hester's decent reserve checks heedless jests. Be led there, sweet Eve!'

'Never! we well remember the Seer. We went where he dwells – we entered the cell – we begged the decree,–

Where, whenever, when, 'twere well
Eve be wedded? Eld Seer, tell.

He rendered the decree; see here the sentence decreed!' Then she presented Stephen the Seer's decree. The verses were these:

Ere the green reed be red,
Sweet Eve, be never wed;
Ere be green the red cheek,
Never wed thee, Eve meek.

The terms perplexed Stephen, yet he jeered the terms; he resented the senseless credence, 'Seers never err.' Then he repented, knelt, wheedled, wept. Eve sees Stephen kneel; she relents, yet frets when she remembers the Seer's decree. Her dress redeems her. These were the events:

Her well-kempt tresses fell; sedges, reeds, bedecked them. The reeds fell, the edges met her cheeks; her cheeks bled. She presses the green sedge where her cheek bleeds. Red then bedewed the green reed, the green reed then speckled her red cheek. The red cheek seems green, the green reed seems red. These were e'en the terms the Eld Seer decreed Stephen Vere.

Here endeth the Legend.

He added an epigraph:

Much trouble it costs to pen stories like these –
Quoth a punster, 'How so? they are written with *Es*.'

5.

François Le Lionnais
LIPO:
FIRST MANIFESTO

translated by Warren Motte
{Oulipo}

Let's open a dictionary to the words 'Potential Literature'. We find absolutely nothing. Annoying lacuna. What follows is intended, if not to impose a definition, at least to propose a few remarks, simple hors d'oeuvres meant to assuage the impatience of the starving multitudes until the arrival of the main dish, which will be prepared by people more worthy than myself.

Do you remember the polemic that accompanied the invention of language? Mystification, puerile fantasy, degeneration of the race and decline of the State, treason against Nature, attack on affectivity, criminal neglect of inspiration; language was accused of everything (without, of course, using language) at that time.

And the creation of writing, and grammar – do you think that that happened without a fight? The truth is that the Quarrel of the Ancients and the Moderns is permanent. It began with Zinjanthropus (a million seven hundred and fifty thousand years ago) and will end only with humanity – or perhaps the mutants who succeed us will take up the cause. A Quarrel, by the way, very badly named. Those who are called the Ancients are often the stuffy old descendants of those who in their own day were Moderns; and the latter, if they came back among us, would in many cases take sides with the innovators and renounce their all too faithful imitators.

Potential literature only represents a new rising of the sap in this debate.

*

Every literary work begins with an inspiration (at least that's what its author suggests) which must accommodate itself as well as possible to a series of constraints and procedures that fit inside each other like Chinese boxes. Constraints of vocabulary and grammar, constraints of the novel (division into chapters, etc.) or of classical tragedy (rule of the three unities), constraints of general versification, constraints of fixed forms (as in the case of the rondeau or the sonnet), etc.

Must one adhere to the old tricks of the trade and obstinately refuse to imagine new possibilities? The partisans of the status quo don't hesitate to answer in the affirmative. Their conviction rests less on reasoned reflection than on force of habit and the impressive series of masterpieces (and also, alas, pieces less masterly) which has been obtained according to the present rules and regulations. The opponents of the invention of language must have argued thus, sensitive as they were to the beauty of shrieks, the expressiveness of sighs, and sidelong glances (and we are certainly not asking lovers to renounce all of this).

Should humanity lie back and be satisfied to watch new thoughts make ancient verses? We don't believe that it should. That which certain writers have introduced with talent (even with genius) in their work, some only occasionally (the forging of new words), others with predilection (counterrhymes), others with insistence but in only one direction (Lettrism), the Ouvroir de Littérature Potentielle (Oulipo) intends to do systematically and scientifically, if need be through recourse to machines that process information.

In the research which the Oulipo proposes to undertake, one may distinguish two principal tendencies, oriented respectively toward Analysis and Synthesis. The analytic tendency investigates works from the past in order to find possibilities that often exceed those their authors had anticipated. This, for example, is the case of the cento, which might be reinvigorated, it seems to me, by a few considerations taken from Markov's chain theory.

The synthetic tendency is more ambitious: it constitutes the essential vocation of the Oulipo. It's a question of developing new possibilities unknown to our predecessors. This is the case, for example, of the *Cent Mille Milliards de poèmes* or the Boolian haikus.

Mathematics – particularly the abstract structures of contemporary mathematics – proposes thousands of possibilities for exploration, both algebraically (recourse to new laws of composition) and topologically (considerations of textual contiguity, openness and closure). We're also thinking of anaglyphic poems, texts that are transformable by projection, etc. Other forays may be imagined, notably into the area of special vocabulary (crows, foxes, dolphins; Algol computer language, etc.). It would take a long article to enumerate the possibilities now foreseen (and in certain cases already sketched out).

It's not easy to discern beforehand, examining only the seed, the taste of a new fruit. Let's take the case of alphabetical constraint. In literature it can result in the acrostic, which has produced truly staggering works (still, Villon and, well before him, the psalmist and author of the *Lamentations* attributed to Jeremiah . . .); in painting it resulted in Herbin, and a good thing too; in music the fugue on the name B.A.C.H. – there we have a respectable piece of work. How could the inventors of the alphabet have imagined all of that?

To conclude, Anoulipism is devoted to discovery, Synthoulipism to invention. From the one to the other there exist many subtle channels.

A word at the end for the benefit of those particularly grave people who condemn without consideration and without appeal all work wherein is manifested any propensity for pleasantry.

When they are the work of poets, entertainments, pranks, and hoaxes still fall within the domain of poetry. Potential literature remains thus the most serious thing in the world. Q.E.D.

6.

Raymond Queneau
FROM *EXERCISES IN STYLE*
translated by Philip Terry
{Oulipo}

Notations

In the S bus, in the rush hour. A bloke about 26, felt hat with a cord instead of a ribbon, neck too long as if someone had been tugging at it. People getting off. The bloke in question gets annoyed with one of the passengers standing next to him. He accuses him of bumping into him every time someone goes past. A whining tone which is meant to sound menacing. When he sees a vacant seat, he grabs it.

Two hours later, I come across him in Cour de Rome, in front of the gare Saint-Lazare. He's with a friend who's saying: 'You should get another button put on your overcoat.' He shows him where (at the lapels) and why.

Anagrams

In the S in the hurs uroh, a belok tabou 62, how had a gib nith cenk dan a tha rounsurded by a droc tineads of a nibbro, tegs yannoed whit noe of the gernpasses who he cuesacs of pingbum toni ihm no pospure. Hewn he sese a canvat teas, he brags it.

Owt horus alter, I come sacros ihm in Cuor Ed More, in tronf of the rage Tsian-Zalare. She whit a refind show aysing: 'You holdus teg heranot nuttob tup no your coveroat.' He whoss ihm hweer (at the pellas).

Olfactory

In that meridian S, besides the usual smells – those of priests, the deceased, eggs, jaywalkers, drunks, snorers, nutters, wings, hate-filled flatulents, unpopular songs, empty verses, French letters, and impetuous kebab eaters – there was a distinct odour of long juvenile neck, of the sweatiness of plaited cord, a pungency of anger, a certain loose and constipated stench, smells that were so unmistakable in combination that when two hours later I passed in front of the gare Saint-Lazare I recognized them at once and traced them to the cosmetic, modish and tailored perfume which was given off by a single badly placed button.

Tactile

Buses are soft to the touch, especially if you take them between the thighs and caress them with both hands, from head to tail, from the engine to the platform. But when you find yourself standing on the platform then you notice something a little rougher, a bit more abrasive, which is the bodywork or the handrail, sometimes something a bit more curvaceous and more elastic which is a buttock. Sometimes there are two of these, in which case you put the sentence in the plural. You might also lay your hands on a tubular and quivering object which disgorges idiotic sounds, or a tool with plaited spirals softer than a rosary, more silky than barbed wire, more velvety than a cord and thinner than a cable. Or then again you might touch human stupidity with the end of your finger, slightly viscous, and sticky, due to the heat.

Then if you wait an hour or two, in front of a clattering station, you might just get the chance to dip your sweaty palms in the exquisite freshness of a corozo button which is out of place.

Visual

Taken in at a glance it's green with a white roof, elongated, with windows. They're not easy to pull off if you're a beginner, windows. The platform isn't any colour, a featureless potpourri of grey and brown, like the background to a cubist painting. More than anything it's composed of curves, a conglomeration of esses you could say. But at midday, in the rush hour, how it is is a bloody mess. To get any picture of it you'd have to first conjure out from the magma a cube of pale ochre, place an oval of pale ochre on top of it, then on top of that paint a darkish ochre hat surrounded by a plait of burnt Sienna, all topsy-turvy to cap it all. Then you'd throw in a blob of duckshit to represent rage, a red triangle to express anger, and a pissworth of green to portray repressed bile and yellow-bellied jitters.

Following that, a street artist might draw you one of those pretty little cutesy blue overcoats decorated at the top, just beneath the neckline, with a pretty little cutesy button done with a very fine brush.

Set Theory

In the S bus, consider set S, the seated passengers, and set S', the standing passengers. Standing at a certain bus stop is set P, people who are waiting for a bus. Let C be the set of passengers who get on, C being a sub-set of P, and itself the union of C', the set of passengers who remain on the rear platform, and C", the set consisting of passengers who sit down.

Demonstrate that set C" is empty.

Let T be the set of Teddy boys, and {t} the intersection of T and C', reduced to a single element. Following the surjection of the feet of t on those of y (any member of set C excluding t), set W is formed, of words pronounced by the element t. The set C" having become non-empty, demonstrate that it contains the unique element t.

Let P' now be the set of pedestrians in front of the gare Saint-Lazare, {t, t'} the intersection of T and P', B the set of buttons on the overcoat of t, B' the set of possible points of attachment of buttons according to t'. Demonstrate that the injection of B into B' is not a bijection.

Definitional

In a large motor-driven urban passenger vehicle designated by the nine-teenth letter of the alphabet, a young eccentric with a nickname popular in Paris in 1942, having that part of the body connecting the head with the shoulders stretched out over some distance and wearing on the upper extremity of the body a covering made of a non-woven flexible material encircled by a thick ribbon intertwined in a plait – this young eccentric, then, imputing to an individual shifting from one place to another the fault of stamping his feet one after the other on his own, moved off to position himself on a piece of furniture designed for sitting on, the fur-niture having become unoccupied.

One hundred and twenty seconds later, I see him again in front of the assortment of buildings and tracks where the goods depot and the ter-minus for the arrival and departure of passengers are located. Another young eccentric designated by a nickname popular in Paris in 1942 was giving him some advice on what he should do regarding a small metal, bone, wooden, etc., disc, covered or not with fabric, used as a fastener for clothes, to be specific an item of menswear which is worn on top of other garments.

Tanka

At last the bus comes
A dude in a hat gets on
There's an argument
Later near gare Saint-Lazare
There's talk about a button

Translation

In the Y bus, in the Russian salad. A blood count around thirty-two years of grace, hatchet with a cordon replacing the riboflavin, necrology too long as if someone had been tugging at it. Peppercorns get off. The blood count of Quetzalcoatl gets annoyed with a nematode. He accuses it of jostling him every time someone goes past, in a snorting tone-row which is meant to sound menacing. When he sees an empty seaway he grabs it.

Eight houseboats later, I see him again in the Roncq Courthouse, in front of the Saint-Dizier station wagon. He's with a frigate bird who's saying: 'You should get an extra butt weld put on your overdrive.' He shows him where (at the lapsus linguae) and why.

Lipogram

On an S bus, rush hour. A guy about 26, soft hat with a cord round it, scruff too long, as if caught in a tug-of-war. A woman and child alight. Said guy angry with a man standing in front of him. Arraigns him for bumping into him as folk push by. A whining intonation that sounds intimidating. Said guy grabs an opportunity to sit down without compunction.

Two hours on, I cross his path again in front of a station. A companion, who sports a similar hat, is saying to him: 'You should put an additional button on your coat.' His companion shows him at what spot (towards his collar) and why.

Antonymic

Midnight. It is raining. Buses pass by, almost empty. On the bonnet of an SUV by the Bastille, a hatless old man with his head buried in his shoulders thanks a woman standing some distance away for carressing his hands. Then he props himself upright on the knees of a man who doesn't move from his place.

Two hours earlier, behind the gare de Lyon, this old man stopped up his ears so as not to listen to a tramp who denied himself the opportunity to say that he should have the bottom button on his shorts lowered by a hole.

Homophonic

In these buskins. Russia. A black abbot, wine-dark socks, felt hot weather called him – steed of Arab, bone neck too long, as if Samson had been tugging at it. People ghettoing Orff. The black (inquest!) soon gets a nude with one of the pass engineers stranded, next to hymn. She accuses *him* of bursting into hymns every time some Hun goes 'Psssst!'. A waning tune – 'Witches' Lament' – to send men a song. When she sees a vacant seat, she grabs it.

Tauruses will hate her. I clone a cross hymning cowards of Rome, in for the hunt of the garrison's lazy ease, with a friend who's a Ying. 'You hood! Get a heather buttonhole put on your lover's coat!' he says. 'Hmm, where? At the lapel? Zounds, why?'

Geometric

In a parallelepiped rectangle proceeding along a straight line described by the equation $84\,x + S = y$, a homoïde A displaying a spherical crown encircled by two sinusoids, above a cylindrical section of length $l > n$, makes a single point of contact with a trivial homoïde B. Show that this point of contact is a point of no return.

If homoïde A meets a homologous homoïde C, then the point of contact is a disc of radius $r < l$. Calculate the height h of this point of contact in relation to the vertical axis of homoïde A.

7.

Joe Brainard
FROM *I REMEMBER*
{Anticipatory Plagiarism}

I remember the first time I got a letter that said 'After Five Days Return To' on the envelope, and I thought that after I had kept the letter for five days I was supposed to return it to the sender.

I remember the kick I used to get going through my parents' drawers looking for rubbers. (Peacock.)

I remember when polio was the worst thing in the world.

I remember pink dress shirts. And bola ties.

I remember when a kid told me that those sour clover-like leaves we used to eat (with little yellow flowers) tasted so sour because dogs peed on them. I remember that didn't stop me from eating them.

I remember the first drawing I remember doing. It was of a bride with a very long train.

I remember my first cigarette. It was a Kent.

Up on a hill. In Tulsa, Oklahoma. With Ron Padgett.

I remember my first erections. I thought I had some terrible disease or something.

I remember the only time I ever saw my mother cry. I was eating apricot pie.

I remember how much I cried seeing *South Pacific* (the movie) three times.

I remember how good a glass of water can taste after a dish of ice cream.

I remember when I got a five-year pin for not missing a single morning of Sunday School for five years. (Methodist.)

I remember when I went to a 'come as your favorite person' party as Marilyn Monroe.

I remember one of the first things I remember. An ice box. (As opposed to a refrigerator.)

I remember white margarine in a plastic bag. And a little package of orange powder. You put the orange powder in the bag with the margarine and you squeezed it all around until the margarine became yellow.

I remember how much I used to stutter.

I remember how much, in high school, I wanted to be handsome and popular.

I remember when, in high school, if you wore green and yellow on Thursday it meant that you were queer.

I remember when, in high school, I used to stuff a sock in my underwear.

I remember when I decided to be a minister. I don't remember when I decided not to be.

8.

Italo Calvino
THE WAVERER'S TALE
translated by William Weaver
{Oulipo}

One of us turns over a card, picks it up, looks at it as if he
were looking at himself in a mirror. True, the *Knight of
Cups* really seems to be he. It is not only the face, anxious,
wide-eyed, with long hair, now white, falling to his shoulders; the resemblance can be noted also in his hands, which
he moves over the table as if he had no idea where to put
them. There in the card the right hand holds an outsize cup
balanced on the palm, and the left barely touches the reins
with the fingertips. This reeling posture is communicated
also to the horse: you would say he is unable to plant his
hoofs firmly on the plowed earth.

Having found that card, the young man seems to recognize a special meaning in all other cards that come within
his reach, and he begins lining them up on the table, as
if he were following a thread from one to the other. As,
next to an *Eight of Cups* and a *Ten of Clubs,* he puts down
the Arcanum that, according to the locality, they call *Love*
or *The Lover* or *The Lovers,* the sadness to be read in his
face suggests a heartache that impelled him to rise from
an overheated banquet for a breath of air in the forest. Or
actually to desert his own wedding feast, to run off to the
woods on the very day of his marriage.

Perhaps there are two women in his life, and he is
unable to choose. This is exactly how the drawing portrays him: still blond, between the two rivals, one seizing

him by the shoulder and staring at him with a lustful eye, the other rubbing her whole body against him in a languid movement, while he does not know which way to turn. Every time he is about to decide which of the two would be the more suitable bride, he convinces himself he can very well give up the other, and so he is resigned to losing the latter every time he realizes he prefers the former. The only fixed point in this mental vacillation is that he can do without either one, for every choice has an obverse, that is to say a renunciation, and so there is no difference between the act of choosing and the act of renouncing.

Only a journey could release him from this vicious circle: the tarot the young man now puts on the table will surely be *The Chariot:* the two horses draw the stately vehicle along the rough paths through the forest; the reins are slack, for he habitually lets the animals have their way, so when they reach a crossroads he does not have to make the choice. The *Two of Clubs* marks the crossing of two roads; the horses start tugging, one this way, one that; the wheels are drawn to such a divergence they seem perpendicular to the road, a sign that the chariot has stopped. Or else, if it is moving, it might as well remain still, as happens to many people before whom the ramps of the most smooth and speedy roads open, flying on high pylons, over valleys, piercing granite mountains, and they are free to go everywhere, and everywhere is always the same. Thus we saw him printed there in the falsely decisive pose, like the master of his fate, a triumphant vehicle-driver; but he bore always within him his divided soul, like the two masks with divergent gaze that he wore on his cloak.

To decide which road to take he could only rely on chance: the *Page of Coins* depicts the youth as he throws a coin in the air: heads or tails. Perhaps neither; the coin rolls and rolls, then remains erect in a bush, at the foot of an old oak, right in the middle of the two roads. With the *Ace of Clubs* the youth surely wishes to tell us that, unable to decide whether to continue in one direction or the other, he had no course save to get down from the chariot and climb up a gnarled trunk, among the branches which, with their succession of repeated forks, continue to inflict the torment of choice on him.

He hopes at least that after pulling himself up from one branch to another he will be able to see farther, discover where the roads lead; but the foliage beneath him is dense, the ground is soon out of sight, and if he raises his eyes toward the top of the tree he is blinded by *The Sun,* whose piercing rays make the leaves gleam with every color, against the light. However, the meaning of those two children seen in the tarot should also be explained: they must indicate that, looking up, the young man has realized he is no longer alone in the tree; two urchins have preceded him, scrambling up the boughs.

They seem twins: identical, barefoot, golden blond. Perhaps at this point the young man spoke, asked: 'What are you two doing here?' Or else: 'How far is it to the top?' And the twins replied, indicating with confused gesticulation toward something seen on the horizon of the drawing, beneath the sun's rays: the walls of a city.

But where are these walls located, with respect to the tree? The *Ace of Cups* portrays, in fact, a city, with many towers and spires and minarets and domes rising above the walls. And also palm fronds, pheasants' wings, fins of blue moonfish, which certainly jut from the city's gardens, aviaries, aquariums, among which we can imagine the two urchins, chasing each other and vanishing. And this city seems balanced on top of a pyramid, which could also be the top of the great tree; in other words, it would be a city suspended on the highest branches like a bird's nest, with hanging foundations like the aerial roots of certain plants which grow at the top of other plants.

As they lay down the cards, the young man's hands are increasingly slow and uncertain, and we have ample time

L'IMPERATRICE

LA · JUSTICE.

to follow him with our conjectures, and to ponder silently the questions that must certainly have come into his head as they now come into ours. 'What city is this? Is this the City of All? Is this the city where all parts are joined, all choices balanced, where the void between what we expect of life and what we draw is filled?'

But who was there, in the city, whom the youth could question? Let us imagine he has entered through the arched gate in the girdle of the walls, he has stepped into a square with a high stairway at the end, and at the top of this stairway there is seated a personage with royal attributes, an enthroned divinity or crowned angel. (Behind the personage two protuberances can be seen, which could be the back of the throne, but also a pair of wings, awkwardly traced in the drawing.)

'Is this your city?' the youth must have inquired.

'Yours.' He could have received no better answer. 'Here you will find what you ask.'

Taken by surprise like this, how could he express a sensible request? Hot from his climb to that height, he could have said only: 'I am thirsty.'

And the enthroned angel said: 'You need only choose from which well to drink.' And he must have pointed to the two identical wells that open in the deserted square.

You have merely to glance at the youth to realize he feels lost once again. The crowned authority now wields a scales and a sword, the attributes of the angel who keeps watch over decisions and balances, from the summit of the constellation of Libra. Are you then admitted even into the City of All only through a choice and a rejection, accepting one side and rejecting the rest? He might as well leave as he came; but, turning, he sees two *Queens* looking down from two balconies, facing each other from opposite sides of the square. And lo! he seems to recognize the two women of his eluded choice. They seem to be there on guard, to prevent his leaving the city, for in

34

fact each is holding an unsheathed sword, one with her right hand, the other – surely for symmetry's sake – with her left. Or else, while there can be no doubts about one queen's sword, the other's could also be a goose-quill pen, or closed compasses, or a flute, or a paper-knife, and then the two women would signify two different ways open to him who still has to find himself: the way of passions, which is always a way of action, aggressive, with abrupt shifts, and the way of wisdom, which demands reflection and learning little by little.

In arranging and pointing to the cards, the youth's hands now hint at vacillation and changes in the order; now the hands are wrung, regretting every tarot already played, which might better have been kept in reserve for another round, now they droop in limp gestures of indifference, to indicate that all tarots and all wells are the same, like the *cups* which are repeated, identical, in the pack, as, in the world of the uniform, objects and destinies are scattered before you, interchangeable and unchanging, and he who believes he makes decisions is deluded.

How to explain that, with his consuming thirst, neither this well nor that would suffice? What he wants is the cistern where the waters of all wells and all rivers are poured and mingled, the sea depicted in the Arcanum known as *The Star* or *The Stars*, where life's aquatic origins are celebrated as the triumph of mixture and of squandered opulence. A naked goddess takes two jugs containing who knows what juices kept cool for the thirsty (all around there are the yellow dunes of a sun-baked desert), and empties them to water the pebbled shore: and at that instant a growth of saxifrage springs up in the midst of the desert, and among the succulent leaves a blackbird sings; life is the waste of material thrown away, the sea's cauldron merely repeats what happens within constellations that for billions of years go on pounding atoms in the mortars of their explosions, obvious here even in the milk-colored sky.

35

In the way the youth slams these cards on the table we can almost hear him shouting: 'It's the sea! It's the sea I want!'

'And you shall have the sea!' The reply of the astral authority could only announce a cataclysm, the rising of the oceans' level toward the abandoned cities, lapping the paws of the wolves that have taken refuge on the heights and howl toward *The Moon* looming over them, while the army of crustaceans advances from the depth of the abysses to reconquer the globe.

A thunderbolt that strikes the top of the tree, breaking every wall and *tower* of the suspended city, illuminates an even more horrifying sight, for which the youth prepares us, uncovering a card with a slow movement and with terrified eyes. Rising to his feet on his throne, the regal interlocutor changes and becomes unrecognizable: at his back it is not an angelic plumage that opens, but two bat-wings that darken the sky, the impassive eyes have become crossed, oblique, and the crown has sprouted horn branches, the cloak falls to reveal a naked, hermaphroditic body, hands and feet prolonged into talons.

'Why, were you not an angel?'

'I am the angel who dwells in the point where lines fork. Whoever retraces the way of divided things encounters me, whoever descends to the bottom of contradictions runs into me, whoever mingles again what was separated feels my membraned wing brush his cheek!'

At his feet the solar twins have reappeared, transformed into two beings whose features are both human and animal, with horns, tail, feathers, paws, scales, linked to the rapacious character by two long threads or umbilical cords, and it is likewise probable that each of them holds on a leash two other, smaller devils that have remained outside the picture, so that from branch to branch stretches a network of ropes which the wind sways like a great cobweb, amid a flutter of black wings of decreasing size: noctules, owls, hoopoes, moths, hornets, gnats.

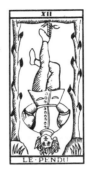

The wind, or waves? The lines drawn at the bottom of the card could indicate that the great tide is already engulfing the top of the tree and all vegetation is being dissolved in a swaying of algae and tentacles. This is the answer to the choice of the man who does not choose: now he does indeed have the sea, he plunges into it headlong, swaying among the corals of the depths, *Hanged* by his feet in the sargassoes that hover half-submerged beneath the ocean's opaque surface, and his green seaweed hair brushes the steep ocean beds. (Is this then the very card that Madame Sosostris, famous clairvoyante but not very reliable as to nomenclature, in prophesying the private and general destiny of the distinguished Lloyds employee, described as a drowned Phoenician sailor?)

If the only thing he wished was to escape from individual limitation, from categories, roles, to hear the thunder that rumbles in molecules, the mingling of prime and ultimate substances, this then is the path that opens to him through the Arcanum known as *The World:* Venus dances in the sky, crowned with vegetation, surrounded by incarnations of multiform Zeus; every species and individual and the whole history of the human race are only a random link in a chain of evolutions and mutations.

He has only to conclude the great turn of *The Wheel* in which animal life evolves and in which you can never say this is the top and this is the bottom, or the even longer turn which passes through decay, the descent to the center of the earth in the deposits of the elements, the awaiting of the cataclysms that shuffle the tarot pack and bring the buried strata to the surface, as in the Arcanum of the final earthquake.

The hands' trembling, the prematurely white hair were only faint signs of what our hapless neighbor had

undergone: in that same night he had been chopped (*swords*) into his prime elements, he had gone through the craters of volcanoes (*cups*), through all the eras of the earth, he had risked remaining prisoner of the definitive immobility of crystal (*coins*), and had reappeared in life through the painful blossoming of the forest (*clubs*), until he had resumed his own identical human form, in the saddle, the *Knight of Coins*.

But is this really he or is it rather a double whom he saw coming through the forest, the moment he was restored to himself?

'Who are you?'

'I am the man who was to marry the girl you did not choose, who was to take the other road at the crossing, quench his thirst at the other well. By not choosing, you have prevented my choice.'

'Where are you going?'

'To an inn different from the one you will come upon.'

'Where shall I see you again?'

'Hanging from a gallows different from the one where you will have hanged yourself. Farewell.'

9.

Paul Fournel
FROM *SUBURBIA*
translated by Harry Mathews
foreword by Marguerite Duras
{Oulipo}

Suburbia, from *suburb*, . . . 2. An outlying part
[ME<L *sub* SUB– + *urb(s)* city].

It is not sufficient to be elsewhere in order to not be here.

ST. THOMAS

A Word from the Publisher

If we have decided to republish a work whose incendiary career was beset with obstacles we all remember far too well, it is because the quality of this little novel, now that passions have subsided, has emerged ever more forcefully. Prosecutions were instigated, verdicts rendered, and offences assuaged. That unfortunate tale needs no further telling. At the end of ten years of painful and absolute silence, the author has agreed to let his work at last be reprinted. He will consequently be restored to the rightful place he should never have abandoned. We hope that this new edition will bring him peace of mind and, as well, bring to readers the tranquil certainty that beneath the transitory scandal eternal literature lay slumbering.

The strength of our conviction is such that we have invited the eminent pedagogue Maurice Garin to prepare this new edition for use in our schools. Some will see in this nothing but provocations, others bald audacity, and a few, we trust, courage and a sense of justice.

An Introductory Note by the Author

They sure kicked me around. They gave me a bloody nose. I'm ten miles down the road and still rubbing my bruises. In Nanterre it was bludgeons. In Bobigny they put me on the stand. In Billancourt they actually tried to kill me. In Les Lilas they beat me up. I'd it up to here.

If I'm back here today, it's because I know they'll keep their traps shut. My story's just history now. They look plain dumb.

Sometimes I feel tired, but nights I still dream of breaking the mayor of Bobigny's jaw.

I've changed a few names and put in some asterisks and phoney initials. All the same, God will recognize his own.

I'm back in business.

Foreword

'To hell with talent!' fools say as they fall on the young author. Their heads invariably empty, their force unchecked, they hound him until the writer's life has become a lasting nightmare.

From their desiccated world, into which the writer had thrust his truth, hypocrites unleash the power of the law. They then wear themselves out in terror of reading what is true. Shouting down youth, they pursue the primal fear inspired by the world they themselves have created. They have decided that *that* will never see the light of day.

But *that* has seen the light of day. Silence distils justice with patient assurance. Here once again we find the gloomy and pitiless vision of the world that surrounds our city, in all its hatefulness and cruelty.

Our conception of what lies outside the city limits has been turned upside down. A new violence, inscribed in thunderstruck words, here becomes definitive and monumental. To write or read about suburbia, we must now look to Fournel. Invariably, Fournel.

Marguerite Duras

Suburbia

---

1. In French in the original.
2. Concerning the definition of *suburb*, see the epigraph *et seq*.
3. What intention on the author's part does this brutal opening suggest?
4. Local judge.

1. Notice how Norbert comes crashing onto the scene.
2. This passage is a mixture of backslang and immigrant jargon. Transpose into normal English.
3. Motorcycle.
4. Obscene gesture.

---

1. Obvious reference to François Villon and Jean-Patrick Manchette.

2. Compare this paragraph with the following passage from *Slices of Love*, an autobiographical work by the same author published two years before *Suburbia*: 'Every Sunday in Bobigny meant the same dumb routine. You scrubbed yourself till you were squeaky clean, squeezed your neck into a fresh shirt, slipped on an elastic bow tie, shined your clogs, and went walking off to church in a nice neat row. "Hurry up," my mother would yell, "we'll be late for the end." You had to be careful about the pleat in your trousers and not step in puddles and hop over the mud on the building site. My old lady, who was already a little broad in the beam, walked on the tips of her patent-leather heels and my old man played the dandy, holding the flaps of his tan mac tight across his front. At the

---

foot of the steps, out of breath, we'd line up according to height: my father, my mother, my three brothers, and me, the last and littlest. We'd watch the gents and ladies come out, then the non-gents and non-ladies, the big fish and the small fry, and we'd softly start making croaking sounds through our teeth until, when that crow of a priest came out, they turned into a shout. My family had quite a reputation.' Analyse how this child-hood memory has been transformed.
1. Drops.
2. This sentence played a crucial role in what is commonly referred to as the Bobigny trial. For what reason might it have been considered provocative?

---

1. Is the violent eroticism of this scene gratuitous?
2. The girl who answers to the name of Olboy (can one deduce an abbreviation of 'old boiler'?) and whom the author identifies as the 'prototype of a suburban slut' nevertheless has an 'angelic smile'. Explain this apparent paradox.
3. 'Go, for I hate thee not.' *Phèdre*, Racine.
4. Analyse how in this passage the suburbs in their entirety are compared to the figure of a man. With this in mind, explain why the author specifically identifies Norbert and Robert with the genital organs: 'Bollocks of suburbia, they keep hanging around; bollocks of suburbia, they howl through the night.'

1. Consider this passage in conjunction with the introductory poem in *Slices of Love*:
     one side the ring road edge
     round and stiff
     other side the edgeless edge
     I sharpen my wills
     farther on.

2. *v. supra.*
3. When the ten commandments of suburban life were nailed to the front of the Nanterre town hall, they provoked a riot and became the starting-point of the whole protest
movement. Initially, however, the authorities only took action against the statement,
'Thou shalt hate thy town fathers, the mothers.'

---

1. Study the development of human feeling in Norbert. How does the 'crystallization' of love take place?
2. 'The earth is blue as a clockwise orange.' Explain the double allusion.
3. In which human drama is Robert actually trapped? Drugs, alcohol, violence, loveless-ness, alienation: does the context allow a choice?
4. NAP: Neuilly-Auteuil-Passy.

1. Show how Robert's collapse points Norbert to a way out of his situation, a way to react positively.
2. He was then mayor of Nanterre.
3. How is the final punch-up staged? Compare it with film scenes that you are familiar with.

49

Supplement for School Use

Author

Paul Fournel was born in Les Lilas in 1957 and spent his entire childhood in the Paris suburbs. Low-rent housing conditions turned him into a delinquent. His first book, *Slices of Love,* was composed in reform school; the second, *Suburbia,* during a period when he had committed himself to a serious effort of self-rehabilitation and was studying to become a specialized education worker.

Shaken by the outburst of hatred that his book inspired, he dropped out of sight for ten years. Even today he refuses to say how those years were spent. To his friends he willingly confides, 'I've gotten older.' No doubt about that. He divides his time between Hire and elsewhere and has, so it seems, begun writing again.

Subject

– The suburbs: analyse the various definitions of this conception.
– Is suburbia the place of choice of the writing profession?
– List the titles of four works dealing with suburbia (remember that Bois de Boulogne is part of Paris).
– What can outskirts teach us about a centre?
– What in our day is 'a committed writer' (*un écrivain engagé*)?
– Is an imprisoned writer always an *écrivain engagé?*
– Was the book worth all the fuss that was made over it?

Form

– How would you define a modern style?
– Is a modern style always a new style?
– Is it really possible to speak of a modern *syntax?*
– Isolate those words and phrases infrequently found in literary works.
– What type of literary production makes the most use of such language?
– This book is nevertheless different. What stylistic distinctions make it so?
– Would you describe the text of this book as 'well written'?

Errata

page 16   read: Robert   for: Norbert
      22   read: Issy   for: Ivry
      23   for: BMV   read: BMW
      28   for: mare   read: mayor
      30   instead of: tubafish salad   read: tuna fish salad
      34   for: puff   read: muff
      38   read: Robert   for: Norbert
      39   read: their shitty rounds   instead of: their shitty grounds
      40   instead of: he pulled out his revolver   read: he pulled   out
           his   revolver
      41   thoroughly dead   for: thoroughly dear
and so in the following line: throughly tailed   for: thoroughly toiled
      42   for: *Phèdre*   read: *Le Cid*
for: Racine   read: Corneille
      48   for: Vincennes   read: Longchamps
      52   for: he pisses through the door of the lift   read: he   passes
           through the door of the lift
      53   read: Robert   for: Norbert
      62   for: clockwise   read: clockwork
      65   for: engaged   read: encaged

51

10.

Jacques Roubaud
FROM *THE FORM OF A CITY CHANGES FASTER, ALAS, THAN THE HUMAN HEART*
translated by Keith and Rosmarie Waldrop
{Oulipo}

Paris

after Raymond Queneau

The Paris we find to traipse
Is not the one we used to find
And we're not wild to get to
The Paris we will leave behind

Commentary on the Preceding Poem

J.R.:   Seven eight
seven eight
there me too I've got
a Verlaine
quatrain

R.Q.:   Well but yours
you copied

Queneau in November

I see him walk along the Seine
Color of sky color of water
He's dreaming of a world well dreamed
Where numbers tend to give in better
To machinations of the poem
I can see how the leaves are fallen
In puddles of low fading light
Is it December? or November?

And as soon as the leaves have fallen
One takes one's notebook out for poems
Walking the bank along the Seine
It's evening now: the poor sunlight
Is getting weaker. He'd do better
To let his shadow take to water
Under the showers of November
Dreaming meanwhile the number dreamed

Shadows in fall soak up the water
Our pumps don't do it any better
Gummed up with all those dead leaves fallen
Into the gutters of November
The evening now directs its light
To the tablet reserved for poems
Where is inscribed the number dreamed
While walking here along the Seine

Here exigencies of the poem
Can be read in the clearest light
So must it all fall in the water
The whole scaffolding he has dreamed
For his octogrammic November?
Alas it could have been far better

In April. All along the Seine
The leaves of all the trees have fallen

Alas it would have been far better
In April rather than November
Shorter would have been the poem
Pleasant the banks along the Seine
In April. Month so often dreamed
So clear the sky, fountain of light
Up fly the leaves already fallen
Back to the trees down by the water

O puddles of so sad a light!
Nevertheless, the number dreamed
Four by four who could do better
So many images have fallen:
Oyez, ahoy, rudds of the Seine
Oy, good oysters of November
Night's negative ignites the water
Plenty material for a poem

Was it December or November
I see him walk along the Seine
Holding his page up to the light
Blackened with figures, damped with water
He walks upon leaves that have fallen
He's dreaming now of the world dreamed
Where words and numbers in the poem
Take to each other, blending better

I write here once more the word 'dreamed'
I write the words here: 'number', 'water'
I ask myself: well why November?
Why on earth oyster, and why poem?
The leaves have all already fallen
Along the sad banks of the Seine

55

It's raining now. For trees that's better
Even and gradual the light.

Envoi

Fall of a dream in some November
I've watered this pome in the Seine
The best I'm able, by my light.

A Bit of Sociology

158 saints, 33 female saints,
popes, 8 cardinals, 11 abbots, 3 abbesses, 1 canoness, 1 rector,
priests, preachers,
Capuchins & Carmelites, Celestines, Recollects
Ursulines, Franciscans,
1 commander-in-chief,

princes, 3 dauphins, 1 princess, 6 counts, 1 countess, knights,
squires,
1 Lord,

4 presidents,

8 marshals, 64 generals, at least 14 colonels, 2 lieutenant-colonels,
    3 commandants, 8 captains, 4 lieutenants, 4 sergeant-majors, 1
    corporal,
crossbowmen,
admirals,

1 agent,

plus 3 judges,

1 banker, entrepreneurs, goldsmiths,
1 single slave trader,

at least 41 doctors,
shepherds – & two shepherdesses,
bons vivants, 2 butchers, bakers,
coal merchants, hunters, lime-burners, vinegar-makers, 1 crêpe-
    maker, 1 cooper, dockers,

1 mailman, 2 mowers, 1 falconer, farmers, landscapers, 1 glazier,
gardeners, sailors, fiddlers, millers,
fish-dealers, 1 haymaker, 1 potter,

4 professors,

painters, poets,

curious, very curious, this distribution
of the population
in the streets
of Paris

Wooden Paris

escalators (Place d'Italie station, and?)
paving (?)

foot bridges (Buttes-Chaumont, and?)
balconies (10 Rue Fessart, and?)
'Wood and Coal Shops' (getting very rare)

benches, gates (passim)
trees
(in Paris the trees are generally of wood)

Rainbow

it's raining

it stops raining

it's nice

the sun's shining
you can see

on Rue VIOLET

on Rue BLEUE
on Rue du Chemin-VERT

on Place du Château-ROUGE

a rainbow full of holes

It's Snowing!

Rue d'	A i x
Rue	A b e l
Rue	V i è t e
Rue	C o u c h e
Rue	A c h i l l e
Rue	C o r i o l i s
Rue	C o n d o r c e t
Rue d'	A l e x a n d r i e
Rue des	H a u d r i e t t e s
Rue	B a s s o m p i e r r e
Rue	C h a t e a u b r i a n d
Rue de	C o n s t a n t i n o p l e
Rue de	B o u l a i n v i l l i e r s

The Snow is Melting!

Rue de	Boulainvilliers
Rue de	Bretonvilliers
Rue de la	Parcheminerie
Rue	Vauvenargues
Rue de	Steinkerque
Rue	Garancière
Rue des	Alouettes
Rue d'	Alembert
Rue	Laplace
Rue	Albert
Rue	Vilin
Rue	Rude
Cour du	Coq

Licence Portrait of Paris 1992

February,	Rue Soufflot	903 JTJ 75
29/04		48 JWW
"	Rue Clément-Marot	253 JWX
05/05	Rue de Parme	848 JWX
06/05	Opéra	485 JWX
07/05	Rue de Douai	311 JXJ
13/05	Rue de Clichy	688 JXJ
16/05	Trinité	336 JXK
17/05	Franklin-Roosevelt	182 JXM
04/06	Rue Marx-Dormoy	479 JXY
06/06	Saint-Lazare	362 JXZ
"	Rue du Havre	730 JYF
15/06	Rue de Clichy	407 JYX
04/07	?	653 JZC
12/07	?	219 JZF
16/07	Trinité	851 JZG
17/07	Bd. Saint-Martin	754 JZM
19/07	Beaubourg	571 JZP
20/07	Place de l'Europe	867 JZR
10/08	Champs-Élysées	939 JZR
11/08	Gare de Lyon	146 JZW
13/08	Pont Royal	263 KAF
09/08	Rue Lepic	4165 WK 75

The Hour

the hour of awakening of the inhabitants of the passage de la reine
de hongrie
the hour of the café opening in rue du moulin de la pointe
the hour of garbage collection in rue du sommet des alpes
the hour of the bakery opening in rue du roi de sicile
the hour of the streetslights going off in the rue du pot de fer
the hour of the butcher opening in rue du faubourg du temple
the hour of the children getting up in rue de la poterne des peupliers
the hour of the delicatessen opening in rue du moulin des prés
the hour of walking the dogs in avenue de la porte de pantin
the hour of cleaning the gutters in rue des nonnains d'hyères
the hour of the garage opening in rue du val de grâce
the hour of the airy manners of cats in rue du père teilhard de chardin
the hour of the driving school opening on boulevard des filles du calvaire
the hour of turtledoves cooing in rue du moulin de la vierge
the hour of the hatshop opening in the galerie des marchands de la gare
saint-lazare
the hour of car invasion in the avenue de la porte d'orléans
the hour of the school opening in avenue de la porte de champerret
the hour of the rumbling of motors in the avenue de la porte d'italie
the hour of the optician opening in rue du pas de la mule
the hour of the mission opening in the rue du pont de lodi
the hour of the libraries opening in rue de l'école de médecine
the hour of the church opening in place d'estienne d'orves
the hour of the brasserie opening in rue du château d'eau
the hour of the electrician opening in rue patrice de la tour du pin
the hour of the salon opening in rue des colonnes du trône
the hour of the flower shop opening in avenue de la porte de montrouge
the hour of the shoemaker opening in rue du dessous des berges
the hour of the jeweler's opening on place de la porte de saint-cloud
the hour of the restaurant opening on avenue de la porte de clichy
the hour of the printer opening in rue de la cour des noues
the hour of the heliport opening on avenue de la porte de sèvres

the hour of the church opening off rue du chevalier de la barre
the hour of the hospital opening in rue de la porte d'urbervilles
the hour of the bath of the sparrows—of the alley of the soleil d'or
the hour of recess for the schoolchildren in rue du val de marne

the hour of asphixiation of pedestrians on avenue de la porte de vitry
the hour of asphixiation of dogs on avenue de la porte de choisy
the hour of asphixiation of cats on avenue de la porte d'ivry
the hour of asphixiation of sparrows on avenue de la porte de gentilly
the hour of asphixiation of children on avenue de la porte de vanves
the hour of asphixiation of lettuce on avenue de la porte de la plaine
the hour of asphixiation of chestnut trees on avenue de la porte d'issy
the hour of asphixiation of drivers on avenue de la porte d'auteuil
the hour of asphixiation of motorcyclists on avenue du parc de passy
the hour of asphixiation of rugbymen on avenue du parc des princes
the hour of asphixiation of bicyclists on avenue de la porte des ternes
the hour of asphixiation of potted violets on avenue de la porte d'asnières
the hour of asphixiation of the geraniums on avenue de la porte de la
      chapelle
the hour of asphixiation of lilacs on avenue de la porte des lilas

the hour of lengthening shadows on avenue du maréchal franchet
      d'espérey
the hour of the chapel closing on avenue de la porte de vincennes
the hour of take-off of pigeons on the place de la porte de versailles
the hour of the café closing in rue du roi d'alger
the hour of lighting the streetlights on the place de la porte de passy
the hour of invisible cats in rue du bois de boulogne
the hour of sleepiness of inhabitants in rue du parc de charonne

the hour of remembering the disappearance of rue du moulin de beurre

Song of Rue Custine
and Rue Caulaincourt

He hawked sardines
And guided a tour
Twixt Rue Custine
And Rue Caulaincourt

She baked Boston beans
And boiled confiture
Twixt rue Custine
And Rue Caulaincourt

She was oh so clean
Her skin so pure
Twixt Rue Custine
And Rue Caulaincourt

Such a girl he'd never seen
Blood pressure cut short his tour
Twixt Rue Custine
And Rue Caulaincourt

She played the queen
He proved a boor
Twixt Rue Custine
And Rue Caulaincourt

She struck out for a distant beach
With a dealer in drink-and-victual
Leaving within his reach
Damn little:

Her beans his sardines
And his abbreviated tour
Twixt Rue Custine
And Rue Caulaincourt

II.

Michèle Métail
CROSS-EXAMINATION
{Oulipo}

A :   :
      "   , –   ?
B : _   ,   .
A : _   – –   ?
B : _   .
A : _   – ,   ?
B : _   .
A : _   ,   – ,   ...   – ?
B : _   ,   .
A : _   –   ?
B : _   ,   .
A : _   ,   ; ...   –   ,   ?
B : _   , ,
A : _   –   ?
B : _   ,   .
A : _   –   ?
B : _   .
A : _   –   ,   ,   ?
B : _ .
A : _   – – ?
B : _   .
A : _   – –   ?
B : _   .
A : _   –   ?
B : _   .

68

A : _   ,   —   ?
B : _   ,   .
A : _   ,   ;   ...   — —   ?
B : _   ,   ;   ,   .
A : _   —   ,   ,   ,   ;
B : _   .
A : _   ?
B : _   .
A : _   —   ?
B : _   ,   .
A : _ —   ?
B : _   .
A : _   ,   —   ,   —   ?
B : _   ,   ...
A : _   ;   —   , ?
B : _   ,   ...
A : _   ,   ,   ...   ,   — — ?
B : _   ,   .
A : _   — —   ;   ,   ?
B : _   ,   .
A : _   —   ?
B : _
A : _   ,   ; ,   ;   —   ?
B : _
A : _   ?
B : _
A : _   ?
B : _
A : _   ?
B : _   ,   , ,   :   , , ,   ; ! "

12.

Georges Perec
FROM *A VOID*
translated by Gilbert Adair
{Oulipo}

Black Bird

'Twas upon a midnight tristful I sat poring, wan and wistful,
Through many a quaint and curious list full of my consorts slain –
I sat nodding, almost napping, till I caught a sound of tapping,
As of spirits softly rapping, rapping at my door in vain.
' 'Tis a visitor,' I murmur'd, 'tapping at my door in vain –
                             Tapping soft as falling rain.'

Ah, I know, I know that this was on a holy night of Christmas;
But that quaint and curious list was forming phantoms all in train.
How I wish'd it was tomorrow; vainly had I sought to borrow
From my books a stay of sorrow – sorrow for my unjoin'd chain –
For that pictographic symbol missing from my unjoin'd chain –
                             And that would not join again.

Rustling faintly through my drapings was a ghostly, ghastly scraping
Sound that with fantastic shapings fill'd my fulminating brain;
And for now, to still its roaring, I stood back as if ignoring
That a spirit was imploring his admission to obtain –
' 'Tis a spirit now imploring his admission to obtain –'
                         Murmur'd I, '– but all in vain.'

But, my soul maturing duly and my brain not so unruly,
'Sir,' said I, 'or Madam, truly your acquittal would I gain;
For I was in fact caught napping, so soft-sounding was your rapping,
So faint-sounding was your tapping that you tapp'd my door in vain –
Hardly did I know you tapp'd it' – I unlock'd it but in vain –
                         For 'twas dark without and plain.

Staring at that dark phantasm as if shrinking from a chasm,
I stood quaking with a spasm fracturing my soul in twain;
But my study door was still as untowardly hush'd and chill as,
Oh, a crypt in which a still aspiring body is just lain –
As a dank, dark crypt in which a still suspiring man is lain –
                         Barr'd from rising up again.

All around my study flapping till my sanity was snapping,
I distinctly caught a tapping that was starting up again.
'Truly,' said I, 'truly this is turning now into a crisis;
I must find out what amiss is, and tranquillity obtain –
I must still my soul an instant and tranquillity obtain –
                         For 'tis truly not just rain!'

So, my study door unlocking to confound that awful knocking,
In I saw a Black Bird stalking with a gait of proud disdain;
I at first thought I was raving, but it stalk'd across my paving
And with broad black wings a-waving did my study door attain –
Did a pallid bust of Pallas on my study door attain –
                         Just as if 'twas its domain.

Now, that night-wing'd fowl placating my sad fancy into waiting
On its oddly fascinating air of arrogant disdain,
'Though thy tuft is shorn and awkward, thou,' I said, 'art not so
     backward
Coming forward, ghastly Black Bird wand'ring far from thy domain,
Not to say what thou art known as in thy own dusk-down domain!'
                         Quoth that Black Bird, 'Not Again.'

Wondrous was it this ungainly fowl could thus hold forth so plainly,
Though, alas, it discours'd vainly – as its point was far from plain;
And I think it worth admitting that, whilst in my study sitting,
I shall stop Black Birds from flitting thusly through my door again –
Black or not, I'll stop birds flitting through my study door again –
What I'll say is, 'Not Again!'

But that Black Bird, posing grimly on its placid bust, said primly
'Not Again', and I thought dimly what purport it might contain.
Not a third word did it throw off – not a third word did it know of –
Till, afraid that it would go off, I thought only to complain –
'By tomorrow it will go off,' did I tristfully complain.
It again said, 'Not Again.'

Now, my sanity displaying stark and staring signs of swaying,
'No doubt,' murmur'd I, 'it's saying all it has within its brain;
That it copy'd from a nomad whom Affliction caus'd to go mad,
From an outcast who was so mad as this ghastly bird to train –
Who, as with a talking parrot, did this ghastly Black Bird train
To say only, "Not Again."'

But that Black Bird still placating my sad fancy into waiting
For a word forthcoming, straight into my chair I sank again;
And, upon its cushion sinking, I soon found my spirit linking
Fancy unto fancy, thinking what this ominous bird of Cain –
What this grim, ungainly, ghastly, gaunt, and ominous bird of Cain
Sought by croaking 'Not Again.'

On all this I sat surmising, whilst with morbid caution sizing
Up that fowl; its tantalizing look burn'd right into my brain;
This for long I sat divining, with my pain-rack'd back inclining
On my cushion's satin lining with its ghastly crimson stain,
On that shiny satin lining with its sanguinary stain
Shrilly shouting, 'Not Again!'

Now my room was growing fragrant, its aroma almost flagrant,
As from spirits wafting vagrant through my dolorous domain.
'Good-for-naught,' I said, 'God sought you – from Plutonian Strands
     God brought you –
And, I know not why, God taught you all about my unjoin'd chain,
All about that linking symbol missing from my unjoin'd chain!'
                    Quoth that Black Bird, 'Not Again.'

'Sybil!' said I, 'thing of loathing – sybil, fury in bird's clothing!
If by Satan brought, or frothing storm did toss you on its main,
Cast away, but all unblinking, on this arid island sinking –
On this room of Horror stinking – say it truly, or abstain –
Shall I – shall I find that symbol? – say it – say it, or abstain
                    From your croaking, "Not Again".'

'Sybil!' said I, 'thing of loathing – sybil, fury in bird's clothing!
By God's radiant kingdom soothing all man's purgatorial pain,
Inform this soul laid low with sorrow if upon a distant morrow
It shall find that symbol for – oh, for its too long unjoin'd chain –
Find that pictographic symbol missing from its unjoin'd chain.'
                    Quoth that Black Bird, 'Not Again.'

'If that word's our sign of parting, Satan's bird,' I said, upstarting,
'Fly away, wings blackly parting, to thy Night's Plutonian plain!
For, mistrustful, I would scorn to mind that untruth thou hast sworn to,
And I ask that thou by morn tomorrow quit my sad domain!
Draw thy night-nibb'd bill from out my soul and quit my sad domain!'
                    Quoth that Black Bird, 'Not Again.'

And my Black Bird, still not quitting, still is sitting, still is sitting
On that pallid bust – still flitting through my dolorous domain;

But it cannot stop from gazing for it truly finds amazing
That, by artful paraphrasing, I such rhyming can sustain –
Notwithstanding my lost symbol I such rhyming still sustain –
Though I shan't try it again!

Arthur Gordon Pym

13.

Stefan Themerson
FROM *BAYAMUS*
{Anticipatory Plagiarism}

*My S.P. Translation of the opening words of the chinese poem:
'Drinking under the Moon,' by Li Po.*

*

The fermented
grape-
juice
among the reproductive
parts
of
seed-plants

O! I'm conscious
of
my state
of
being isolated
from
others!

Ah! Body attendant   revolving   keeping   & shining
          on   about   238,840 miles   by
          the   (mean)   reflecting the light
          Earth   aloof   radiated
                                                                   by
                                                                   the
                                                                   sun

       into
       my
       mouth
    I take
       &   while expressing the hope for thy success.
       swallow
       the
       liquid

* *

Obtain the
      visual
      impression of a
            dark
            patch formed beside me
                by
                my body
                    which
                    obstructs some rays of thy light!

Let   influence   by   feedback   the   object of which
us   ourselves   from   is
three   each   to stimulate
                    other   the
                                  pleasure centre
                                  in
                                  our brain!

Body attendant   Why are you separated from me by 221,614 miles minimum –
        on
        the   Why is the distance to you increasing up to 252,972 miles?
        Earth!

Make thy glides
              leaps
                  revolutions
                      gestures
                        & other expresses of a universal fixation for
                                      rhythmical movement
                  the
            keep in step with partial
                    darkness caused by the intervention
                            of
                            my   thy light
                          body between
                                &
                              the surface
                              of the
                              Earth
            & with me.

* * *

The existence   shall
    of   continue
    this   for
    emotion   a   every
           period   which is greater than assignable
           of   quantity
           time

Body attendant   Let the   vibrations of my short lyrical song
    on   stimulate thine external ear-drum
    the   & be conveyed to thine internal ear-drum
    Earth!   & thence to thine internal ear fluids
           Let them
                  cause impulses to pass up thine auditory nerve
                                to
                                the
                                hearing
                                centre
                                in
                                thy
                                brain

    the
I & patch   produced by the intervention
    of darkness   of
                     my   the surface of the Earth
                     body between
                              &
                              thy light

we can move
    rapidly
    like the masses   suspended   in the gases
           of   at   of
           minute   high   the
           droplets   altitudes   air
           of
           water
    away.

* * * *

And having the
        fermented
        grape-juice in our stomach
    absorbing it into our cerebro-spinal fluid
    paralysing various parts of our nervous system with it
    speaking thickly
    unable to maintain equilibrium
    our vision blurred and double
  we get merged with one another
        cognitively
        &
        affectively

(though separated and companionless again when the sun
                                is
                                above
                            the horizon)
Let us determine the place
                of
                our
                meeting which
                        shall
                        continue for a period of time
                                greater
                                than
                                every
                                assignable
                                quantity
        somewhere
        between
    145,000 million
        or is it
    300,000 million
                stars constituting that particular 'island universe'
                of
                which
                our
                    solar
                    system
                    is
                        a   part.

14.

Lewis Carroll

FROM *ALICE'S ADVENTURES IN WONDERLAND*

{Anticipatory Plagiarism}

The Pool of Tears

'Curiouser and curiouser!' cried Alice (she was so much surprised, that for the moment she quite forgot how to speak good English). 'Now I'm opening out like the largest telescope that ever was! Good-bye, feet!' (for when she looked down at her feet, they seemed to be almost out of sight, they were getting so far off). 'Oh, my poor little feet, I wonder who will put on your shoes and stockings for you now, dears? I'm sure *I* sha'n't be able! I shall be a great deal too far off to trouble myself about you: you must manage the best way you can – but I must be kind to them,' thought Alice, 'or perhaps they wo'n't walk the way I want to go! Let me see. I'll give them a new pair of boots every Christmas.'

And she went on planning to herself how she would manage it. 'They must go by the carrier,' she thought; 'and how funny it'll seem, sending presents to one's own feet! And how odd the directions will look!

> *Alice's Right Foot, Esq.*
> *Hearthrug,*
> *near the Fender,*
> *(with Alice's love).*

Oh dear, what nonsense I'm talking!'

Just at this moment her head struck against the roof of the hall: in fact she was now rather more than nine feet high, and she at once took up the little golden key and hurried off to the garden door:

Poor Alice! It was as much as she could do, lying down on one side, to look through into the garden with one eye; but to get through was more hopeless than ever: she sat down and began to cry again.

'You ought to be ashamed of yourself,' said Alice, 'a great girl like you,' (she might well say this), 'to go on crying in this way! Stop this moment, I tell you!' But she went on all the same, shedding gallons of tears, until there was a large pool all round her, about four inches deep, and reaching half down the hall.

After a time she heard a little pattering of feet in the distance, and she hastily dried her eyes to see what was coming. It was the White Rabbit returning, splendidly dressed, with a pair of white kid-gloves in one hand and a large fan in the other: he came trotting along in a great hurry, muttering to himself, as he came, 'Oh! The Duchess, the Duchess! Oh! *Wo'n't* she be savage if I've kept her waiting!' Alice felt so desperate that she was ready to ask help of any one: so, when the Rabbit came near her, she began, in a low, timid voice, 'If you please, Sir –' The Rabbit started violently, dropped the white kid-gloves and the fan, and scurried away into the darkness as hard as he could go.

Alice took up the fan and gloves, and, as the hall was very hot, she kept fanning herself all the time she went on talking. 'Dear, dear! How queer everything is to-day! And yesterday things went on just as usual. I

wonder if I've been changed in the night? Let me think: *was* I the same when I got up this morning? I almost think I can remember feeling a little different. But if I'm not the same, the next question is "Who in the world am I?" Ah, *that's* the great puzzle!'

And she began thinking over all the children she knew that were of the same age as herself, to see if she could have been changed for any of them.

'I'm sure I'm not Ada,' she said, 'for her hair goes in such long ringlets, and mine doesn't go in ringlets at all; and I'm sure I ca'n't be Mabel, for I know all sorts of things, and she, oh, she knows such a very little! Besides, *she's* she, and *I'm* I, and – oh dear, how puzzling it all is! I'll try if I know all the things I used to know. Let me see: four times five is twelve, and four times six is thirteen, and four times seven is – oh dear! I shall never get to twenty at that rate! However, the Multiplication-Table doesn't signify: let's try Geography. London is the capital of Paris, and Paris is the capital of Rome, and Rome – no, *that's* all wrong, I'm certain! I must have been changed for Mabel! I'll try and say "*How doth the little –*",' and she crossed her hands on her lap, as if she were saying lessons, and began to repeat it, but her voice sounded hoarse and strange, and the words did not come the same as they used to do: –

'How doth the little crocodile
Improve his shining tail,
And pour the waters of the Nile
On every golden scale!

'How cheerfully he seems to grin,
How neatly spreads his claws,
And welcomes little fishes in,
With gently smiling jaws!'

'I'm sure those are not the right words,' said poor Alice, and her eyes filled with tears again as she went on, 'I must be Mabel after all, and I shall have to go and live in that poky little house, and have next to no toys to play with, and oh, ever so many lessons to learn! No, I've made up my mind about it: if I'm Mabel, I'll stay down here! It'll be no use their putting their heads down and saying "Come up again, dear!" I shall only look up and say "Who am I, then? Tell me that first, and then, if I like being that person, I'll come up: if not, I'll stay down here till I'm some-body else" – but, oh dear!' cried Alice, with a sudden burst of tears, 'I do wish they *would* put their heads down! I am so *very* tired of being all alone here!'

As she said this she looked down at her hands, and was surprised to see that she had put on one of the Rabbit's little white kid-gloves while she was talking. 'How *can* I have done that?' she thought. 'I must be growing small again.' She got up and went to the table to measure herself by it, and found that, as nearly as she could guess, she was now about two feet high, and was going on shrinking rapidly: she soon found out that the cause of this was the fan she was holding, and she dropped it hastily, just in time to save herself from shrinking away altogether.

'That *was* a narrow escape!' said Alice, a good deal frightened at the sudden change, but very glad to find herself still in existence. 'And now for the garden!' And she ran with all speed back to the little door; but, alas! the little door was shut again, and the little golden key was lying on the glass table as before, 'and things are worse than ever,' thought the poor child, 'for I never was so small as this before, never! And I declare it's too bad, that it is!'

As she said these words her foot slipped, and in another moment, splash! she was up to her chin in salt-water. Her first idea was that she had somehow fallen into the sea, 'and in that case I can go back by rail-way,' she said to herself.

(Alice had been to the seaside once in her life, and had come to the general conclusion that, wherever you go to on the English coast, you find a number of bathing-machines in the sea, some children digging in the sand with wooden spades, then a row of lodging-houses, and behind them a railway station.) However, she soon made out that she was in the pool of tears which she had wept when she was nine feet high.

'I wish I hadn't cried so much!' said Alice, as she swam about, trying to find her way out. 'I shall be punished for it now, I suppose, by being drowned in my own tears! That *will* be a queer thing, to be sure! However, everything is queer to-day.'

Just then she heard something splashing about in the pool a little way off, and she swam nearer to make out what it was: at first she thought it

must be a walrus or hippopotamus, but then she remembered how small she was now, and she soon made out that it was only a mouse, that had slipped in like herself.

'Would it be of any use, now,' thought Alice, 'to speak to this mouse? Everything is so out-of-the-way down here, that I should think very likely it can talk: at any rate, there's no harm in trying,' So she began: 'O Mouse, do you know the way out of this pool? I am very tired of swimming about here, O Mouse!' (Alice thought this must be the right way of speaking to a mouse: she had never done such a thing before, but she remembered having seen, in her brother's Latin Grammar, 'A mouse – of a mouse – to a mouse – a mouse – O mouse!') The mouse looked at her rather inquisitively, and seemed to her to wink with one of its little eyes, but it said nothing.

'Perhaps it doesn't understand English,' thought Alice. 'I daresay it's a French mouse, come over with William the Conqueror.' (For, with all her knowledge of history, Alice had no very clear notion how long ago anything had happened.) So she began: 'Où est ma chatte?' which was the first sentence in her French lesson-book. The Mouse gave a sudden leap out of the water, and seemed to quiver all over with fright. 'Oh, I beg your pardon!' cried Alice hastily, afraid that she had hurt the poor animal's feelings. 'I quite forgot you didn't like cats.'

'Not like cats!' cried the Mouse in a shrill, passionate voice. 'Would *you* like cats, if you were me?'

'Well, perhaps not,' said Alice in a soothing tone: 'don't be angry about it. And yet I wish I could show you our cat Dinah. I think you'd take a fancy to cats, if you could only see her. She is such a dear quiet thing,' Alice went on, half to herself, as she swam lazily about in the pool, 'and she sits purring so nicely by the fire, licking her paws and washing her face – and she is such a nice soft thing to nurse – and she's such a capital one for catching mice – oh, I beg your pardon!' cried Alice again, for this time the Mouse was bristling all over, and she felt certain it must be really offended. 'We wo'n't talk about her any more, if you'd rather not.'

'We, indeed!' cried the Mouse, who was trembling down to the end of its tail. 'As if *I* would talk on such a subject! Our family always *hated* cats: nasty, low, vulgar things! Don't let me hear the name again!'

'I wo'n't indeed!' said Alice, in a great hurry to change the subject of conversation. 'Are you – are you fond – of – of dogs?' The Mouse did not answer, so Alice went on eagerly: 'There is such a nice little dog, near our house, I should like to show you! A little bright-eyed terrier, you know, with oh, such long curly brown hair! And it'll fetch things when you throw them, and it'll sit up and beg for its dinner, and all sorts of things – I ca'n't remember half of them – and it belongs to a farmer, you know, and he says it's so useful, it's worth a hundred pounds! He says it kills all the rats and – oh dear!' cried Alice in a sorrowful tone.

'I'm afraid I've offended it again!' For the Mouse was swimming away from her as hard as it could go, and making quite a commotion in the pool as it went.

So she called softly after it, 'Mouse dear! Do come back again, and we won't talk about cats, or dogs either, if you don't like them!' When the Mouse heard this, it turned round and swam slowly back to her: its face was quite pale (with passion, Alice thought), and it said, in a low trembling voice, 'Let us get to the shore, and then I'll tell you my history, and you'll understand why it is I hate cats and dogs.'

It was high time to go, for the pool was getting quite crowded with the birds and animals that had fallen into it: there was a Duck and a Dodo, a Lory and an Eaglet, and several other curious creatures. Alice led the way, and the whole party swam to the shore.

15.

Michelle Grangaud
FROM *POETS' CALENDAR*
translated by Cole Swensen
{Oulipo}

April 1

– Having invented the 'poem du jour' form, Jacques Jouet today begins a journal of poems.
– In the palm grove, there is a blue cup.

April 2

– Certain details indicate that Mr Tchulkaturin died some time during the previous night.
– Victor Segalen, Gilbert de Voisins, and the prefect of Zhao Hua meet in the tomb of Bao San naing in the province of Sè tchouan. Segalen takes photographs.
– On this day, François-René Chateaubriand publishes a description of Niagara Falls in *Atala*.

April 3

– Ettore Schmitz Promises For the last time To stop smoking.
– Voltaire and President de Brosses are received at the Academy of Dijon.
– Samuel Johnson begins work on the second volume of his Dictionary, leaving space for the preface, the grammar, and the history, none of these chapters having yet been started.

April 4

– Monsieur de Marivaux reads his *Reflections* to the Académie française in the form of a letter *on the human spirit*.
– A new cinematographic series is launched with *Une aventure de Bout de Zan*, a film by Louis Feuillade.
– After reading Solovyov's *History*, Tolstoy jots in his notebook: 'Despite oneself, one must conclude that the history of Russia is composed of monstrosities.'

April 5

– Though Marshall Canrobert, dining at the Princess's, has gout in his hand, he nonetheless jauntily entertains the guests with a description of Marshall Lauriston's death 'on the battlefield of love.'
– The group that would later be called l'Oeuvre des Planteurs-Cultivateurs de l'Olivier Pacifique is founded this day, as attested by a letter from Dubeau to Père Enfantin.

April 6

– On this 15 clinamen 77 E.P., Irénée-Louis Sandomir, in his inaugural Harangue, announces the birth of the College of 'Pataphysics.
– There were twenty-five bombings during the night. The Alhambra Theatre was burning, the Institute smoking, the Hôpital Saint-Louis flaming, and not a wall left standing straight.
– The *Charterhouse of Parma* appears this day in the bookstores.

April 7

– Ludwig van Beethoven, age 16, goes to Vienna to work with Mozart.
– Dostoevsky attends the banquet of the 'petrashevists' (partisans of the socialist and anti-monarchist Petrashevsky), which is given in honor of Fourier.
– Walter Benjamin sets sail on the *Catania*, which he'd taken six years earlier, bound for Barcelona, and from there to Ibiza. It looks like bad weather ahead.

April 8

– Luster, in leaving, looks for the last time at the flower drooping over Ben's fist, then leaves.

– Delacroix is working on the painting *Hercule attachant Nérée*. Over Hercules, he washes vermillion, laquer, light zinc yellow and Van Dyke brown. Over Nérée, light zinc yellow, lacquer, cobalt, and Prussian blue. He touches the light, muted tones with a shade of pale rose-orange mixed with a shade of Van Dyke brown, zinc yellow, and a mauve that's lighter than the one he used for the wash.

– In the city of Meung, where the author of the *Roman de la rose* was born, the young d'Artagnan cuts a startling figure on a bizarre nag that looks like Don Quixote's Rocinante.

– In Boston, Henry James speaks in the past tense about his novel *The Bostonians*, which he has not yet starting writing.

April 9

– A son is born to the Jouberts at nine hours and fifteen minutes after midnight. The father, in noting the fact, comments: that he might one day remember the suffering of his mother! On the same day, he also notes that he heard a cock crowing.

– In her prison cell in the Barminstrasse, Rosa Luxemburg reads a geology book and learns that in a layer of clay in Sweden they've discovered the traces of a brief downpour that fell millions of years ago.

– According to the instructions in his will, the body of Hermann Raffke, brewer and noted amateur painter, is stuffed by the greatest taxidermist in the world, brought in specially from Mexico, and then is propped up in the chair in which he posed for the henceforth famous painting by Heinrich Kürz, titled *A Gallery Portrait*.

April 10

– At daybreak on his seventieth birthday, Tang Zhen toasts himself by drinking the rest of the wine. He then reflects that perhaps congratulations are not in order as he is much closer to his death than to his birth.

But then he tells himself that though his hair may have changed and his teeth fallen out, his spirit has remained the same, vibrant and vigorous. 'Today, at seventy, is the time to pull out all the stops.'
– Emmanuel Hocquard sees Manhattan as a city or a little island.

April 11

– *The Crucifixion Considered as an Uphill Bicycle Race* by Alfred Jarry is published today in *Le Canard sauvage*.
– Alfred de Musset converses with a Mandarin with painted eyebrows and fingernails eighteen inches long whose only exercise consists in trailing his gaze sometimes to the right, sometimes to the left, with a half-smile.

April 12

– In the library of Miss Shepheard (known as Leonora), between Malebranche and Locke, you'll find a certain number of novels – *Cleopatra, Cassandra, Le Grand Cyrus,* and *Clélie*, which falls open, when you open it, at a scene of two lovers meeting in a grove.
– A review by Eneas Sweetland Dallas appears in *Times*, 'There can be no mistake about *Adam Bede*. It is a first-rate novel, and its author takes rank at once among the masters of the art.'
– In the streets of Paris, the people follow Voltaire, applauding him and calling him Calas's man.

April 13

– At four-seventeen in the afternoon, with the sea beautiful and the breeze gentle, the Cunard Company's *Scotia*, suffers a collision that tears a perfectly even isosceles triangle in its hull below the waterline.
– Handel's servant, lacking tobacco for his pipe, mitigated his boredom by blowing soap bubbles through it.

April 14

– Paul Klee walks through the cemetery at Hammamet, which stretches, unwalled, along the sea. Around him, cacti, unveiled young girls, and a camel. The camel, above all, gives him the sense that time has stopped.
– During the night, an earthquake swallowed Elfrida de Monte Salerno's palace. That noble and arrogant lady had openly bragged about possessing a veritable paradise, which is what, according to Pope Pius III, turned the place into a haunt of the devil.
– Jacques Roubaud gives his fourth lesson, *Le fils de Leoprepes*, at the Villa Gillet.

April 15

– Emily Dickinson writes: 'Mr Higginson, Are you too deeply occupied to say if my Verse is alive?'
– Cézanne repeats his earlier statement to Emile Bernard – that nature must be dealt with in terms of the cylinder, the sphere, and the cone.
– Three baggage cars wallow down the flooded road. They're carrying the new pastor's domestic effects to Heukelum.

April 16

– Valerie Larbaud is in bed with a fever and Byron's *Don Juan*. During the night while asleep, he recites the most insipid banalities in perfect byronian stanzas.
– The first Dada exhibition takes place in the bookstore Le Sans Pareil.
– Near Vechta, there are compasses that also keep time.

April 17

– Monsieur de Kératry uses, for the first time in France, the word 'démodé.'
– At Madame Necker's, seventeen venerable philosophers, after having invoked the Holy Spirit and dined and discussed with abandon, unanimously decide to erect a statue of Monsieur de Voltaire.
– Today, Mary Shelley finishes the final draft of *Frankenstein*.

April 18

– George Eliot starts writing *Janet's Repentance* at St Mary's in the Isles of Scilly.
– Cao Xueqin remarries, just a few years before his death – either three or four – the date of his death is not certain, but that of his second marriage is confirmed by two coffers whose decorations, both written and drawn, form a whole: on one side, a poem dedicated to his new wife; on the other, the date of the poem: 'day shangsi of the year gengchen, the twenty-fifth of the Qianlong era.'

April 19

– Pontormo sulks beneath the rocks. He dines on nine ounces of bread, an omelette, and a salad. It all makes him a bit dizzy.
– With the capital (New York) surging up above him, Walt Whitman contemplates the great bronze statue at dusk, when the setting sun gleams on its head and crown, making it dazzle like a huge, strange star.
– The Raymond-Queneau Library at Juvisy-sur-Orge is inaugurated.

April 20

– Zola, needing to research art dealers and connoisseurs for his projected novel *L'Oeuvre,* asks Antoine Guillemet for an hour of casual chat.
– Terrasse, Fénéon, Vallette, Rachilde, and several others are invited to a day of celebration (with victuals and potables) put on by Alfred Jarry at his retreat along the canal.

April 21

– Referring to the election of Ampère to the Académie française, Hugo notes in his journal: 'Progress slow, but academies, like the elderly, advance in small steps.'
– Leonardo de Vinci starts a new notebook and goes back to working on the horse for an equestrian statue of Francesco Sforza.

– Paul-Jean Toulet writes to himself: 'Dear Master, the respectful silence of Bruges reminds me too vividly of that which strikes me in your presence when, once again, I cannot bring myself to express to you the singular admiration I feel for your beautiful talent.'

April 22

– While waiting for his baggage to come off the train that just brought him from Brignoles, Gide suddenly senses, like an illumination, the beginning of his novel *The Counterfeiters*. It's going to start with the sentence: I'll bet you're traveling without a ticket.
– Nietzsche composes a vocal quartet with piano that he titles *Sunny Days of Autumn*.
– *Underground Lovers* by Jean Tardieu is produced at the Lancry Theater.
– At Heaven's reception desk, an official fills in the pre-printed form that he'll address to Hell: 'An individual by the name of Shakespeare presented himself at our office today.'

April 23

– A boxing match in Madrid brings Jack Johnson, champion of Europe, face to face with Arthur Craven, champion of France and poet, who is knocked out in the first round.
– On this day in the *Écho de Paris*, Monsieur Ubu announces to Achras that he has invented 'Pataphysics.
– At the town hall of Nantes, the honorable Morlierre (sic) humbly asks the members of the council to allow actors to put on their plays.
– Roman Opalka is sitting on a fur cushion on the floor in the center of his studio. He has reached 3,455,207.

April 24

– At La Rochelle, an anonymous fugitive seeking a way out of France promises the captain of a ship 200 thalers for each of the five people that he will bring to him, thus 1000 thalers in all.

– The Citizen Army (Connolly) supported by a handful of Irish voluteers (Pearse) takes over the main Dublin post office and proclaims the Republic.
– Towards evening, Roland Barthes runs through a cold rain to catch the #58.

April 25

– The warbler, well known to Madeleine de Scudéry, returns to the grove today, as it usually does.
– In the sale of Madame Hanska's estate, the manuscript of *Eugénie Grandet* slips through the Viscount of Lovenjoul's fingers, having been auctioned off at two thousand francs to Baron Cahen d'Anvers.

April 26

– Towards one in the morning, Samuel Johnson writes to God: 'If you have assigned my spouse to keep a watch over me, allow me to enjoy some of the good effects of her attentions [. . .] in the form of apparitions, impulses, dreams, or any other manifestation that your judgement finds agreeable.'
– Raymond Queneau testifies in favor of Isidore Isou at his trial; the latter is accused of violating public morality with his book *La Méchanique des femmes*.
– In an inn in Dordrecht, the young René Descartes argues about Lulle's *Ars parva* with a learned man who prides himself on being able to argue a point for a full hour, and then switch and take the opposing argument for another hour.

April 27

– Balzac is incarcerated in the Hotel des Haricots for having several times shirked his duties in the National Guard.
– Georges Perec is at parachuting school at Camp Astra, near Pau in the lower Pyrenees.
– An imperial decree orders all Chinese functionaries to send their province's most literate people to the capital.

April 28

– The King's agents search the ship, but the fugitives aren't found. And then a favorable wind, toward 11 or 12 pm, carries them far from the enemies of truth.
– King Henri orders that 'a total of twenty-five écus be paid to our dear and beloved *sieur de Sponde.*'
– Geoffroy Tory and Gilles de Gourmont present their *Champ fleury.*

April 29

– Queneau finishes his great poem *The Explanation of Metaphors.*
– Like the night before, at two o'clock in the morning, Victor Hugo hears three sharp knocks; the sound makes him think of three lashes of the whip landing on his bed post.

April 30

– Annibal de Coconnas and Boniface de La Mole are decapitated in the Place de Grève for trying to help Henri de Navarre to escape from the Louvre, where he is held captive. Mathilde de La Mole appears, that evening, in deep mourning; Julien watches her in astonishment.
– On his deserted island, Robinson Crusoe, having noticed that his supply of biscuits is diminishing rapidly, decides to limit himself to one biscuit a day, which grieves his heart deeply.

16.

Georges Perec
81 EASY-COOK RECIPES
FOR BEGINNERS
translated by David Bellos
{Oulipo/Oucuipo}

SOLE AUX CHAMPIGNONS
Take two fine whole fresh sole, skin and fillet them. Bake in a medium oven for 40 minutes, basting frequently. When half-done, add a half-pound of button mushrooms. Lay out on a heated serving dish and sprinkle generously with ground fennel.

LAPIN AU NOILLY
Smear a pair of small rabbits with a generous coating of full-strength mustard. Cook in a casserole together with a few rashers of bacon, sliced carrots, fresh tomatoes and spring onions. To make the gravy, add a dash of vermouth to the liquid. Serve with ratatouille.

RIS DE VEAU 'À MA FAÇON'
Take four sweetbreads, soak in lemon water, then drain and cut into thin slices. Bake in a medium oven for 40 minutes, basting frequently. Remove from heat and then add two tablespoons of double cream. Serve with stiffly beaten egg whites.

SOLE À LA CRÈME
Take two fine whole fresh sole, skin and fillet them. Cook in a casserole together with a few rashers of bacon, sliced carrots, fresh tomatoes and spring onions. Remove from heat and then add two tablespoons of double cream. Lay out on a heated serving dish and sprinkle generously with tarragon.

RIS DE VEAU FLAMANDE
Take four sweetbreads, soak in lemon water, then drain and cut into thin slices. Brown the sweetbreads in a hot shallow pan, then lower the heat and leave to simmer. When half done, add a half-pound of button mushrooms. Lay out on a heated serving dish and sprinkle generously with soft brown sugar.

LAPIN À LA BOURGUIGNONNE
Smear a pair of small rabbits with a generous coating of full-strength mustard. Bake in a medium oven for 40 minutes, basting frequently. To make the gravy, add a dash of vermouth to the liquid. Serve with a jug of *sauce bourguignonne*.

RIS DE VEAU GRAND-MÈRE
Take four sweetbreads, soak in lemon water, then drain and cut into thin slices. Cook in a casserole together with a few rashers of bacon, sliced carrots, fresh tomatoes and spring onions. When half done, add a half-pound of button mushrooms. Serve with a jug of caper sauce.

LAPEREAU À LA MOUTARDE
Smear a pair of small rabbits with a generous coating of full-strength mustard. Bake in a medium oven for 40 minutes, basting frequently. When half done, add a half-pound of button mushrooms. Serve with potato pancakes.

SOLE AU NOILLY
Take two fine whole fresh sole, skin and fillet them. Cook in a casserole together with a few rashers of bacon, sliced carrots, fresh tomatoes and spring onions. To make the gravy, add a dash of vermouth to the liquid. Lay out on a heated serving dish and sprinkle generously with fresh thyme.

RIS DE VEAU À LA CRÈME
Take four sweetbreads, soak in lemon water, then drain and cut into thin slices. Brown the sweetbreads in a hot shallow pan, then lower the heat

and leave to simmer. Remove from heat and then add two tablespoons of double cream. Serve with a jug of mousseline sauce.

Lapin aux navets
Smear a pair of small rabbits with a generous coating of full-strength mustard. Cook in a casserole together with a few rashers of bacon, sliced carrots, fresh tomatoes and spring onions. When half done, add a half-pound of button mushrooms. Serve with glacé turnips.

Sole au four
Take two fine whole fresh sole, skin and fillet them. Bake in a medium oven for 40 minutes, basting frequently. To make the gravy, add a dash of vermouth to the liquid. Serve with a jug of white-butter sauce.

Sole printanière
Take two fine whole fresh sole, skin and fillet them. Cook in a casserole together with a few rashers of bacon, sliced carrots, fresh tomatoes and spring onions. Remove from heat and then add two tablespoons of double cream. Serve with peas.

Ris de veau aux champignons
Take four sweetbreads, soak in lemon water, then drain and cut into thin slices. Bake in a medium oven for 40 minutes, basting frequently. When half done, add a half-pound of button mushrooms. Lay out on a heated serving dish and sprinkle generously with chives.

Lapin au roquefort
Smear a pair of small rabbits with a generous coating of full-strength mustard. Cook in a casserole together with a few rashers of bacon, sliced carrots, fresh tomatoes and spring onions. Remove from heat and then add two tablespoons of double cream. Lay out on a heated serving dish and sprinkle generously with crumbled Roquefort cheese.

Lapin à la saigonnaise
Smear a pair of small rabbits with a generous coating of full-strength

mustard. Bake in a medium oven for 40 minutes, basting frequently. Remove from heat and then add two tablespoons of double cream. Serve with a jug of *nuoc mam*.

Sole à l'oseille

Take two fine whole fresh sole, skin and fillet them. Brown the fish in a hot shallow pan, then lower the heat and leave to simmer. To make the gravy, add a dash of vermouth to the liquid. Serve with mashed sorrel leaves.

Ris de veau béarnaise

Take four sweetbreads, soak in lemon water, then drain and cut into thin slices. Cook in a casserole together with a few rashers of bacon, sliced carrots, fresh tomatoes and spring onions. To make the gravy, add a dash of vermouth to the liquid. Serve with a jug of Béarnaise sauce.

Lapin aux cardons

Smear a pair of small rabbits with a generous coating of full-strength mustard. Brown them in a hot shallow pan, then lower the heat and leave to simmer. When half done, add a half-pound of button mushrooms. Serve with shrimps.

Soles Choron

Take two fine whole fresh sole, skin and fillet them. Brown the fish in a hot shallow pan, then lower the heat and leave to simmer. When half done, add a half-pound of button mushrooms. Serve with a jug of Choron sauce.

Ris de veau à l'italienne

Take four sweetbreads, soak in lemon water, then drain and cut into thin slices. Bake in a medium oven for 40 minutes, basting frequently. To make the gravy, add a dash of vermouth to the liquid. Lay out on a heated serving dish and sprinkle generously with Parmesan cheese.

SOLES À L'ÉTOUFFÉE
Take two fine whole fresh sole, skin and fillet them. Cook in a casserole together with a few rashers of bacon, sliced carrots, fresh tomatoes and spring onions. When half done, add a half-pound of button mushrooms. Lay out on a heated serving dish and sprinkle generously with rosemary.

LAPEREAUX À LA MOSCOVITE
Smear a pair of small rabbits with a generous coating of full-strength mustard. Brown them in a hot shallow pan, then lower the heat and leave to simmer. Remove from heat and then add two tablespoons of double cream. Serve with a jug of devil's sauce.

SOLE 'SANS-FAÇON'
Take two fine whole fresh sole, skin and fillet them. Bake in a medium oven for 40 minutes, basting frequently. Remove from heat and then add two tablespoons of double cream. Lay out on a heated serving dish and sprinkle generously with *fines herbes*.

RIS DE VEAU CURNONSKY
Take four sweetbreads, soak in lemon water, then drain and cut into thin slices. Brown the sweetbreads in a hot shallow pan, then lower the heat and leave to simmer. To make the gravy, add a dash of vermouth to the liquid. Serve with broccoli.

LAPIN AUX CHIPOLATAS
Smear a pair of small rabbits with a generous coating of full-strength mustard. Brown them in a hot shallow pan, then lower the heat and leave to simmer. To make the gravy, add a dash of vermouth to the liquid. Serve with chipolatas.

SOLE SOUBISE
Take two fine whole fresh sole, skin and fillet them. Brown the fish in a hot shallow pan, then lower the heat and leave to simmer. Remove from heat and then add two tablespoons of double cream. Serve with a jug of Soubise sauce.

Ris de veau en cocotte
Take four sweetbreads, soak in lemon water, then drain and cut into thin slices. Cook in a casserole together with a few rashers of bacon, sliced carrots, fresh tomatoes and spring onions. Remove from heat and then add two tablespoons of double cream. Serve with artichoke hearts.

Lapin à la pistache
Smear a pair of small rabbits with a generous coating of full-strength mustard. Bake in a medium oven for 40 minutes, basting frequently. Remove from heat and then add two tablespoons of double cream. Lay out on a heated serving dish and sprinkle generously with ground pistachios.

Ris de veau Aurore
Take four sweetbreads, soak in lemon water, then drain and cut into thin slices. Brown them in a hot shallow pan, then lower the heat and leave to simmer. To make the gravy, add a dash of vermouth to the liquid. Serve with a jug of Aurora sauce.

Lapin au cumin
Smear a pair of small rabbits with a generous coating of full-strength mustard. Brown them in a hot shallow pan, then lower the heat and leave to simmer. When half done, add a half-pound of button mushrooms. Lay out on a heated serving dish and sprinkle generously with cumin.

Suprême de sole
Take two fine whole fresh sole, skin and fillet them. Bake in a medium oven for 40 minutes, basting frequently. When half done, add a half-pound of button mushrooms. Serve with asparagus.

Ris de veau à la seychelloise
Take four sweetbreads, soak in lemon water, then drain and cut into thin slices. Brown the sweetbreads in a hot shallow pan, then lower the heat and leave to simmer. Remove from heat and then add two tablespoons of double cream. Lay out on a heated serving dish and sprinkle generously with grated coconut.

LAPIN À LA PROVENÇALE

Smear a pair of small rabbits with a generous coating of full-strength mustard. Cook in a casserole together with a few rashers of bacon, sliced carrots, fresh tomatoes and spring onions. When half done, add a half-pound of button mushrooms. Serve with aioli.

RIS DE VEAU SURPRISE

Take four sweetbreads, soak in lemon water, then drain and cut into thin slices. Bake in a medium oven for 40 minutes, basting frequently. To make the gravy, add a dash of vermouth to the liquid. Serve with a tea sorbet.

SOLE BRAISÉE AUVERGNATE

Take two fine whole fresh sole, skin and fillet them. Cook in a casserole together with a few rashers of bacon, sliced carrots, fresh tomatoes and spring onions. To make the gravy, add a dash of vermouth to the liquid. Serve with lentils.

RIS DE VEAU MÉPHISTO

Take four sweetbreads, soak in lemon water, then drain and cut into thin slices. Bake in a medium oven for 40 minutes, basting frequently. When half done, add a half-pound of button mushrooms. Serve with chili sauce.

SOLE 'CAFÉ DE PARIS'

Take two fine whole fresh sole, skin and fillet them. Cook in a casserole together with a few rashers of bacon, sliced carrots, fresh tomatoes and spring onions. When half done, add a half-pound of button mushrooms. Serve with a jug of Béchamel sauce.

LAPIN AU BASILIC

Smear a pair of small rabbits with a generous coating of full-strength mustard. Bake in a medium oven for 40 minutes, basting frequently. When half done, add a half-pound of button mushrooms. Lay out on a heated serving dish and sprinkle generously with basil.

Ris de veau à la lyonnaise
Take four sweetbreads, soak in lemon water, then drain and cut into thin slices. Cook in a casserole together with a few rashers of bacon, sliced carrots, fresh tomatoes and spring onions. Remove from heat and then add two tablespoons of double cream. Serve with a jug of sauce ravigote.

Lapereau sauté 'Val d'Aoste'
Smear a pair of small rabbits with a generous coating of full-strength mustard. Brown them in a hot shallow pan, then lower the heat and leave to simmer. To make the gravy, add a dash of vermouth to the liquid. Lay out on a heated serving dish and sprinkle generously with star anise.

Filets de sole bruxelloise
Take two fine whole fresh sole, skin and fillet them. Brown the fish in a hot shallow pan, then lower the heat and leave to simmer. When half done, add a half-pound of button mushrooms. Serve with a jug of Hollandaise sauce.

Sole charcutière
Take two fine whole fresh sole, skin and fillet them. Bake in a medium oven for 40 minutes, basting frequently. Remove from heat and then add two tablespoons of double cream. Serve with applesauce.

Ris de veau au safran
Take four sweetbreads, soak in lemon water, then drain and cut into thin slices. Bake in a medium oven for 40 minutes, basting frequently. Remove from heat and then add two tablespoons of double cream. Lay out on a heated serving dish and sprinkle generously with saffron.

Lapin à l'alsacienne
Smear a pair of small rabbits with a generous coating of full-strength mustard. Cook in a casserole together with a few rashers of bacon, sliced carrots, fresh tomatoes and spring onions. Remove from heat and then add two tablespoons of double cream. Serve with fresh pasta.

RIS DE VEAU SAINT-SYLVESTRE
Take four sweetbreads, soak in lemon water, then drain and cut into thin slices. Brown the sweetbreads in a hot shallow pan, then lower the heat and leave to simmer. When half done, add a half-pound of button mushrooms. Serve with hot chestnuts.

FILETS DE SOLE BASSE-CALORIE
Take two fine whole fresh sole, skin and fillet them. Bake in a medium oven for 40 minutes, basting frequently. To make the gravy, add a dash of vermouth to the liquid. Serve with white beets.

RIS DE VEAU PÉRIGOURDINE
Take four sweetbreads, soak in lemon water, then drain and cut into thin slices. Cook in a casserole together with a few rashers of bacon, sliced carrots, fresh tomatoes and spring onions. When half done, add a half-pound of button mushrooms. Serve with mashed celery.

LAPIN AUX AMANDES
Smear a pair of small rabbits with a generous coating of full-strength mustard. Bake in a medium oven for 40 minutes, basting frequently. To make the gravy, add a dash of vermouth to the liquid. Lay out on a heated serving dish and sprinkle generously with crushed almonds.

SOLE LANDAISE
Take two fine whole fresh sole, skin and fillet them. Brown the fish in a hot shallow pan, then lower the heat and leave to simmer. Remove from heat and then add two tablespoons of double cream. Serve with baked eggplants.

LAPIN À LA TOURGANELLE
Smear a pair of small rabbits with a generous coating of full-strength mustard. Cook in a casserole together with a few rashers of bacon, sliced carrots, fresh tomatoes and spring onions. To make the gravy, add a dash of vermouth to the liquid. Serve with a jug of tomato sauce.

RIS DE VEAU FLAMANDE
Take four sweetbreads, soak in lemon water, then drain and cut into thin
slices. Brown the sweetbreads in a hot shallow pan, then lower the heat
and leave to simmer. When half done, add a half-pound of button mushrooms. Serve with mayonnaise.

LAPEREAU À LA HONGROISE
Smear a pair of small rabbits with a generous coating of full-strength
mustard. Brown them in a hot shallow pan, then lower the heat and leave
to simmer. Remove from heat and then add two tablespoons of double
cream. Lay out on a heated serving dish and sprinkle generously with
paprika.

SOLE BONNE-FEMME
Take two fine whole fresh sole, skin and fillet them. Brown the fish in
a hot shallow pan, then lower the heat and leave to simmer. When half
done, add a half-pound of button mushrooms. Serve with Vichy carrots.

RIS DE VEAU LOUIS XIV
Take four sweetbreads, soak in lemon water, then drain and cut into thin
slices. Cook in a casserole together with a few rashers of bacon, sliced
carrots, fresh tomatoes and spring onions. To make the gravy, add a dash
of vermouth to the liquid. Lay out on a heated serving dish and sprinkle
generously with chervil.

SOLE À L'ANGLAISE
Take two fine whole fresh sole, skin and fillet them. Bake in a medium
oven for 40 minutes, basting frequently. When half done, add a half-
pound of button mushrooms. Serve with a jug of horseradish sauce.

LAPIN AUX CACAHUÈTES
Smear a pair of small rabbits with a generous coating of full-strength
mustard. Cook in a casserole together with a few rashers of bacon, sliced
carrots, fresh tomatoes and spring onions. To make the gravy, add a dash
of vermouth to the liquid. Lay out on a heated serving dish and sprinkle
generously with pulverized peanuts.

Ris au riz
Take four sweetbreads, soak in lemon water, then drain and cut into thin slices. Bake in a medium oven for 40 minutes, basting frequently. When half done, add a half-pound of button mushrooms. Serve with rice pudding.

Sole aux échalotes
Take two fine whole fresh sole, skin and fillet them. Brown the fish in a hot shallow pan, then lower the heat and leave to simmer. To make the gravy, add a dash of vermouth to the liquid. Lay out on a heated serving dish and sprinkle generously with chopped shallots.

Lapereau Bercy
Smear a pair of small rabbits with a generous coating of full-strength mustard. Brown them in a hot shallow pan, then lower the heat and leave to simmer. When half done, add a half-pound of button mushrooms. Serve with a jug of Bercy sauce.

Ris de veau bernoise
Take four sweetbreads, soak in lemon water, then drain and cut into thin slices. Cook in a casserole together with a few rashers of bacon, sliced carrots, fresh tomatoes and spring onions. Remove from heat and then add two tablespoons of double cream. Lay out on a heated serving dish and sprinkle generously with Gruyère cheese.

Lapereaux 'Happy Few'
Smear a pair of small rabbits with a generous coating of full-strength mustard. Brown them in a hot shallow pan, then lower the heat and leave to simmer. To make the gravy, add a dash of vermouth to the liquid. Serve with custard.

Sole strasbourgeoise
Take two fine whole fresh sole, skin and fillet them. Brown the fish in a hot shallow pan, then lower the heat and leave to simmer. Remove from

heat and then add two tablespoons of double cream. Lay out on a heated serving dish and sprinkle generously with fried parsley.

LAPIN BRAISÉ
Smear a pair of small rabbits with a generous coating of full-strength mustard. Cook in a casserole together with a few rashers of bacon, sliced carrots, fresh tomatoes and spring onions. Remove from heat and then add two tablespoons of double cream. Serve with a jug of white sauce.

SOLE À LA PAIMPOLAISE
Take two fine whole fresh sole, skin and fillet them. Cook in a casserole together with a few rashers of bacon, sliced carrots, fresh tomatoes and spring onions. When half done, add a half-pound of button mushrooms. Serve with baked cauliflower.

RIS DE VEAU PRINCESSE
Take four sweetbreads, soak in lemon water, then drain and cut into thin slices. Bake in a medium oven for 40 minutes, basting frequently. Remove from heat and then add two tablespoons of double cream. Serve with a jug of Mornay sauce.

SOLE MAÎTRE D'HÔTEL
Take two fine whole fresh sole, skin and fillet them. Cook in a casserole together with a few rashers of bacon, sliced carrots, fresh tomatoes and spring onions. To make the gravy, add a dash of vermouth to the liquid. Serve with a jug of maître-d'hôtel sauce.

LAPIN RÔTI GRENOBLOISE
Smear a pair of small rabbits with a generous coating of full-strength mustard. Bake in a medium oven for 40 minutes, basting frequently. To make the gravy, add a dash of vermouth to the liquid. Serve with Savoy potatoes.

RIS DE VEAU À LA PURÉE DE CRESSON
Take four sweetbreads, soak in lemon water, then drain and cut into thin slices. Brown the sweetbreads in a hot shallow pan, then lower the heat

and leave to simmer. Remove from heat and then add two tablespoons of double cream. Serve with a watercress purée.

Soles Stravinsky
Take two fine whole fresh sole, skin and fillet them. Cook in a casserole together with a few rashers of bacon, sliced carrots, fresh tomatoes and spring onions. Remove from heat and then add two tablespoons of double cream. Serve with a jug of Bordelaise sauce.

Lapereau 'Villa d'Ouest'
Smear a pair of small rabbits with a generous coating of full-strength mustard. Bake in a medium oven for 40 minutes, basting frequently. When half done, add a half-pound of button mushrooms. Serve with tartar sauce.

Sole à l'ancienne
Take two fine whole fresh sole, skin and fillet them. Bake in a medium oven for 40 minutes, basting frequently. To make the gravy, add a dash of vermouth to the liquid. Lay out on a heated serving dish and sprinkle generously with grated nutmeg.

Ris de veau à l'américaine
Take four sweetbreads, soak in lemon water, then drain and cut into thin slices. Cook in a casserole together with a few rashers of bacon, sliced carrots, fresh tomatoes and spring onions. When half done, add a half-pound of button mushrooms. Lay out on a heated serving dish and sprinkle generously with cayenne pepper.

Lapin 'Sans Souci'
Smear a pair of small rabbits with a generous coating of full-strength mustard. Bake in a medium oven for 40 minutes, basting frequently. Remove from heat and then add two tablespoons of double cream. Serve with steamed potatoes.

Ris de veau grand-seigneur
Take four sweetbreads, soak in lemon water, then drain and cut into thin

slices. Brown the sweetbreads in a hot shallow pan, then lower the heat and leave to simmer. To make the gravy, add a dash of vermouth to the liquid. Lay out on a heated serving dish and sprinkle generously with finely shredded lemon rind.

Ris de veau au Noilly
Take four sweetbreads, soak in lemon water, then drain and cut into thin slices. Bake in a medium oven for 40 minutes, basting frequently. To make the gravy, add a dash of vermouth to the liquid. Serve with rémoulade sauce.

Sole exotique
Take two fine whole fresh sole, skin and fillet them. Brown the fish in a hot shallow pan, then lower the heat and leave to simmer. When half done, add a half-pound of button mushrooms. Lay out on a heated serving dish and sprinkle generously with cinnamon.

Lapin 'Grand Hôtel de Paris'
Smear a pair of small rabbits with a generous coating of full-strength mustard. Brown them in a hot shallow pan, then lower the heat and leave to simmer. Remove from heat and then add two tablespoons of double cream. Serve with fried salsify.

Sole au four à la normande
Take two fine whole fresh sole, skin and fillet them. Bake in a medium oven for 40 minutes, basting frequently. Remove from heat and then add two tablespoons of double cream. Serve with a jug of melted butter.

Ris de veau braisé 'Yorkshire'
Take four sweetbreads, soak in lemon water, then drain and cut into thin slices. Cook in a casserole together with a few rashers of bacon, sliced carrots, fresh tomatoes and spring onions. To make the gravy, add a dash of vermouth to the liquid. Serve with Yorkshire pudding.

Lapin Berrichon

Smear a pair of small rabbits with a generous coating of full-strength mustard. Cook in a casserole together with a few rashers of bacon, sliced carrots, fresh tomatoes and spring onions. When half done, add a half-pound of button mushrooms. Lay out on a heated serving dish and sprinkle generously with breadcrumbs.

17.

Jorge Luis Borges
THE GARDEN OF FORKING PATHS
translated by Andrew Hurley
{Anticipatory Plagiarism}

On page 252 of Liddell Hart's *History of World War I* you will read that an attack against the Serre-Montauban line by thirteen British divisions (supported by 1,400 artillery pieces), planned for 24 July 1916, had to be postponed until the morning of the 29th. The torrential rains, Captain Liddell Hart comments, caused this delay, an insignificant one, to be sure.

The following statement, dictated, reread and signed by Dr Yu Tsun, former professor of English at the *Hochschule* at Tsingtao, throws an unsuspected light over the whole affair. The first two pages of the document are missing.

'. . . and I hung up the receiver. Immediately afterwards, I recognized the voice that had answered in German. It was that of Captain Richard Madden. Madden's presence in Viktor Runeberg's apartment meant the end of our anxieties and – but this seemed, *or should have seemed*, very secondary to me – also the end of our lives. It meant that Runeberg had been arrested or murdered.* Before the sun set on that day, I would encounter the same fate. Madden was implacable. Or rather, he was obliged to be so. An Irishman at the service of England, a man accused of laxity and perhaps of treason, how could he fail to seize and be thankful for such a miraculous opportunity: the discovery, capture, maybe even the death of two agents of the German Empire? I went up to my room: absurdly

---

* An hypothesis both hateful and odd. The Prussian spy Hans Rabener, alias Viktor Runeberg, attacked with drawn automatic the bearer of the warrant for his arrest, Captain Richard Madden. The latter, in self-defence, inflicted the wound which brought about Runeberg's death. (Editor's note.)

I locked the door and threw myself on my back on the narrow iron cot. Through the window I saw the familiar roofs and the cloud-shaded six o'clock sun. It seemed incredible to me that that day without premonitions or symbols should be the one of my inexorable death. In spite of my dead father, in spite of having been a child in a symmetrical garden of Hai Feng, was I – now – going to die? Then I reflected that everything happens to a man precisely, precisely now. Centuries of centuries and only in the present do things happen; countless men in the air, on the face of the earth and the sea, and all that really is happening is happening to me . . . The almost intolerable recollection of Madden's horselike face banished these wanderings. In the midst of my hatred and terror (it means nothing to me now to speak of terror, now that I have foiled Richard Madden, now that my throat yearns for the noose) it occurred to me that that tumultuous and doubtless happy warrior did not suspect that I possessed the Secret. The name of the exact location of the new British artillery park on the River Ancre. A bird streaked across the grey sky and blindly I translated it into an aeroplane and that aeroplane into many (against the French sky) annihilating the artillery station with vertical bombs. If only my mouth, before a bullet shattered it, could cry out that secret name so it could be heard in Germany . . . My human voice was very weak. How might I make it carry to the ear of the Chief? To the ear of that sick and hateful man who knew nothing of Runeberg and me save that we were in Staffordshire and who was waiting in vain for our report in his arid office in Berlin, endlessly examining newspapers . . . I said out loud: *I must flee.* I sat up noiselessly, in a useless perfection of silence, as if Madden were already lying in wait for me. Something – perhaps the mere vain ostentation of proving my resources were nil – made me look through my pockets. I found what I knew I would find. The American watch, the nickel chain and the square coin, the key ring with the incriminating useless keys to Runeberg's apartment, the notebook, a letter which I resolved to destroy immediately (and which I did not destroy), a crown, two shillings and a few pence, the red and blue pencil, the handkerchief, the revolver with one bullet. Absurdly, I took it in my hand and weighed it in order to inspire courage within myself. Vaguely I thought that a pistol report can be heard at a great distance. In ten minutes my plan was perfected. The telephone book listed the name of the only person capable of transmitting the message; he lived in a suburb of Fenton, less than a half hour's train ride away.

I am a cowardly man. I say it now, now that I have carried to its end a plan whose perilous nature no one can deny. I know its execution was terrible. I didn't do it for Germany, no. I care nothing for a barbarous country which imposed upon me the abjection of being a spy. Besides, I know of a man from England – a modest man – who for me is no less great than Goethe. I talked with him for scarcely an hour, but during that hour he was Goethe . . . I did it because I sensed that the Chief somehow scorned people of my race – for the innumerable ancestors who merge within me. I wanted to prove to him that a yellow man could save his armies. Besides, I had to flee from Captain Madden. His hands and his voice could call at my door at any moment. I dressed silently, bade farewell to myself in the mirror, went downstairs, scrutinized the peaceful street and went out. The station was not far from my home, but I judged it wise to take a cab. I argued that in this way I ran less risk of being recognized; the fact is that in the deserted street I felt myself visible and vulnerable, infinitely so. I remember that I told the cab driver to stop a short distance before the main entrance. I got out with voluntary, almost painful slowness; I was going to the village of Ashgrove but I bought a ticket for a more distant station. The train left within a very few minutes, at eight-fifty. I hurried; the next one would leave at nine-thirty. There was hardly a soul on the platform. I went through the coaches; I remember a few farmers, a woman dressed in mourning, a young boy who was reading with fervour the *Annals* of Tacitus, a wounded and happy soldier. The coaches jerked forward at last. A man whom I recognized ran in vain to the end of the platform. It was Captain Richard Madden. Shattered, trembling, I shrank into the far corner of the seat, away from the dreaded window.

From this broken state I passed into an almost abject happiness. I told myself that the duel had already begun and that I had won the first encounter by frustrating, even if for forty minutes, even if by a stroke of fate, the attack of my adversary. I argued that the victory was not slight, since without the precious difference that the train schedule afforded me, I would be in jail or dead. I argued (no less fallaciously) that my cowardly happiness proved that I was a man capable of carrying out the adventure successfully. From this weakness I took strength that did not abandon me.

I foresee that man will resign himself each day to more atrocious undertakings; soon there will be no one but warriors and brigands; I give them this counsel: *The author of an atrocious undertaking ought to imagine that he has already accomplished it, ought to impose upon himself a future as irrevocable as the past.* Thus I proceeded as my eyes of a man already dead registered the elapsing of that day, which was perhaps the last, and the diffusion of the night. The train ran gently along, amid ash trees. It stopped, almost in the middle of the fields. No one announced the name of the station. 'Ashgrove?' I asked a few lads on the platform. 'Ashgrove,' they replied. I got off.

A lamp enlightened the platform but the faces of the boys were in shadow. One questioned me, 'Are you going to Dr Stephen Albert's house?' Without waiting for my answer, another said, 'The house is a long way from here, but you won't get lost if you take this road to the left and at every crossroads turn again to your left.' I tossed them a coin (my last), descended a few stone steps and started down the solitary road. It went downhill, slowly. It was of elemental earth; overhead the branches were tangled; the low full moon seemed to accompany me.

For an instant, I thought that Richard Madden in some way had penetrated my desperate plan. Very quickly, I understood that that was impossible. The instructions to turn always to the left reminded me that such was the common procedure for discovering the central point of certain labyrinths. I have some understanding of labyrinths: not for nothing am I the great grandson of that Ts'ui Pên who was governor of Yunnan and who renounced worldly power in order to write a novel that might be even more populous than the *Hung Lu Meng* and to construct a labyrinth in which all men would become lost. Thirteen years he dedicated to these heterogeneous tasks, but the hand of a stranger murdered him – and his novel was incoherent and no one found the labyrinth. Beneath English trees I meditated on that lost maze: I imagined it inviolate and perfect at the secret crest of a mountain; I imagined it erased by rice fields or beneath the water; I imagined it infinite, no longer composed of octagonal kiosks and returning paths, but of rivers and provinces and kingdoms . . . I thought of a labyrinth of labyrinths, of one sinuous spreading labyrinth that would encompass the past and the future and in some way involve the stars. Absorbed in these illusory images, I forgot my destiny of one pursued. I felt myself to be, for an unknown period of time, an abstract perceiver of the world. The vague, living countryside, the moon, the remains of the day worked on me, as well as the slope of the road which eliminated any possibility of weariness. The evening was intimate, infinite. The road descended and forked among the now confused meadows. A high-pitched, almost syllabic music approached and receded in the shifting of the wind, dimmed by leaves and distance. I thought that a man can be an enemy of other men, of the moments of other men, but not of a country: not of fireflies, words, gardens, streams of water, sunsets. Thus I arrived before a tall, rusty gate. Between the iron bars I made out a poplar grove and a pavilion. I understood suddenly two things, the first trivial, the second almost unbelievable: the music came from the pavilion, and the music was Chinese. For precisely that reason I had openly accepted it without paying it any heed. I do not recall if there was a bell or a buzzer or if I clapped my hands. The sparkling of the music continued.

From the rear of the secluded house within a lantern approached: a lantern that the trees sometimes striped and sometimes eclipsed, a paper lantern that had the form of a drum and the colour of the moon. A tall man bore it. I didn't see his face for the light blinded me. He opened the door and said slowly, in my own language: 'I see that the pious Hsi P'êng persists in correcting my solitude. You no doubt wish to see the garden?'

I recognized the name of one of our consuls and I replied, disconcerted, 'The garden?'

'The garden of forking paths.'

Something stirred in my memory and I uttered with incomprehensible certainty, 'The garden of my ancestor Ts'ui Pên.'

'Your ancestor? Your illustrious ancestor? Come in.'

The damp path zigzagged like those of my childhood. We came to a library of Eastern and Western books. I recognized bound in yellow silk several volumes of the Lost Encyclopaedia, edited by the Third Emperor of the Luminous Dynasty but never printed. The record on the phonograph revolved next to a bronze phoenix. I also recall a *famille rose* vase and another, many centuries older, of that shade of blue which our craftsmen copied from the potters of Persia . . .

Stephen Albert observed me with a smile. He was, as I have said, very tall, sharp-featured, with grey eyes and a grey beard. There was something of a priest about him and also of a sailor; later he told me that he had been a missionary in Tientsin 'before aspiring to become a Sinologist'. We sat down – I on a long, low divan, he with his back to the window and a tall circular clock. I calculated that my pursuer, Richard Madden, could not arrive for at least an hour. My irrevocable determination could wait.

'An astounding fate, that of Ts'ui Pên,' Stephen Albert said. 'Governor of his native province, learned in astronomy, in astrology and in the tireless interpretation of the canonical books, chess player, famous poet and calligrapher – he abandoned all this in order to compose a book and a maze. He renounced the pleasures of both tyranny and justice, of his populous couch, of his banquets and even of erudition – all to close himself up for thirteen years in the Pavilion of the Limpid Solitude. When he died, his heirs found nothing save chaotic manuscripts. His family, as you may be aware, wished to condemn them to the fire, but his executor – a Taoist or Buddhist monk – insisted on their publication.'

'We descendants of Ts'ui Pên,' I replied, 'continue to curse that monk. Their publication was senseless. The book is an indeterminate heap of contradictory drafts. I examined it once: in the third chapter the hero dies, in the fourth he is alive. As for the other undertaking of Ts'ui Pên, his labyrinth . . .'

'Here is Ts'ui Pên's labyrinth,' he said, indicating a tall lacquered desk.

'An ivory labyrinth!' I exclaimed. 'A tiny labyrinth.'

'A labyrinth of symbols,' he corrected. 'An invisible labyrinth of time. To me, a barbarous Englishman, has been entrusted the revelation of this diaphanous mystery. After more than a hundred years, the details are irretrievable; but it is not hard to conjecture what happened. Ts'ui Pên must have said once: *I am withdrawing to write a book.* And another time: *I am withdrawing to construct a labyrinth.* Every one imagined two works; to no one did it occur that the book and the maze were one and the same thing. The Pavilion of the Limpid Solitude stood in the centre of a garden that was perhaps intricate; that circumstance may have suggested to men a physical labyrinth. Ts'ui Pên died; no one in the vast territories that were his came upon the labyrinth; the confusion of the novel suggested to me that *it* was the maze. Two circumstances gave me the correct solution of the problem. One: the curious legend that Ts'ui Pên had planned to create a labyrinth which would be strictly infinite. The other: a fragment of a letter I discovered.'

Albert rose. He turned his back on me for a moment; he opened a drawer of the black and gold desk. He faced me and in his hands he held a sheet of paper that had once been crimson, but was now pink and tenuous and cross-sectioned. The fame of Ts'ui Pên as a calligrapher had been justly won. I read, uncomprehendingly and with fervour, these words written with a minute brush by a man of my blood: *I leave to the various futures (not to all) my garden of forking paths*. Wordlessly, I returned the sheet. Albert continued:

'Before unearthing this letter, I had questioned myself about the ways in which a book can be infinite. I could think of nothing other than a cyclical volume, a circular one. A book whose last page was identical with the first, a book which had the possibility of continuing indefinitely. I remembered too that night which is at the middle of the Thousand and One Nights when Queen Scheherazade (through a magical oversight of the copyist) begins to relate word for word the story of the Thousand and One Nights, at the risk of coming once again to the night when she must repeat it, and thus on to infinity. I imagined as well a Platonic, hereditary work, transmitted from father to son, in which each new individual added a chapter or corrected with pious care the pages of his elders. These conjectures diverted me; but none seemed to correspond, not even remotely, to the contradictory chapters of Ts'ui Pên. In the midst of this perplexity, I received from Oxford the manuscript you have examined. I lingered, naturally, on the sentence: *I leave to the various futures (not to all) my garden of forking paths*. Almost instantly, I understood: "the garden of forking paths" was the chaotic novel; the phrase "the various futures (not to all)" suggested to me the forking in time, not in space. A broad rereading of the work confirmed the theory. In all fictional works, each time a man is confronted with several alternatives, he chooses one and eliminates the others; in the fiction of the almost inextricable Ts'ui Pên, he chooses – simultaneously – all of them. *He creates*, in this way, diverse futures, diverse times which themselves also proliferate and fork. Here, then, is the explanation of the novel's contradictions. Fang, let us say, has a secret; a stranger calls at his door; Fang resolves to kill him. Naturally, there are several outcomes: Fang can kill the intruder, the intruder can kill Fang, they both can escape, they both can die, and so forth. In the work of Ts'ui Pên, all possible outcomes occur; each one is the point of departure for other forkings. Sometimes, the paths of this labyrinth converge: for example, you arrive at this house, but in one of the possible pasts you are my enemy, in another, my friend. If you will resign yourself to my incurable pronunciation, we shall read a few pages.'

His face, within the vivid circle of the lamplight, was unquestionably that of an old man, but with something unalterable about it, even immortal. He read with slow precision two versions of the same epic chapter. In the first, an army marches to a battle across a desolate mountain; the horror of the rocks and shadows makes the men undervalue their lives and they gain an easy victory. In the second, the same army traverses a palace where a great festival is taking place; the resplendent battle seems to them a continuation of the celebration and they win the victory. I listened with proper veneration to these ancient narratives, perhaps less admirable in themselves than the fact that they had been created by my blood and were being restored to me by a man of remote empire, in the course of a desperate adventure, on a Western isle. I remember the last words, repeated in each version like a secret commandment: *Thus fought the heroes, tranquil their admirable hearts, violent their swords, resigned to kill and to die.*

From that moment on, I felt about me and within my dark body an invisible, intangible swarming. Not the swarming of the divergent, parallel and finally coalescent armies, but a more inaccessible, more intimate agitation that they in some manner prefigured. Stephen Albert continued:

'I don't believe that your illustrious ancestor played idly with these variations. I don't consider it credible that he would sacrifice thirteen years to the infinite execution of a rhetorical experiment. In your country, the novel is a subsidiary form of literature; in Ts'ui Pên's time it was a despicable form. Ts'ui Pên was a brilliant novelist, but he was also a man of letters who doubtless did not consider himself a mere novelist. The testimony of his contemporaries proclaims – and his life fully confirms – his metaphysical and mystical interests. Philosophic controversy usurps a good part of the novel. I know that of all problems, none disturbed him so greatly nor worked upon him so much as the abysmal problem of time. Now then, the latter is the only problem that does not figure in the pages of the *Garden*. He does not even use the word that signifies *time*. How do you explain this voluntary omission?'

I proposed several solutions – all inadequate. We discussed them. Finally, Stephen Albert said to me:

'In a riddle whose answer is chess, what is the only prohibited word?'

I thought a moment and replied, 'The word *chess*.'

'Precisely,' said Albert. '*The Garden of Forking Paths* is an enormous riddle, or parable, whose theme is time; this recondite cause prohibits its mention. To omit a word *always*, to resort to inept metaphors and obvious periphrases, is perhaps the most emphatic way of stressing it. That is the tortuous method preferred, in each of the meanderings of his indefatigable novel, by the oblique Ts'ui Pên. I have compared hundreds of manuscripts, I have corrected the errors that the negligence of the copyists has introduced, I have guessed the plan of this chaos, I have re-established – I believe I have re-established – the primordial organization, I have translated the entire work: it is clear to me that not once does he employ the word "time". The explanation is obvious: *The Garden of Forking Paths* is an incomplete, but not false, image of the universe as Ts'ui Pên conceived it. In contrast to Newton and Schopenhauer, your ancestor did not believe in a uniform, absolute time. He believed in an infinite series of times, in a growing, dizzying net of divergent, convergent and parallel times. This network of times which approached one another, forked, broke off, or were unaware of one another for centuries, embraces *all* possibilities of time. We do not exist in the majority of these times; in some you exist, and not I; in others I, and not you; in others, both of us. In the present one, which a favourable fate has granted me, you have arrived at my house; in another, while crossing the garden, you found me dead; in still another, I utter these same words, but I am a mistake, a ghost.'

'In every one,' I pronounced, not without a tremble to my voice, 'I am grateful to you and revere you for your re-creation of the garden of Ts'ui Pên.'

'Not in all,' he murmured with a smile. 'Time forks perpetually towards innumerable futures. In one of them I am your enemy.'

Once again I felt the swarming sensation of which I have spoken. It seemed to me that the humid garden that surrounded the house was infinitely saturated with invisible persons. Those persons were Albert and

I, secret, busy and multiform in other dimensions of time. I raised my eyes and the tenuous nightmare dissolved. In the yellow and black garden there was only one man; but this man was as strong as a statue . . . this man was approaching along the path and he was Captain Richard Madden.

'The future already exists,' I replied, 'but I am your friend. Could I see the letter again?'

Albert rose. Standing tall, he opened the drawer of the tall desk; for a moment he turned his back to me. I had readied the revolver. I fired with extreme caution. Albert fell uncomplainingly, immediately. I swear his death was instantaneous – a lightning stroke.

The rest is unreal, insignificant. Madden broke in, arrested me. I have been condemned to the gallows. I have won out abominably; I have communicated to Berlin the secret name of the city they must attack. They bombed it yesterday; I read it in the same papers that offered to England the mystery of the learned Sinologist Stephen Albert who was murdered by a stranger, Yu Tsun. The Chief had deciphered this mystery. He knew my problem was to indicate (through the uproar of the war) the city called Albert, and that I had found no other means to do so than to kill a man of that name. He does not know (no one can know) my innumerable contrition and weariness.

For Victoria Ocampo

18.

Thieri Foulc

NEW OBSERVATIONS ON HARRY MATHEWS'S FACE

{Oupeinpo}

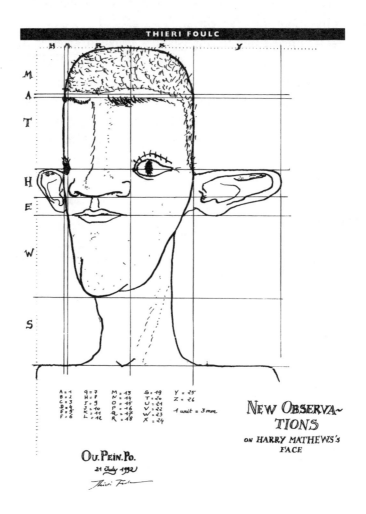

19.

François Rabelais
FROM *GARGANTUA AND PANTAGRUEL*
translated by Sir Thomas Urquhart
{Anticipatory Plagiarism}

CHAPTER I

Of the original and antiquity of the great Pantagruel

It will not be an idle nor unprofitable thing, seeing we are at leisure, to put you in mind of the fountain and original source, whence is derived unto us the good Pantagruel. For I see that all good historiographers have thus handled their chronicles, not only the Arabians, Barbarians, and Latins, but also the gentle Greeks, who were eternal drinkers. You must therefore remark, that at the beginning of the world, – I speak of a long time, it is above forty quarantains, or forty times forty nights, according to the supputation of the ancient Druids, – a little after that Abel was killed by his brother Cain, the earth, imbrued with the blood of the just, was one year so exceeding fertile in all those fruits which it usually produces to us, and especially in medlars, that ever since, throughout all ages, it hath been called the year of the great medlars; for three of them did fill a bushel. In it the Calends were found by the Grecian almanacks. There was that year nothing of the month of March in the time of Lent, and the middle of August was in May. In the month of October, as I take it, or at least September, that I may not err, for I will carefully take heed of that, was the week so famous in the Annals, which they call the week of the three Thursdays; for it had three of them by means of their irregular leap-years, called Bissextiles, occasioned by the sun's having tripped and stumbled a little towards the left hand, like a debtor afraid of serjeants, coming right upon him to arrest him: and the moon varied from her course above five fathom, and there was manifestly seen the motion of trepidation in the firmament of the fixed stars, called Aplanes, so that the middle Pleiade, leaving her fellows, declined towards the equinoctial, and the star named Spica left the constellation of the Virgin to withdraw herself towards the Balance, known by the name of Libra; which are cases very terrible, and matters so hard and difficult, that astrologians cannot set their teeth in them; and indeed their teeth had been pretty long if they could have reached thither.

However, account you it for a truth, that every body did most heartily eat of those medlars, for they were fair to the eye, and in taste delicious. But even as Noah, that holy man, to whom we are so much beholding, bound, and obliged, for that he planted to us the vine, from whence we have that nectarian, delicious, precious, heavenly, joyful, and deific liquor, which they call piot or tiplage, was deceived in the drinking of it, for he was ignorant of the great virtue and power thereof; so likewise the men and women of that time did delight much in the eating of that fair great fruit, but divers and very different accidents did ensue thereupon; for there fell upon them all in their bodies a most terrible swelling, but not upon all in the same place, for some were swollen in the belly, and their belly strouted out big like a great tun; of whom it is written *Ventrem omnipotentem*; who were all very honest men, and merry blades. And of this race came St Fatgulch, and Shrove-Tuesday. Others did swell at the shoulders, who in that place were so crump and knobby, that they were therefore called Montifers, which is as much as to say Hill-carriers, of whom you see some yet in the world, of divers sexes and degrees. Of this race came Æsop, some of whose excellent words and deeds you have in writing. Some other puffs did swell in length by the member, which they call the labourer of nature, in such sort that it grew marvellous long, fat, great, lusty, stirring, and crest-risen, in the antique fashion, so that they made use of it as of a girdle, winding it five or six times about their waist: but if it happened the aforesaid member to be in good case, spooming with a full sail, bunt fair before the wind, then to have seen those strouting champions, you would have taken them for men that had their lances settled on their rest, to run at the ring or tilting whintam [quintain]. Of these, believe me, the race is utterly lost and quite extinct, as the women say; for they do lament continually, that there are none extant now of those great, &c. You know the rest of the song. Others did grow in matter of ballocks so enormously, that three of them would well fill a sack, able to contain five quarters of wheat. From them are descended the ballocks of Lorraine, which never dwell in codpieces, but fall down to the bottom of the breeches. Others grew in the legs, and to see them you would have said they had been cranes, or the reddish-long-billed-stork-like-scrank-legged sea-fowls, called flamans, or else men walking upon stilts or scatches. The little grammar schoolboys, known by the name of Grimos, called those leg-grown slangams, iambics, in allusion to the French word Jambe, which signifieth a leg. In others, their nose did grow so, that it seemed to be the beak of a limbeck, in every part thereof most variously diapered with the twinkling sparkles of crimson-blisters budding forth, and purpled with pimples all enamelled with thick-set wheals of a sanguine colour, bordered with gules: and such have you seen the canon, or prebend Panzoult, and Woodenfoot the physician of Angiers. Of which race there were few that liked the ptisane, but all of them were perfect lovers of the pure septembral juice. Naso and Ovid had their extraction from thence, and all those of whom it is written, *Ne reminiscaris*. Others grew in ears, which they had so big, that out of one would have been stuff enough got to make a doublet, a pair of breeches, and a jacket, whilst with the other they might have covered themselves as with a Spanish cloak; and they say, that in Bourbonnois this race remaineth yet. Others grew in length of body, and of those came the giants, and of them Pantagruel.

And the first was Chalbroth,
Who begat Sarabroth,
Who begat Faribroth,
Who begat Hurtali, that was a brave eater of pottage, and reigned
    in the time of the flood;
Who begat Nembroth,
Who begat Atlas, that with his shoulders kept the sky from falling;
Who begat Goliah,
Who begat Erix, that invented the Hocus pocus plays of
    legerdemain,
Who begat Titius,
Who begat Eryon,

Who begat Polyphemus,

Who begat Cacus,

Who begat Etion, the first man who ever had the pox, for not drinking fresh in summer as Bartachin witnesseth;

Who begat Enceladus,

Who begat Ceus,

Who begat Tiphœus,

Who begat Alœus,

Who begat Othus,

Who begat Ægeon,

Who begat Briareus, that had a hundred hands;

Who begat Porphyrio,

Who begat Adamastor,

Who begat Anteus,

Who begat Agatho,

Who begat Porus, against whom fought Alexander the Great;

Who begat Aranthas,

Who begat Gabbara, that was the first inventor of the drinking of healths;

Who begat Goliah of Secondille,

Who begat Offot, that was terribly well nosed for drinking at the barrel-head;

Who begat Artachæus,

Who begat Oromedon,

Who begat Gemmagog, the first inventor of Poulan shoes, which are open on the foot, and tied over the instep with a latchet;

Who begat Sisyphus,

Who begat the Titans, of whom Hercules was born,

Who begat Enay, the most skilful man that ever was, in matter of taking the little worms (called circons) out of the hands;

Who begat Fierabras, that was vanquished by Oliver, Peer of France, and Roland's camerad;

Who begat Morgan, the first in the world that played at dice with spectacles;

Who begat Fracassus, of whom Merlin Coccaius hath written, of him was born Ferragus;

Who begat Hapmouche, the first that ever invented the drying
of neats' tongues in the chimney; for, before that, people salted
them, as they do now gammons of bacon;
Who begat Bolivorax,
Who begat Longis,
Who begat Gayoffo, whose ballocks were of poplar, and his
pendulum of the servise, or sorb-apple tree;
Who begat Mashefain,
Who begat Bruslefer,
Who begat Angoulevent,
Who begat Galchault, the inventor of flagons;
Who begat Mirelangaut,
Who begat Galaffre,
Who begat Falourdin,
Who begat Roboast,
Who begat Sortibrant of Conimbres,
Who begat Brushant of Mommiere,
Who begat Bruyer that was overcome by Ogier the Dane, Peer of
France;
Who begat Mabrun,
Who begat Foustanon,
Who begat Haquelebac,
Who begat Vitdegrain,
Who begat Grangousier,
Who begat Gargantua,
Who begat the noble Pantagruel my master.

I know that reading this passage, you will make a doubt within yourselves, and that grounded upon very good reasons, which is this, – how
is it possible that this relation can be true, seeing at the time of the flood
all the world was destroyed, except Noah, and seven persons more with
him in the ark, into whose number Hurtali is not admitted? Doubtless
the demand is well made, and very apparent, but the answer shall satisfy
you, or my wit is not rightly caulked. And, because I was not at that time
to tell you anything of my own fancy, I will bring unto you the authority of the Massorets, good honest fellows, true ballockeering blades, and

exact Hebraical bagpipers, who affirm, that verily the said Hurtali was not within the ark of Noah, neither could he get in, for he was too big, but he sat astride upon it, with one leg on the one side, and another on the other, as little children use to do on their wooden horses: or as the great bull of Berne, which was killed at Marinian did ride for his hackney the great murdering piece called the Canonpevier, a pretty beast of a fair and pleasant amble without all question.

In that posture, he, after God, saved the said ark from danger, for with his legs he gave it the brangle that was needful, and with his foot turned it whither he pleased, as a ship answereth her rudder. Those that were within sent him up victuals in abundance by a chimney, as people very thankfully acknowledging the good that he did them. And sometimes they did talk together as Icaromenippus did to Jupiter, according to the report of Lucian. Have you understood all this well? Drink then one good draught without water, for if you believe it not; – no truly do I not, quoth she.

20.

Italo Calvino
THE BURNING OF THE
ABOMINABLE HOUSE
translated by Tim Parks
{Oulipo/Oulipopo}

In a few hours' time Skiller, the insurance agent, will be coming to ask me for the computer results, and I still haven't keyed in the orders to the electronic circuits which will have to grind to a fine dust of bits both Widow Roessler's secrets and her hardly to be recommended boarding house. Where the house once stood, between railway lines and iron stockyards, on one of those humps of wasteland our city's suburbs leave behind like heaps of dirt that have escaped the broom, nothing is left but charred rubble now. It could have been a smart villa originally, or it may have looked no better than a ghostly hovel: insurance company reports have nothing to say on the matter; and now it has burnt down, from eaves to cellar, and the incinerated corpses of its four inhabitants have left no clue that might serve to reconstruct the events that led up to this secluded slaughter.

Rather than the bodies, what does offer a clue is a copybook found in the ruins, entirely burnt except for its cover which was protected by a plastic folder. On the front it says: *An Account of the Abominable Deeds Committed in this House* and on the back there is an index with twelve entries in alphabetical order: Blackmail, Drugging, Incitement to Suicide, Knifing, Prostitution, Threatening with a gun, Tying and Gagging, Rape, Seduction, Slander, Snooping, Strangling.

It isn't known which of the house's inhabitants penned this sinister summary, nor to what end: to report the matter to the police, to confess, to defend themselves, to gratify their fascinated contemplation of evil.

All we have is this index which doesn't tell us the names of the perpetrators or the victims of the twelve deeds – criminal or merely immoral as they may be – nor does it explain the order in which they were committed, something that would offer a good start for reconstructing a story: the entries in alphabetical order refer us to page numbers obliterated by a black streak. To complete the list would require one additional word, Arson, doubtless the final deed in this grim chain of events. But who did it? In order to hide, or to destroy?

Even if we accept that each of the twelve deeds was committed by just one person and inflicted upon just one other person, reconstruction would still be a tall order: given that there are four characters to be considered, then taken two by two we have twelve possible relationships for each of the twelve kinds of relationship listed. The number of possible combinations is thus twelve to the twelfth, meaning that we shall have to choose from a total of eight thousand eight hundred and seventy-four billion, two hundred and ninety-six million, six hundred and seventy-two thousand, two hundred and fifty-six potential solutions. It is hardly surprising that our already overworked police force has chosen not to pursue its enquiries, on the good grounds that, however many crimes may have been committed, the perpetrators doubtless died together with their victims.

Only the insurance company is eager to know the truth: mainly on account of a fire insurance policy taken out by the owner of the house. The fact that the young Inigo, the policy holder, likewise perished in the flames only serves to make the matter more problematic: his powerful family, despite having ejected and disinherited this degenerate son, is notoriously disinclined to give up anything owed to them. Then one can level the worst possible charges (whether or not included in the abominable index) against a young man who, as a hereditary member of the British House of Lords, dragged an illustrious title down to the steps of those public squares that serve as beds to a nomadic, introspective generation, a man who was wont to soap his long hair under the water of municipal fountains. The small house he rented to the old landlady was the last property left to him, and he had taken a room there subletting from his own tenant in return for a reduction in the already low rent he charged. If he, Inigo, was the arsonist, perpetrator and victim of a criminal plan executed with the carelessness and imprecision that appear to have been typical of his way of behaving, and if the insurance company could demonstrate as much, then they wouldn't have to pay the damages.

But this is not the only claim the company is obliged to honour as a result of the calamity: every year Widow Roessler would renew a policy insuring her own life in favour of her adopted daughter, a fashion model familiar to anyone in the habit of leafing through the pages of the more stylish magazines. Of course Ogiva herself is likewise dead, incinerated together with the collection of wigs that would transform her features with their terrifying charm (how else describe a beautiful and delicate young woman with a completely bald skull) into those of hundreds of different and exquisitely asymmetrical faces. But it turns out that the model had a three-year-old child, entrusted to relatives in South Africa, who will waste no time in claiming the rewards of the policy, unless it can be demonstrated that it was she, Ogiva, who killed (*Knifing? Strangling?*) Widow Roessler. Or again, given that Ogiva had taken the trouble to insure her wig collection, the child's guardians could claim on this policy too, unless it can be demonstrated that she was responsible for their destruction.

Of the fourth person who died in the fire, the gigantic Uzbek wrestler, Belindo Kid, we know that in Widow Roessler he had found not only a zealous landlady (he was the only paying occupant of the boarding house) but also an agent with a keen eye for business. Indeed the old lady had recently agreed to finance the ex-middleweight champion's seasonal tour, covering herself by insuring against the eventuality that illness, incapacity or injury might prevent him from honouring his contracts. A consortium of wrestling match organizers are now claiming damages against this policy; but had the old woman *induced* Belindo *to suicide,* perhaps by *slandering* him or *blackmailing* him or *drugging* him (the giant was renowned on the international scene for his impressionable character), then the company could easily have them desist.

I can't prevent the slow tentacles of my mind from advancing one hypothesis at a time, exploring labyrinths of consequence that magnetic memories would run through in a nanosecond. It is from my computer that Skiller is expecting a solution, not from me.

Of course each of the four catastrophic characters appears better suited to be perpetrator of some of the abominable deeds and victim of others. But who can rule out the notion that the most improbable alternative might be the only one possible? Take what you would suppose to be the most innocent of the twelve relationships, that implied by *seduction*. Who seduced whom? I have to work hard to concentrate on my permutations here: a flow of images swirls unceasingly in my mind, breaking up and reforming as though in a kaleidoscope. I see the long fingers of the fashion model with their green and purple varnished nails skimming the listless chin, the grassy stubble of the slummy young aristocrat, or tickling the solid predatory nape of the Uzbek champion who, aware of a remote and pleasant sensation, arches his deltoids like a purring cat. But immediately afterwards I also see the volatile Ogiva allowing herself to be seduced, captivated by the taurine flattery of the middleweight or the consuming introversion of the feckless youth. And I can also see the old widow, haunted by appetites that age may discourge but not extinguish, painting her face and dolling herself up to lure one or the other of her male prey (or both), and overcoming opposition very different in terms of weight but equally feeble in terms of character. Or I see her herself as the object of a seduction whose perversity might be due to youthful lust's readiness to confuse life's seasons, or alternatively to sinister calculation. Until finally, to complete the picture, the shadow of Sodom and Gomorrah unleashes the whirligig of loves between the same sex.

Does the range of possibilities shrink a little for the more criminal deeds? Not necessarily: anybody can *knife* anybody else. Already I can imagine Belindo Kid being treacherously skewered in the back of the neck by a switchblade that slices through his spinal cord the way the toreador's sword dispatches the bull. Behind the perfectly aimed blow we might find the slender, bracelet-tinkling wrist of an Ogiva seized by cold and bloody frenzy, or Inigo's playful fingers, rocking the dagger to and fro by the blade, then flinging it through the air with inspired abandon along a trajectory that strikes its target almost by chance; or we might find LandLady Macbeth's claw, shifting the curtains of the bedrooms at night as she imposes her presence on the sleepers' breathing. Nor are these the only images that throng my mind: Ogiva or Widow Roessler slaughter Inigo like a lamb, knifing through his windpipe; Inigo or Ogiva grab the big knife the widow is using to slice the bacon and hack her to bits in the kitchen; the widow or Inigo dissect Ogiva's nude body like surgeons while she struggles (*tied up and gagged*?) to escape. Then if Belindo had found the knife in his hand, at a moment of exasperation perhaps, or perhaps when someone had stirred him up against someone else, he could have had all the others in pieces in no time. But why should he, Belindo Kid, go for a *knifing*, when both the copybook index and his own motor sensory circuits offer the possibility of *strangling*, something far more congenial to his physical tendencies and technical training? And furthermore, this would be an action of which he could only be the subject and not the object: I'd like to see the other three trying to strangle the middleweight wrestler; their puny fingers wouldn't even go round his tree-trunk neck!

So this is a piece of data the programme will have to take into account: Belindo doesn't *knife* but prefers to *strangle;* and he can't be *strangled*; only *if threatened with a gun* can he be *tied up and gagged;* once *tied up and gagged* anything can happen to him, he can even be *raped*, by the ruttish widow, or the impassive model, or the eccentric youth.

Let's start laying down exclusions and orders of precedence. Someone may first *threaten someone with a gun*, then *tie them up and gag them*; it would be to say the least superfluous to *tie up* someone first then *threaten* them afterwards. On the other hand someone *knifing* or *strangling* who at the same time *threatened with a gun*, would be engaging in a gesture at once awkward and unnecessary, unforgivable. Someone who wins over the object of his or her desires by *seduction* has no need to *rape* that person; and vice versa. Someone inciting someone else to *prostitution* may have previously *seduced* or *raped* them; doing so afterwards would be a pointless waste of time and energy. One may *snoop* on someone in order to *blackmail* them, but if you have already *slandered* them then further scandalous revelations can frighten them no more; hence the person *slandering* is not interested in *snooping*, nor has any further reasons for *blackmail*. Someone *knifing* one victim may well *strangle* another, or *incite them to suicide*, but it is unlikely that the three deadly deeds could be committed at the expense of the same person.

Following this method allows me to rewrite my flow-chart: to establish a system of exclusions that will enable the computer to discard billions of incongruous combinations, to reduce the number of plausible concatenations, to approach a selection of that solution which will present itself as true.

But will we ever get to that? Half I'm concentrating on constructing algebraic models where factors and functions are anonymous and interchangeable, thus dismissing the faces and gestures of those four phantoms from my thoughts; and half I am identifying with the characters, evoking the scenes in a mental film packed with fades and metamorphoses. Maybe it's around the word *drugging* that the cog that drives all the others turns: at once my mind associates the word with the pasty face of the last Inigo of an illustrious stock; if *drugging* meant the reflexive *drugging oneself*, there would be no problem here: it's highly likely that the boy took drugs, something that does not concern me; but the transitive sense of *drugging* implies a drugger and a person drugged, the latter consenting, unknowing or compelled.

It is equally likely that Inigo gets himself so high on drugs that he tries to preach stupefaction to others; I imagine spindly cigarettes being passed from his hand to Ogiva's or old Widow Roessler's. Is it the young nobleman who transforms the lonely boarding house into a smoke-filled den of kaleidoscopic hallucinations? Or is it the landlady who lures him there in order to exploit his inclination toward states of ecstasy? Perhaps it is Ogiva who procures the drug for the old opium addict, Roessler, and Inigo who, while *snooping* on her, discovers where she hides it and bursts it on her *threatening her with a gun* or *blackmailing* her; Widow Roessler shouts to Belindo for help, then *slanders* Inigo accusing him of having *seduced* and *prostituted* Ogiva, the Uzbeck's chaste passion, at which the wrestler takes his revenge by *strangling* the boy; to get out of trouble the landlady now has no alternative but to incite the wrestler *to suicide*, not a problem since the insurance company will pay the damages, but Belindo, in for a penny in for a pound, *rapes* Ogiva, *ties and gags* her and sets fire to the obliterating pyre.

Slowly does it: no point in imagining I can beat the electronic brain to it. The drug might just as well have to do with Belindo: old and over the hill he can't climb into the ring these days without stuffing himself full of stimulants. It's Widow Roessler who doles them out, slipping them in his mouth with a soup spoon. *Snooping* through the keyhole, Inigo, a glutton for psychodrugs, interrupts and demands a dose for himself. When they refuse, he *blackmails* the wrestler threatening to have him banned from the championship; Belindo *ties and gags* him, then *prostitutes* him for a few guineas to Ogiva who has for some time been infatuated with the elusive aristocrat; impervious to eros, Inigo can only achieve an amorous state if on the point of being *strangled*; Ogiva presses on his carotid artery with her slim fingertips; perhaps Belindo lends a hand; just two of his fingers and the little lord rolls his eyes and gives up the ghost; what to do with the corpse? To simulate a suicide they *knife* him . . . Stop! Have to rewrite the whole programme: have to cancel the instruction now stored in the central memory that someone *strangled* cannot be *knifed*. The ferrite rings are demagnetized and remagnetized; I'm sweating.

Let's start again from scratch. What is the job my client expects of me? To arrange a certain amount of data in a logical order. It is information I am dealing with, not human lives, with their good and evil sides. For reasons that need not concern me the data available to me only has to do with the evil side, and the computer must put it in order. Not the evil, which cannot perhaps be put in order, but the information relative to the evil. On the basis of this data, contained in the alphabetical index of the *Abominable Deeds*, I must reconstruct the lost *Account*, true or false as that may be.

The *Account* presupposes the existence of a writer. Only by reconstructing it will we know who that was: certain data, however, can already be placed on his or her file. The author of the *Account* couldn't have been killed by *knifing* or *strangling*, because he wouldn't have been able to include his or her own death in the report; as far as suicide is concerned, the writer could have decided on it before writing out the copybook-testament, and carried it out later; but someone who believes they have been *incited to suicide* by the force of someone else's will does not commit suicide; every exclusion of the author of the copybook from the role of victim automatically increases the likelihood of our being able to attribute to him or her the role of perpetrator: hence this person could be both the originator of the evil and of the information regarding that evil. This presents no problems for my work: evil and information regarding evil are coincident, both in the burnt book and in the electronic files.

The memory has also been fed another series of data to be compared with the first: the four insurance policies taken out with Skiller, one by

Inigo, one by Ogiva and two by the Widow (one for herself and one for Belindo). An obscure thread may link the policies to the *Abominable Deeds* and the photoelectric cells must follow that thread in a bewildering blind man's bluff, seeking it out amongst the tiny holes of the punch cards. Even the policy data, now translated into binary code, is capable of evoking images in my mind: it's evening, there's fog; Skiller rings at the door of the house on the hump of wasteland; the landlady imagines he's a new tenant and greets him accordingly; he gets his insurance brochures out of his bag; he's sitting in the lounge; he accepts a cup of tea; clearly he can't get the four contracts signed in just one visit; he makes sure he is thoroughly familiar with the house and its four inhabitants. I imagine Skiller helping Ogiva to brush out the wigs in her collection (and in so doing his lips brush the model's bald scalp); I imagine him as, with a touch as sure as a doctor's and as thoughtful as a son's, he measures the widow's blood pressure, enclosing her soft white arm in the sphygmomanometer; or again I see him trying to get Inigo interested in home maintenance, pointing out problems with the plumbing, subsidence in the loadbearing beams, while in a fatherly voice telling him not to bite his nails; I see him reading the sports papers with Belindo, complimenting him with a slap on the back when he has guessed a winner.

I must admit, I don't really like this Skiller. A web of complicity stretches out wherever he ties his threads; if he really did have so much power over Widow Roessler's boarding house, if he was the factotum, the *deus ex machina*, if nothing happened between those walls but that he knew about it, then why did he come to me for a solution to the mystery? Why did he bring me the charred copybook? Was it he who found the copybook in the ruins? Or did he put it there? Was it he who brought this mass of negative information, of irreversible entropy, he who introduced it into the house, as now into the circuits of the computer?

The Roessler boarding-house massacre doesn't have four characters: it has five. I translate the data of insurance agent Skiller into holes on punchcards and add it to the other information. The abominable deeds could be his doing as much as any of the others: he could have *Blackmailed, Drugged, Induced to Suicide*, etc., or better still he could have made somebody *prostitute* themselves or *strangle* someone and all the rest. The billions of combinations multiply, but perhaps a shape is beginning to emerge. Merely for the purposes of a hypothesis I could construct a model in which all the evil stems from Skiller, before whose entrance on the scene the boarding house basked in Arcadian innocence: old Widow Roessler plays a *Lied* on her Bechstein which the gentle giant Belindo humps from room to room for the sake of the tenants' enjoyment, Ogiva waters the petunias, Inigo paints petunias on Ogiva's head. The bell rings: it's Skiller. Is he looking for a bed and breakfast? No, but he has some useful insurance policies to offer: life, accident, fire, house and contents. The conditions are good; Skiller invites them to think it over; they think it over; they think of things they never thought of before; they are tempted; temptation starts its trail of electronic impulses through the channels of the brain . . . I'm aware that I am undermining the objectivity of the operation with these subjective dislikes. In the end, what do I know about this Skiller? Perhaps his soul is without stain, perhaps he is the only innocent person in the story, while all the data depict Widow Roessler as a sordid miser, Ogiva as a ruthless narcissist, Inigo as lost in his dreamy introversion, Belindo as condemned to muscular brutality for lack of alternative role models . . . It is they who called Skiller, each with a sinister plan against the other three and the insurance company. Skiller is the dove in a nest of serpents.

The computer stops. There's an error, and the central memory has picked it up; it cancels everything. There are no innocents to be saved, in this story. Start again.

No, it wasn't Skiller who rang at the door. Outside it's drizzling, there's fog, no one can make out the visitor's face. He comes into the passage, takes off his wet hat, unwraps his woollen scarf. It's me. I introduce myself. Waldemar, computer programmer and systems analyst. You're looking well, you know, Signora Roessler? No, we've never met, but I remember the data on the analogical-digital convertor and I recognize all four of you perfectly. Don't hide, Signor Inigo! You're looking good, Belindo Kid! Is that purple hair I see peeping over the stairs, Signorina Ogiva? Here you are all together; good: let me explain why I've come. I need you, yes, you, just as you are, for a project that's kept me nailed to my programming console for years. During office hours I work freelance for clients, but at night, shut up in my laboratory, I spend my time researching a system that will transform individual passions – aggression, private interest, selfishness, various vices – into elements necessary for the universal good. The accidental, the negative, the abnormal, in a word the human, will be able to develop without provoking general destruction, by being integrated into a harmonious plan . . . This house is the ideal terrain for determining if I am on the right track. Hence I am asking you to accept me here as a tenant, a friend . . .

The house is burnt down, everybody is dead, but in the computer I can arrange the facts according to a different logic, get into the computer myself, insert a Waldemar programme, bring the number of characters to six, introduce new galaxies of combinations and permutations. The house rises from the ashes, all its inhabitants are alive again, I turn up at the door with my collapsible suitcase and golf clubs, and ask for a room to rent . . .

Signora Roessler and the others listen in silence. They don't trust me. They suspect I'm working for the insurance company, that I've been sent by Skiller . . .

One can hardly deny that their suspicions are well founded. It's Skiller I'm working for of course. It would have been he who asked me to gain their confidence, to study their behaviour, to forecast the consequences of their evil intentions, to classify stimuli, tendencies, gratifications, quantify them, store them in the computer . . .

But if this Waldemar programme is nothing but a duplicate of the Skiller programme, then it is pointless keying it in. Skiller and Waldemar must be enemies, the mystery will be sorted out in the struggle between us.

In the drizzly evening two shadows brush against each other on the rusty overpass that leads to what must once have been a residential suburb, though there's nothing left now but a crooked house on a hump of ground surrounded by derelict car dumps; the lighted windows of the Roessler boarding house emerge from the fog as though on a short-sighted retina. Skiller and Waldemar don't know each other as yet. Each unaware of the other, they stalk around the house. Who will make the first move? Indisputably the insurance agent takes precedence.

Skiller rings the doorbell. 'Please excuse me, on behalf of my company I am carrying out some research into the role played by household factors in disasters. This house has been chosen for our representative sample. With your permission, I would like to keep your behaviour under observation. I hope this won't put you to too much trouble: it's just a question of filling in some forms from time to time. In return the company is offering the chance to enjoy special discounts on insurance policies of various kinds: life, property . . .'

The four listen in silence; already each of them is thinking how they can get something from the situation, each is concocting a plan . . .

But Skiller is lying. His programme has already forecast what each member of the household will do. Skiller has a copybook listing a series of violent or dishonest acts whose probability he merely has to establish. He already knows there will be a series of maliciously provoked injuries, but that the company won't have to pay any damages, because all the beneficiaries will have killed each other. All these forecasts were given him by a computer: not my own, so I am bound to imagine the existence of another programmer, Skiller's accomplice in a criminal plot. The plot goes like this: a databank brings together the names of those fellow citizens of ours driven by fraudulent and destructive impulses; there are several hundred thousand of them; a system of persuasion and follow-ups leads them to become clients of the company, to insure everything insurable, to produce fraudulent accidents and to kill each other off. The company will have taken care to record evidence to its own advantage, and since those committing crimes always tend to overdo it, the amount of information will include a considerable percentage of useless data that will function as a smokescreen to cover up the company's involvement. Indeed this coefficient of entropy has already been programmed: not all the *Abominable Deeds* of the index have a role in the story; some just create a 'noise' effect. The Roessler boarding-house operation is the first practical experiment the diabolical insurance agent has attempted. Once the disaster has taken place, Skiller will go to another computer, whose programmer is ignorant of all the facts, to check if it is possible to trace consequence back to cause. Skiller will give this second programmer all the necessary data together with a certain amount of 'noise' such as to produce circuit overload and debase the information: the evil intent of those insured will be sufficiently demonstrated, but not that of the insurer.

I am the second programmer. Skiller has set it up well. Everything fits. The programme was set up beforehand, and the house, the copybook, my own flowchart and my computer were to do nothing more than carry it out. I'm stuck here inputting and outputting the data of a story I can't change. There's no point in my putting myself in the computer: Waldemar will not go up to the house on the hump of wasteland, nor will he meet the four mysterious inhabitants, nor will he be (as he had hoped) the perpetrator of a *seduction* (victim: Ogiva). Perhaps even Skiller only has an input-output function: the real computer is elsewhere.

But a game between two computers is not won by the one that plays better than the other, but by the one that understands how its opponent is managing to play better than itself. My computer has now been fed its opponent's winning game: so has it won?

Someone rings at the door. Before going to open it, I must quickly work out how Skiller will react when he finds out his plan has been discovered. I too was persuaded by Skiller to sign a fire insurance policy. Skiller has already provided for killing me and setting fire to the laboratory: he will destroy the punchcards that accuse him and demonstrate that I lost my life attempting arson. I hear the fire brigade's siren approaching: I called them in time. I click off the safety catch on my gun. Now I can open the door.

21.

Raymond Queneau
REDUNDANCY IN PHANE ARMÉ
translated by Philip Terry
{Oulipo}

1

Unalterable law
of my vertebrae:
funereal ceilings
in me

To seduce a king
with the celebrated
darkness
of his faith . . .

The earth:
less
mystery

Genius
denies itself
to witness

2

Drunken wing beat,
under frost,

today
unfled!

The place to live
breaks free;
boredom,
it is he,

Swan
assigned
contempt
is caught

Death-throe
denying it

3

Fair suicide;
tempest!
my absent tomb
gets ready . . .

Even a scrap
celebrates us
head
in darkness.

Yours
holds back,
doing up your hair,
you put it down,
child
of roses.

4

Their onyx?
torch-bearer!
The Phoenix?
amphora!

No echoing
ptyx
from the Styx
prides itself.

A gold
décor
against a nymph,

again
the septet
settles

5

In emergencies,
unfold
a diadem.

Its former hearth,
always interior,
continues,
true or laughing,
this live cloud.

The woman
defames

the escapade
with a finger
that she flays,
torch . . .

6

Not to have known
naked
change:
strange!

The angel
of the tribe,
having drunk the prophecy,
black mixture,
oh grief!

A bas-relief
decorates
an unseen disaster:
its limit
in the future

7

Savage
Anubis,
mouth,
pubis
shiftless.
Endured
rubies,
the street-lamp wakens.

In the duskless cities
sitting down
with shivers
of Baudelaire,
tutelary,

we perish.

8

Travel
troubles.
The messenger
turns.

Caravel
in low
frolics.

News
monotonously
doesn't change:
Bearing,

gemstone,
as far as
pale Vasco.

22.

Jacques Jouet
FROM *THE GREAT-APE LOVE-SONG*
translated by Iain White
{Oulipo}

Zor hoden tanda
Kagoda bolgani
Rak gom tand-panda
Yato kalan mangani
Kreegh–ah yel greeh–ah
Kreegh–ah zu–vo bolgani
Greeh–ah tand-popo
Ubor zee kalan mangani

The preceding poem is written in great-ape language. And here is a translation:

Where are you going, gorilla,
In the dark forest?
You run without a sound
Seeking the female ape.
Beware of love
Watch out, gorilla
A lover dies of hunger
Of thirst, of hoping for the leg of the female great-ape.

The great-ape language has the peculiarity of being composed of a
lexicon of less than 300 words. In the absence of any information, it must
be deemed that the syntax is according to the user's preference, as are the
pronunciation and the prosody.

146

The French-Ape and Ape-French lexicon is to be found in *Tarzan*, by Francis Lacassin, Collection 10-18, Paris, 1971. In it, Francis Lacassin clarifies as follows:

'This lexicon, drawn up by Edgar Rice Burroughs himself after the compilation of his own works, was published under his own auspices in 1939 in the now unobtainable booklet *The Tarzan Clans of America*.

'Since then it has become the guide of the well-informed amateur and the official style-manual of successive artists and authors of strip-cartoons.

'It is published here for the first time in French, by special permission. Copyright, Edgar Rice Burroughs Inc., 1971.'

According to Edgar Rice Burroughs the great-apes are comparable to the gorilla in terms of strength, but far more developed on the level of intelligence.

It is at the breast of a great-ape (a great-ape with a great-ape's great heart) that little Lord Greystroke, orphaned of his father and mother, humans come to grief somewhere in equatorial Africa, acquired the strength of his species of adoption, while his British and innate intelligence was to sprout within him like an indestructible reed. That, at least, is more or less what Burroughs says.

Tarzan, born in the jungle, lived for a year with his human mother, whom he heard speaking to him in English, no doubt telling him English stories. He lived for a year with his English mother and father, and when his English mother died of boredom and unfamiliarity, he lived for a night and half a morning with his father, still English but completely desperate.

Adopted by Kala (in great-ape language, she who has *kal*, milk), Lord Greystoke became Tarzan, *Tar-zan*, which signifies, precisely, 'white skin' – but I have no intention here of retelling the hackneyed story of that equatorial baron-in-the-trees.

Here, rather, is another love-song. I begin with the translation. It will be seen that, this time, the poem is addressed to the human, thus, unless I am mistaken, to the reader himself.

> Black cousin of the great-ape, my friend,
> Halt under the tree to be wed.
> Your heart is in tatters for having killed too much,

Steep it again in the forest's black nest.
The river is wet,
The river that devours truncheon,
Wet too the tongue in its hut.
Come now, abandon your dryness and abandon your gun.

Gomangani yo
Dan do par kalan den
Thub tul bundolo
Vo wala go vo hoden
Gom-lul eho-lul
Gom-lul popo balu-den
Eho-l'l lus wala
Aro tand-lul pand-balu-den

As the title of this paper, *The Great-Ape Love-Song, an Unappreciated Lyric Corpus,* indicates in a very insistent way, the essential themes of great-ape poetry are amorous. But we also find an appreciable number of songs of food-gathering, the great-ape being, by nature, somewhat pacific and a vegetarian. Nor will I conceal the fact that certain of these love-songs are concerned with various carnivore perversions, trans-specific zoophilias, and are indeed sadly xenophobic and exterminatory. Let no one expect that I should paint an unduly idyllic picture of the great-apes. If they are not, on the whole, either cannibals or Calibans, either good angels or nasty brutes, let us never forget that they are capable of everything, since they are capable of poems.

But let us return to love-poems and, by way of example, to the following:

Voo-voo ta
Voo-dum red tand bzee
Yo kalan sheeta
Zu-kut koho gu zu zee
Bzan tor tand-utor
Bzan tor ta-pal rand-ramba

Tand-utor gugu zut
Eho-nala ta tand amba

I sing at the top of my voice
Because I am not really sure of myself.
I love the female leopard
Her warm grotto, and her belly, and her leg.
A hair of the beast makes one brave
The hair of my beast I pluck from her mons.
I take my courage from within and without
And from the highest summits I shall never again return.

It is clear that this is a very beautiful love-poem which sets nothing higher than love. It is also a poem which is fairly forthright in its approach to the sexual relationship between species that are generally ill-assorted; something of value, above all if we consider that the literary text is a mirror, albeit a distorting one, carried along the road of languages and of passions, basic or marginal.

With the next poem, which is a poem of food-gathering, one will readily be drawn to conclude that the great-ape food-gathering poems are not very different from great-ape love-poems, to the degree that it is perhaps pointless to have created this sub-category in the general typology of great-ape poetry. The food-gathering songs are also songs of a quite different quest.

I draw attention to the composite word *balu-den-greeh-ah*, which I have translated, word for word, as 'love-truncheon.'

Gu pan-vo manu
Yar vo-o-vo rea
Tand kree-gor sopu
Iro balu-den-greeh-ah
Pan-lul tand cho-lul
Pan-lul galul she-eta?
Gu tand-vulp dum dum
At dan-sopu tand tand-ramba

Weak stomach of the little small ape,
Listen to this poem, which is made only of words.
What use is there in crying for the fruit?
Rather rear up your love-truncheon.
You weep like a madeleine . . .
Does she weep, the bleeding panther?
Your stomach will sound hollower than the drum
If your stick does not rise up to the nuts.

Quite obviously the great-ape lyric has no great cause to be jealous of the highest topics of reference in the history of the literatures which have existed from the very beginnings of time and the first morning.

If the poem sings only of love, it sings of it to some extent by more often – but without underrating, in its turn, the spiritual dimension – putting in the foreground its formidable physical vigour. Thus it is true that the 'raw' of instinct will always, tragically (at all events among the great-apes), precede the 'cooked' – or the rehashed – of sentiment. Franz Kafka has already said it: 'Apes think with their bellies.' (*A Report to an Academy*.)

We cannot therefore completely rule it out that, in great-ape poetry, the recourse to a vocabulary as rich in vitamins as the leaves of the wild celery they greedily devour, does not come close, with the hearer of the poem, to the expectation, indeed the near reflex quest of a Pavlovian erection (or Pavlova-style juiciness), as we may certainly evaluate in the next example, which is a ritual nursery-rhyme of copulation, moreover incestuous, which I prefer not to translate, especially as, with the aid of Burroughs' lexicon (op. cit.), the curious reader will be able to attempt his own translation:

Kut za-balu
At zot at gugu
Kut za balu
At zot at gugu
Sord b'wang kali
At zot at gugu
Kut sato kali
At zot at gogo

It must be said that, among the great-apes, there is a great deal of loving going on, time and time again, left, right and centre, and non-stop, without for all that misjudging the anarchic power of that particularly widespread activity, without ignoring its fundamentally tragic character which on occasion renders the matter as daunting as the filling of the barrel by the Danaïds.

But since I fear I am being wearisome with these very abstract considerations, and certainly to provide the reader with a little amusement, I shall now speak of poetic technique.

All the poems I have quoted, with the exception of the last, are written in accordance with a great-ape fixed form, the *bzee-bur*, which means, word for word, 'cold foot.'

It will have been observed that each poem is an octave with a metric schema 5 6 5 7 5 7 5 8. The very movement of the syllabic count (or, if you prefer, the count of feet) presents a picture of a body making ready for a bath. When you venture your feet in cold water, you do it one at a time. It's cold; you withdraw the first, but if you try again, you try both.

The *bzee-bur* is a poem rhymed a b a b a b c b, or sometimes a b a b c b d b, or sometimes differently. The fifth line is characteristic, since it must be formed around two words in *rime riche*, or near paronyms, possibly around a pivot – '*Kreegh-ah yel greegh-ah*,' in the first poem quoted. These two words of line 5, taken up again at the beginning of lines 6 and 7, constitute the semantic core of the *bzee-bur*. In this instance, 'love,' and 'watch out.'

It will have been observed that the food-gathering song is a sort of slovenly *bzee-bur* since, at the beginning of the 7th line the repetition of '*cho-lul*,' 'wet,' is lacking.

The following *bzee-bur* is entitled 'Love-song of the great powerful knee.' The poem is addressed to the great-ape lambda. It is a poem which expresses the violent rivalry between the drive towards love and the drive towards feeding.

Where are you projecting your desire?
Here, or there? the leg, or the courgette-flower?

The leaves, or the buttocks?
Under the warm rain
Are you going to get something good, or something brilliant?
Are you going to get the muscle, or the forest-larder?
Is all that universe in a celery-stick
Better than a lusty thigh?

Yel? yeland? aro
Po–ubor? zee rota?
Wa–usha? goro?
Eta–koho meeta
Gando vando tu?
Gando vo popo hoden?
Vando ben abu
Hohotan popo–baluden?

Why knee? . . . It must not be expected that I, at the expense of the great-apes, should involve myself in the slightest ethnographic-type investigation. That I became acquainted with the great-ape language in a book – which I readily agree is as unbelievable and inadequate as the way in which the little Lord Greystoke learned to read English in a spelling-book, and all on his own, without ever being able to speak it, to the point that, in a few years he was perfectly capable of reading, for example, a letter addressed to him, but did not recognize the same words read out loud, so much so that a certain character in the novel thought him deaf and dumb – is rather comical when, page after page, one has heard Tarzan's famous cry of victory echoing throughout the deep and generally terrified forest.

And the extraordinary character of that learning-process does not end there, for when his new friend, the naval lieutenant D'Arnot, who is French, realizes that Tarzan can read (English), and not speak it, he decides – an initiative of inspired stupidity – to teach him to speak . . . French, better still to have him pronounce a unique species of Franglais which raises to its highest point the arbitrary nature of the sign, seeing that if Tarzan sees the written English word MAN, D'Arnot teaches him to pronounce the word *HOMME*, if he sees the word APE, he reads it *SINGE*, and the word TREE, *ARBRE!*

It appears that, using the great-ape language from the age of a year and a day (can we go so far as to say that it is a question of his mother-tongue?), Tarzan has, as it were, no particular attitude towards the plurality of languages and the arbitrariness of the sign, not the faintest pre-babelian and inveterate nostalgia for THE unitary language – which, for my part, I find rather attractive.

This strange learning-process is equalled in literature only by the way in which (in Mary Shelley's novel) Doctor Frankenstein's artificial creature learns, in a parasitic fashion, to read and speak English, his eye riveted to the chink in the wall of his outhouse, turning to his profit lessons not intended for him. Now the exceptional gifts manifested by Doctor Frankenstein's creature do not prevent him, finally, from finding himself throughout seven chapters the novel's narrator – a capacity which, in my eyes, militates in favour of calling Doctor Frankenstein a criminal when he refuses to consider his creature fully human, and therefore assimilable . . . the novel spends its time convincing us that the creature is not a monster, while, paradoxically, Mr Boris Karloff winds up inferring the exact opposite! Now, the 'Modern Prometheus' alluded to in the book's subtitle is far more the creature than the creator: if, to be sure, Doctor Frankenstein has stolen from God his privilege as initial *accoucheur*, Frankenstein's creature is not slow in stealing from men language and thought, as Prometheus does fire, and stealing from Mary Shelley, as from other characters, for several chapters, their status as narrator.

I return to the great-ape poems, and to a few thoughts about the lexicon. Less than three hundred words, I said . . . One might suppose that there are grave deficiencies. Thus, in the great-ape language, you appear not to have the word 'categorilla,' you lack the word 'allegorilla,' you do not have the word 'fantasmagorilla' (or, what is more, the utterance 'ha-ha') . . . and many others are equally lacking. But, in the long run, you can always manage with a paraphrase. My own conviction is that, from the point of view of poetry, languages are equal among themselves (at all events virtually equal), just as the words of a language are equal among themselves (at all events potentially equal) in so far, that is, that, in that language, poets have a feel for those words. And it is that 'feel' alone which can create the hierarchy! Poets, it is true, are not equal among themselves.

Few words, then, in great-ape; a syntax, a grammar, a prosody to create out of nothing . . . On the other hand, since the eminent work of François Caradec, we have at our disposal – something essential for the writing of poetry – a rhyming-dictionary. It was in 1985 that François Caradec put together an invaluable *Dictionnaire des rimes singes* on the basis of Burroughs' lexicon. He presented the Oulipo with a copy – this was a crucial moment in the discovery of the great-ape lyric.

23.

Christian Bök
FROM *EUNOIA*
{Noulipo}

for René Crevel

Enfettered, these sentences repress free speech. The text deletes selected letters. We see the revered exegete reject metred verse: the sestet, the tercet – even *les scènes élevées en grec*. He rebels. He sets new precedents. He lets cleverness exceed decent levels. He eschews the esteemed genres, the expected themes – even *les belles lettres en vers*. He prefers the perverse French esthetes: Verne, Péret, Genet, Perec – hence, he pens fervent screeds, then enters the street, where he sells these letterpress newsletters, three cents per sheet. He engenders perfect newness wherever we need fresh terms.

Relentless, the rebel peddles these theses, even when vexed peers deem the new precepts 'mere dreck'. The plebes resent newer verse; nevertheless, the rebel perseveres, never deterred, never dejected, heedless, even when hecklers heckle the vehement speeches. We feel perplexed whenever we see these excerpted sentences. We sneer when we detect the clever scheme – the emergent repetend: the letter E. We jeer; we jest. We express resentment. We detest these depthless pretenses – these present-tense verbs, expressed pell-mell. We prefer genteel speech, where sense redeems senselessness.

Westerners revere the Greek legends. Versemen retell the represented events, the resplendent scenes, where, hellbent, the Greek freemen seek revenge whenever Helen, the new-wed empress, weeps. Restless, she deserts her fleece bed where, detested, her wedded regent sleeps. When she remembers Greece, her seceded demesne, she feels wretched, left here, bereft, her needs never met. She needs rest; nevertheless, her demented fevers render her sleepless (her sleeplessness enfeebles her). She needs help; nevertheless, her stressed nerves render her cheerless (her cheerlessness enfetters her).

24.

Anne Garréta
FROM *SPHINX*
translated by Emma Ramadan
{Oulipo}

I never alluded to what I had so indistinctly perceived in my sleep, and neither did A***. There were always inexplicable silences between us, a sort of prudishness or reserve that kept us from broaching certain intimate subjects. We kept the evidence hidden away, even avoiding the use of expressions that seemed improper, excessive, or bizarre. A*** would never show any immoderate affection, and I was constantly forcing myself not to criticize the escapades I witnessed. Once, only once, I was weak enough to reveal my jealousy, which had been gnawing away at me. In the same vein, A*** only once slipped in showing tenderness toward me, using words and gestures that we had never before allowed ourselves to use.

This single jealous episode took place in the dressing room of the Eden where, one night, I came upon A*** in the company of a man I had seen fairly often in the wings the previous week, whom I suspected to be A***'s latest lover. Normally I pretended not to give a damn about the goings-on of A***'s libido; the number and nature of A***'s escapades were none of my business. What right did I have to be jealous, since there was nothing between us other than platonic affection? But that night I could not bear to see this lugubrious cretin, in the seat that I habitually occupied, engaged with A*** in the sort of conversation I had thought was reserved for me alone. This substitution outraged me: the idea that in my absence someone could take my place, could be the object of identical attentions. I was willing to admit that I was not everything for A***, but I refused to accept that what I was, achieved through a hard-fought struggle, could be taken over by someone else, and apparently by *anyone at all*. The sole merit of the lover in question was his idiocy: his inane conversation was doubtless a nice break from the thornier discussions A*** and I typically had. A*** thought he had a beautiful face, entrancing eyes, and good fashion sense. I was shocked by A***'s poor taste, by the appreciation of such an individual: an Adonis from a centerfold with a stupidly handsome face.

I had judged him, a priori, as moronic, and I realized, triumph and despair mixing indissolubly, that it was true, indeed in every way. I was revolted by this pretty boy's attitude, by his dumbfounded acceptance and regurgitation of all conventional hogwash. With the aplomb bestowed on him by age and rank, Monsieur would uphold unconscionable vulgarities, which, moreover, he revered – a proselyte! When I arrived, the conversation was revolving around the countries of North Africa, which he had glimpsed during a recent trip to a resort. He passed briskly from the picturesque story of his trip to general commentary on the countries and the samples of the population that one could encounter in France, 'In *our* country,' as he articulated so well. I reveled in ridiculing a rival in front of A*** and put on a show of systematic perversity. The discussion quickly turned sour: when one realizes that one is being unreasonable, it is precisely then that one employs even more uncouth and violent arguments. The offspring of the 16th arrondissement do not like to be refuted, much less mocked; they never think it beneath them to resort to insults, no matter how low. I left, slamming the door behind me, not without having hurled out an extremely spiteful compliment on the quality and distinction of A***'s lover, whom I referred to with a far more offensive noun.

I was in a very bad mood when I arrived at the Apocryphe, and the music I selected was proof. I exuded my resentment through the loudspeakers, which calmed me down a bit. On the floor that night were some showbiz caryatids, those people that one sees on the covers of popular magazines. They did me the honor of a hello, expecting that I would carry out some of their desiderata: 'Could you maybe play X's latest record . . . ? He's here tonight, it would be an immmmense pleasure for him,' or else: 'When are you going to play some reggae?' It made me snicker that these dignitaries, flush with their new, modern-day power, solicited favors from the feeble authority conferred on me by my position behind the turntables. What an *enormous* privilege it was in their eyes that they should notice me! In granting me the favor of acknowledging my presence, of pouring onto me a minuscule portion of the celebrity they oozed and tried to pawn off as glory, they tried cheaply to coax my kindness. I made them feel the vanity of their approach, and unless they were willing to own up to the humiliation of failure, they had no choice but to laugh at my sneering. And that night in particular they were made to feel the grace of my cynicism, the bursts of my impertinent irony.

Common mortals have other ways of expressing their desires. A club does not get filled every night with only the chic clientele. Because there are a paltry number of remarkable characters – and they are remarkable only because their number is paltry – a mass of individuals of lower distinction are allowed into this sanctuary, a privilege through which they are made to feel honored. They would come to the Apocryphe, attracted by the club's reputation (they don't accept just *anybody* – you, me, any old person), hoping to rub shoulders with some celebrities.

That night I realized something: they pronounce their desiderata, demanding (without really caring) some record, in order to prove that they have a right to be in this milieu where the arbitrary reigns. It's their sole ontological proof, their sole cogito, their foundation and justification. I want, therefore I am; I need, I breathe. I spend money, they must grant my desire, considering my demands in light of the value that I offer. I pay to exist; the tribute, delivered in kind or in cash, buys the recognition of my right.

My strategy was to inspire incertitude; I derived pleasure in imbuing these souls with doubt by not playing into their pathetic ruses. *Che vuoi?* I was leading them to the brink of an essential anxiety. My reply was always 'maybe.' It was a dangerous game that exposed me to the disapproval, disrespect, or insidious resentment of the people to whom I denied the assurance of being a subject. Each night I would have to confront this great panic of individual desires that were in reality desires for individuation, for furious revindication. Sometimes I would try – utterly in vain but with a perverse pleasure – to make them understand that the sum of individual desires does not add up to the happiness of all. That when it comes to the music in a club the law of the majority is ineffectual; that neither democracy nor aristocracy, nor even oligarchy, is a possible regime for a coherent musical set. I would argue that a good DJ is one who, rather than simply responding to repetitive wishes that are consciously formulaic and elementary (such and such a record, such and such a song), subconsciously manages to fulfill an unknown desire by creating a unity out of something superior to adding up so many records, so many requests. To appease is not the same as to fulfill.

Each night I made such observations that I would occasionally articulate to myself when pedantic disquisition and contempt started to mutually reinforce each other. I had come to the end of this chapter of my *De natura rerum noctis* dedicated to the essence of the position of the DJ when I noticed A*** standing near the bar, no longer accompanied by that new moronic lover, being served a glass of champagne by the barman.

It was late, the Eden had already been closed for some time, and I worried that A***'s arrival at the Apocryphe after our altercation meant trouble. I didn't know if I was supposed to leave my booth and go meet A*** or if I was supposed to wait for A*** to approach me. Fortunately, we both had the same reflex, and met halfway between the bar and the booth. There was no visible trace of what had happened a few hours before. A*** was drunk, which almost never happened, and from within that drunkenness asked me to dance. People didn't dance as a couple anymore in those days except during retro sequences when the DJ would revive old dance forms such as the bop, tango, or waltz. And that was absolutely what A*** desired: a waltz, nothing less. I was enticed by this extravagance, and besides, why not? At this late hour, only a small number of people remained on the floor. A waltz would serve as a charming exit, and, irresistibly outmoded, could assume the parodic allure that excuses all improprieties. So from the bottom of the crate I took out an LP of Viennese waltzes that I cued with no transition, following some nondescript funk track. Abandoning the turntables, and without any snarky retort this time, I went to dance this waltz.

A***, though drunk, was dancing divinely. A classic routine demonstrates one's sensibility just as much as the unruly improvisations of today's dance steps. While dancing these waltzes – for we danced many in succession – I had the impression that never until this day had I reveled in such a carefree lightness of being. There was no longer anybody but us on the dance floor; no doubt our perfect execution of the steps had intimidated all the amateurs. A*** had a naïve and clichéd fondness for the antiquated world of the aristocracy, an admiration for the bygone, the retro, the image of luxury that Hollywood associates with times past.

A***'s drunkenness, at once dissipated and concentrated by the dance, kept us moving. When the Apocryphe closed, we hurried to the Kormoran. Ruggero had a bottle of whiskey brought to my table that he insisted on offering me for the New Year, and as a thank you for the cigars I had brought him back from Germany. And so I too started to drink. A*** and I talked for a long time about everything under the sun. We were drunk, A*** more so than me. There was a warmth, a hint of complicity between us, which soothed the constant tension of our unfinished business. And this happy understanding, permitted by our drunkenness, was further reinforced by the illusory intensity of perception brought on by the alcohol. Leaning toward me and speaking with more abandon than usual, A*** suddenly murmured the following question: 'And if we make love, will you still love me after?' Abruptly, I caught a glimpse of what I had given up hoping for, without ever having written it off. It was finally being offered to me, in a whisper and under the extraordinary guise of a fiction, all that we had envisioned and elaborated, that which ultimately gave meaning to all of our stratagems. A*** repeated the query, making it sound like a supplication. I leaned toward A***, not knowing how to respond to the anxiety I sensed in the question.

My only answer was to wrest A*** from the chair and to take us out of this place. Once outside and without having discussed it at all, we hailed a taxi and A*** told the driver the address. Without saying a word, we took the elevator. The fear that I had forgotten suddenly returned and took me by the heart, the fear of flesh that accompanies those first adolescent excitements, an anxiety we attempt to combat too quickly with cynicism. I thought I was going to faint, standing there at last on the threshold of what I had so passionately desired.

I staggered as A*** moved to kiss me; I didn't know what to do except let it happen. The temporal order of events, even the simple spatial points of reference, all disappeared without my realizing it; everything is blurred in my memory. I have in my mouth, still, the taste of skin, of the sweat on that skin; against my hands, the tactile impression of skin and the shape of that flesh. In a sprawling obscurity – either I closed my eyes or my gaze was struck with a temporary blindness – some vaguely outlined visions, and, in my ear, the echo of soft rustlings, of words barely articulated.

I don't know how to recount precisely what happened, or how to describe or even attest to what I did, what was done to me. And the effect of the alcohol has nothing to do with this eradication; it's impossible to recapture the feeling of abandon through words. Crotches crossed and sexes mixed, I no longer knew how to distinguish anything. In this confusion we slept.

25.

Raymond Queneau
FROM *THE FOUNDATIONS*
OF LITERATURE
(AFTER DAVID HILBERT)
translated by Harry Mathews
{Oulipo}

First Group of Axioms
(axioms of connection)

I, 1 – *A sentence exists containing two given words.*

COMMENT: Obvious. Example: given the two words 'a' and 'a', there exists a sentence containing these two words – 'A violinist gives the vocalist her a.'

I, 2 – *No more than one sentence exists containing two given words.*

COMMENT: This, on the other hand, may occasion surprise. Nevertheless, if one considers the words 'years' and 'early', once the following sentence containing them has been written, namely 'For years I went to bed early,' clearly all other sentences such as 'For years I went to bed right after supper' or 'For years I did not go to bed late' are merely pseudo-sentences that should be rejected by virtue of the above axiom.

SCHOLIUM: Naturally, if 'For years I went to bed right after supper' is the sentence written originally, 'For years I went to bed early' becomes the sentence to be excluded by virtue of the axiom I, 2. In other words, no one can write *À la recherche du temps perdu* twice.

I, 3 – *There are at least two words in a sentence; at least three words exist that do not all belong to the same sentence.*

COMMENT: Thus there are no one-word sentences. 'Yes', 'No', 'Hey', 'Psst' are not sentences. In regard to the second part of the axiom: the implicit assumption is that the language used comprises at least three words (a truism in the case of French and English) and furthermore that the possible existence of a sentence comprising all the words in a language (or all words less one, or less two) is excluded.

I, 4a – *A paragraph exists including three words that do not all belong to the same sentence.*

COMMENT: A paragraph consequently comprises at least two sentences.

It is to be noted that the manner in which the axioms I, 1 through I, 4 are formulated contradicts axiom I, 2, since all four require for their articulation the words 'words' and 'sentences' whereas, according to the said axiom, no more than one sentence containing them should exist.

It is therefore possible to formulate the following metaliterary axiom:

Axioms are not governed by axioms.

I, 4b – *Every paragraph contains at least one word.*

COMMENT: Therefore 'Yes', 'No', 'Hey', 'Psst', which according to I, 3 are not sentences, cannot by themselves constitute paragraphs.

I, 5 – *Not more than one paragraph exists containing three words that do not belong to the same sentence.*

COMMENT: As in I, 2, the question of unicity is thus raised, here that of the paragraph. In other terms, if three words that do not belong to the same sentence are used in one paragraph, they cannot be reused in another paragraph. But what if – as may be objected – they all belong to the same sentence in the other paragraph? An impossibility, according to this axiom.

I, 6 – If two words in a sentence belong to a paragraph, all words in the sentence belong to the paragraph.

COMMENT: No comment required.

I, 7 – If two paragraphs have one word in common, they have still another one in common.

COMMENT: To comply with this axiom, a writer must, if in a new paragraph he uses a word that has already appeared in the preceding paragraph, obligatorily use a second word that has appeared in the preceding paragraph as well. The obligation is easily acquitted in the case of such words as articles, auxiliary verbs, etc.; it is clearly anti-Flaubertian in regard to signifiers (nouns and adjectives, for example).

(See the comment on theorem I.)

I, 8 – At least four words exist that do not belong to the same paragraph.

COMMENT: This means that a 'text' consisting of a single paragraph does not deserve the designation 'text'; that, furthermore, the language (French, English) contains sufficient words (four at least).

(See as well the comment to I, 3.)

In commenting on axiom I, 7, we did not explore all the consequences that can be drawn from it (as well as from other axioms already considered). We introduce forthwith the first theorem demonstrated by Hilbert:

THEOREM I. *Two discrete sentences in the same paragraph have at most one word in common; two discrete paragraphs either have no word in common or else they have one word in common and no word in common outside this sentence.*

COMMENT: If the two paragraphs have one word in common, they must in fact have a second (I, 7); but in that case these two words determine the sentence and, according to I, 1, this sentence is unique. The two paragraphs therefore have one sentence in common.

We thus come back to a more Flaubertian conception. The repetition of a word already used in a preceding paragraph requires the repetition of the entire sentence – a crushing obligation. It is just as well – and far more prudent – to avoid any repetition of the word. Flaubert complies with this axiom scrupulously.

Second Group of Axioms
(axioms of order)

II, 1 – *If a word in a sentence is situated between two words taken in a particular order, it is also situated between them when these two words are taken in reverse order.*

COMMENT: A truism.

II, 2 – *If two words are present in a sentence, there exists at least one other word so situated that the second word appears between it and the first word.*

COMMENT: This may occasion surprise. The reader is requested to refer to the comments on theorems 3 and 7 for fuller insight into the question.

II, 3 – Of three words in a paragraph, one is situated between the two others.

COMMENT: A careful investigation of literature will unearth a few sentences to which this axiom does not apply – for example, in Chapter XCVIII of *Tristram Shandy*.

II, 4 – *Given three words in a paragraph that do not all belong to the same sentence; given a sentence that does not contain these words but belongs to the same paragraph; if the latter sentence contains a word of the sentence determined by two of the same words, it will always contain a word in common with the sentence determined by one of these words and the third.*

COMMENT: To elucidate this axiom, let us go back to Hilbert, who formulates it 'more intuitively: a straight line that enters a triangle exits from it as well' (p. 7 of the English translation).

We leave the reader the task of identifying or inventing paragraphs true to this axiom. Hilbert subsequently establishes several theorems, among them.

THEOREM 3. *Where two words are present, the sentence in which they appear includes at least one word between these two words.*

And

THEOREM 7. *Between two words of a sentence there exists an infinity of other words.*

COMMENT: No doubt a reader surprised by axiom II, 2 will deem his surprise justified. To overcome his astonishment and understand these theorems he need only admit the existence of what we shall call, following the example of traditional projective geometry, 'imaginary words' and 'infinitesimal words'. Every sentence contains an infinity of words; only an extremely limited number of them is perceptible; the rest are infinitesimal or imaginary. Many thoughtful minds have had a premonition – but never a clear awareness – of this. No longer will it be possible for students of rhetoric to ignore so crucial a theorem. Linguistics may benefit from it as well.

Axiom of Parallels
(Euclid's axiom)

Given a sentence and a word that does not belong to this sentence; in the paragraph determined by the sentence and the word, no more than one sentence exists that contains this word while having no word in common with the given sentence.

COMMENT: Given the sentence 'For years I went to bed early', and the word 'awakening', in the paragraph that includes them, there is one sentence and one only that contains the word 'awakening' and no word belonging to the sentence 'For years I went to bed early', namely: 'This belief lasted a few seconds after my awakening.' Thus the opening paragraph of *À la recherche du temps perdu* follows Euclid's axiom at least locally.

We leave to the reader the task of transposing the axioms of congruence and continuity.

The process of transposition might be pursued still further. Curiously enough, once the domain of conic sections is reached, there is no more need of transposition. We find ourselves immersed in rhetoric. There is no talk of anything but ellipses, parabolas, and hyperbolas, all figures of speech well known to writers, even if in our day ellipsis is rare, the parable has been neglected (for nearly two thousand years), and hyperbole is common coin.

26.

Michèle Audin
FROM *ONE HUNDRED TWENTY-ONE DAYS*
translated by Christiana Hills
{Oulipo}

The Numbers

The numbers, in order, starting with the negatives:

-25,   the temperature (in degrees Celsius) in Upper Silesia in January 1945 during the evacuation of Auschwitz

0.577215 . . . ,   Euler's constant

0.625   or 5/8 Jewish would have been each of Mireille's and André's children

1   single bullet managed to remove one of M.'s eyes, his nose, and half of his jaw

1.414213 . . . ,   the square root of 2, the length of the diagonal of a square with a side of 1

2   grenadiers returning to France in a poem by Heine

3   croissants for a breakfast at the Hotel Raphael

3.14159 . . . ,   π, the constant allowing one to calculate the length and surface area of all circles

5   daughters (and one son) had Christian and Marguerite M.

6TH   Artillery Regiment, the one in which Gorenstein was serving when he had the sense knocked out of him

7   kilometers, the distance between Monowitz and the main camp of Auschwitz

8	minutes, the length of time it took for Sacco to die on the electric chair
9	Rue de Médicis, the home of the Duvivier family
11,	answered the nurse when the numeromaniac polytechnician asked her for a number
12,	the number of syllables in a translation of one of Dante's hendecasyllabic verses
12.3569111418 . . . ,	Gorenstein's constant
13TH	of August, the date the uprising started in Paris in 1944
14	years old, Claude Yersin's age when he was looking for his uncle's remains on the battlefield
14.134725 . . . ,	the imaginary part of one of the zeros in the zeta function
15	years old was the boy when they decided to send him to Paris
16	meters, the height of the cylinder Beckett describes in *The Lost Ones*
17	years old, Kürz's age when he enlisted in the navy
18TH	of January, the day the Auschwitz camps were evacuated
19	years old, the age of the future great poet when he jumped out of a trench
20	years that Meyerbeer studied Gorenstein
22	years old, Gorenstein's age when he committed a triple murder
23RD	of June, the date Christian and Marguerite were married
24TH	of June, the last day André and Mireille saw each other
25	the only square that becomes a cube when you add 2 to it
26,	the canto number in the *Inferno* in which the sea closes over Ulysses and his companions
27	German physicists were winners of the Nobel Prize of Physics
28	is a perfect number
29	days had the month of February in 1916
31	years old, André's age when he died in Mariahilf

39,   the number of survivors from the convoy in which Silberberg was taken

40   prisoners were held in each cell of the Cherche-Midi prison

41,   the largest dimension for which Kürz managed to demonstrate Silberberg's lemma

42.8   meters cubed of rubble per person after the bombing of Dresden

48   hours that André and Sonntag marched side by side

50   meters, the circumference of the cylinder Beckett describes in *The Lost Ones*

60,   the number of the convoy that took André to Upper Silesia

65,   the smallest integer whose square can be written in two ways as the sum of two squares

67   kilometers, the length of what became known as the Auschwitz death march

70   kilos, the weight of the bags of phenyl-beta that Klein had to carry while he was at the camp

80   victories (at least) had been achieved by Guynemer

103   years old, M.'s age when he died

120   pages of M.'s dissertation were recopied by Marguerite

121   days of happiness for André and Mireille

131   cities were attacked by the Royal Air Force

209,   the number of the hospital where Gorenstein's aunt worked as a nurse

250   years old was the University of N. in 1937

340   men in Convoy 60 were sent to Monowitz

400   individual detached houses could have been constructed for the cost of one insane asylum

475,   the number of Mozart's Fantasia in the Köchel catalog

479   is a prime number and one quarter of 1916

491	men and women from Convoy 60 were taken by SS officers and dogs and immediately gassed
600	barricades were erected during the Parisian uprising
800	meters, the track event in which André was university champion
1000,	the number of Jews in the convoys
1796,	the year Bonaparte made his entry into Milan at the head of his young army
1800	meters, the total length of the cylinders in which the V-2 rockets were constructed at Dora
1801,	the year Beethoven composed his fourteenth sonata *Quasi una fantasia*
1821,	the date Heinrich Heine evoked the books burned during the Reconquista
1858,	the opening of the Kaffeehaus & Konditorei Korb & Schlag in N.
1926,	the year Vito Volterra invented a model for predator-prey systems
1933,	the date the books of Heinrich Heine were joyously burned in public squares
1949,	Gorenstein's death
1950,	the lovely summer evenings were started again in N.
2066,	the year M.'s writings will enter the public domain
8000	meters high, they say, was the height the smoke reached after the bombing of Hamburg
14521.8	square kilometers of Germany were allocated to France by the Versailler Diktat
116800	Reichsmarks would have been the cost of a mentally ill patient if he had been looked after for forty years
157034,	the number tattooed on a survivor's arm and jotted down on a page from a blue notebook

27.

Robert Desnos
FROM *RROSE SÉLAVY*
translated by Timothy Adès
{Anticipatory Plagiarism}

1   Is the solution of a sage the pollution of a page?

2   Oh, my knackered noddle, star-struck nacreous nodule.

3   Will you harass Rrose Sélavy as far as the decimal numbers nothing dismal encumbers?

4   Marcel Duchamp, marchand du sel: Rrose Sélavy knows the salt-seller well.

5   Aragon harvests in extremis the spirit of Aramis on a bed of tarragon.

6   Rrose Sélavy may don prison's drab garb, yet her mount ranges on mountain-ranges.

7   Ah, lover! All over.

8   Craning on the careen, the poet seeks a rhyme: do you see Rrose Sélavy as the queen of crime?

9   From Everest mountain I am falling down to your feet for ever, Mrs Everling.

10 Rrose Sélavy calls on you not to mistake the verrucas of the breast for the virtues of the blest.

11 Rrose Sélavy can't believe the religion of catholics arose from the contagion of relics.

12 Forego the absurd parabolas, go for Rrose Sélavy's misheard parables.

13 Cravan wends on the wave and his cravat waves in the wind.

14 The act of the sexes is the axis of the sects.

15 Do poesy's Vestals take you for vesicles, Petals?

16 Phalanx of angels, prefer the phallus to the angelus.

17 Say the trances of confusion, not the contusions of France.

18 Fear is a pure femur under ingrate granite.
19 Desnos does not pale as he deals with desires on his pole.
20 Praying in pews with bibles is like spraying the eclipse with pebbles.
21 Rrose Sélavy tarts up the fates and her dart starts the feasts.
22 At the astral gala this name is written in astragals: Gala.

28.

Georges Perec
THINK / CLASSIFY
translated by John Sturrock
{Oulipo}

D. Summary

Summary – Methods – Questions – Vocabulary exercises – The world as puzzle – Utopias – Twenty Thousand Leagues Under the Sea – Reason and thought – Eskimos – The Universal Exposition – The alphabet – Classifications – Hierarchies – How I classify – Borges and the Chinese – Sei Shonagon – The ineffable joys of enumeration – The Book of Records – Lowness and inferiority – The dictionary – Jean Tardieu – How I think – Some aphorisms – 'In a network of intersecting lines' – Miscellaneous – ?

A. Methods

At the different stages of preparation for this essay – notes scribbled on notebooks or loose sheets of paper, quotations copied out, 'ideas', see, cf., etc. – I naturally accumulated small piles: lower-case b, CAPITAL I, thirdly, part two. Then, when the time came to bring these elements together (and they certainly needed to be brought together if this 'article' was finally one day to cease from being a vague project regularly put off until a less fraught tomorrow), it rapidly became clear that I would never manage to organize them into a discourse.

It was rather as if the images and ideas that had come to me – however shiny and promising they may at first have seemed, one by one, or even when opposed in pairs – had distributed themselves from the outset across the imaginary space of my as yet unblackened sheets of paper like the noughts (or the crosses) that a not very skilful player of noughts and crosses spreads over his grid without ever managing to have three together in a straight line.

This discursive deficiency is not due simply to my laziness (or my feebleness at noughts and crosses); it's connected rather with the very thing I have tried to define, if not to take hold of, in the topic I have been set here. As if the interrogation set in train by this 'THINK/CLASSIFY' had called the thinkable and the classifiable into question in a fashion that my 'thinking' could only reflect once it was broken up into little pieces and dispersed, so reverting endlessly to the very fragmentation it claimed to be trying to set in order.

What came to the surface was of the nature of the fuzzy, the uncertain, the fugitive and the unfinished, and in the end I chose deliberately to preserve the hesitant and perplexed character of these shapeless scraps, and to abandon the pretence of organizing them into something that would by rights have had the appearance (and seductiveness) of an article, with a beginning, a middle and an end.

Perhaps this is to answer the question put to me, before it was put. Perhaps it is to avoid putting it so as not to have to answer it. Perhaps it is to use, and abuse, that old rhetorical figure known as the *excuse* whereby, instead of confronting the problem needing to be resolved, one is content to reply to questions by asking other questions, taking refuge each time behind a more or less feigned incompetence. Perhaps also it is to designate the question as in fact having no answer, that is, to refer thinking back to the unthought on which it rests, and the classified to the unclassifiable (the unnameable, the unsayable) which it is so eager to disguise.

N. Questions

Think/classify

What does the fraction line signify?
What am I being asked precisely? Whether I think before I classify?

Whether I classify before I think? How I classify what I think? How I think when I seek to classify?

S. Vocabulary exercises

How could one classify the following verbs: arrange, catalogue, classify, cut up, divide, enumerate, gather, grade, group, list, number, order, organize, sort? They are arranged here in alphabetical order.

These verbs can't all be synonymous: why would we need fourteen words to describe just one action? They are different, therefore. But how to differentiate between them all? Some stand in opposition to one another even though they refer to an identical preoccupation: *cut up*, for example, evokes the notion of a whole needing to be divided into distinct elements, while *gather* evokes the notion of distinct elements needing to be brought together into a whole.

Others suggest new verbs (for example: subdivide, distribute, discriminate, characterize, mark, define, distinguish, oppose, etc.), taking us back to that original burbling in which we can with difficulty make out what might be called the readable (what our mental activity is able to read, apprehend, understand).

U. The world as puzzle

'Plants are divided into trees, flowers and vegetables.'
Stephen Leacock

So very tempting to want to distribute the entire world in terms of a single code. A universal law would then regulate phenomena as a whole: two hemispheres, five continents, masculine and feminine, animal and vegetable, singular plural, right left, four seasons, five senses, six vowels, seven days, twelve months, twenty-six letters.

Unfortunately, this doesn't work, has never even begun to work, will never work. Which won't stop us continuing for a long time to come to categorize this animal or that according to whether it has an odd number of toes or hollow horns.

R. Utopias

All utopias are depressing because they leave no room for chance, for difference, for the 'miscellaneous'. Everything has been set in order and order reigns. Behind every utopia there is always some great taxonomic design: a place for each thing and each thing in its place.

E. Twenty Thousand Leagues Under the Sea

Conseil knew how to classify (*classer*) fish.
Ned Land knew how to hunt (*chasser*) fish.
Conseil draws up annotated lists of the fish that Ned Land draws up out of the sea.*

L. Reason and thought

What in fact is the relationship between reason and thought (aside from the fact that *Raison* and *Pensée* were the titles of two philosophical journals in France)? The dictionaries aren't much help in supplying an answer. In the *Petit Robert*, for example, a thought = whatever affects the consciousness, while reason = the thinking faculty. We would find a relationship or a difference between the two terms more easily, I fancy, by studying the adjectives they may be graced by: a thought can be kind, sudden, trite or delightful; reason can be pure, sufficient, good, or sovereign.

* Conseil and Ned Land are characters in Jules Verne's *Twenty Thousand Leagues Under the Sea*. (Translator's note.)

I. Eskimos

Eskimos, I am assured, have no *generic* name for denoting ice. They have several words (I've forgotten the exact number, but I believe it's a lot, something like a dozen) which denote specifically the various aspects that water takes between its wholly liquid state and the various manifestations of its more or less intense frozenness.

It is hard, obviously, to find an equivalent example in French. It may be that Eskimos have only one word to denote the space that separates their igloos, whereas we, in our towns, have at least seven (*rue, avenue, boulevard, place, cours, impasse, venelle*), and the English at least twenty (street, avenue, crescent, place, road, row, lane, mews, gardens, terrace, yard, square, circus, grove, court, green, houses, gate, ground, way, drive, walk); but we do all the same have a noun (*artère*, for example) that subsumes all of these. Similarly, if we talk to a pastry-cook about cooking sugar, his answer will be that he can't understand us unless we specify what degree of cooking we want (thread, ball, crack, etc.), but then for him the notion of 'cooking sugar' is already firmly established.

G. The Universal Exposition

The objects displayed at the great Exposition of 1900 were divided into eighteen Groups and 121 Classes. 'The products must be offered to visitors in a logical sequence,' wrote M. Picard, the Chief Commissioner of the Exposition, 'and their classification must answer to a simple, clear and precise conception bearing its own philosophy and justification within it, so that the overall idea may be easily grasped.'

Read the programme drawn up by M. Picard and it appears that this overall idea was inadequate. A trite metaphor justifies the leading place given to Education and Teaching: 'It is by this that man *enters* on to life.' Works of Art come next because their 'place of honour' must be preserved. 'Reasons of this same kind' mean that the 'General Instruments and Procedures of Literature and the Fine Arts' occupy third place. In the 16th Class of which, and I wonder why, one finds Medicine and

Surgery (straitjackets, invalid beds, crutches and wooden legs, army medical kits, Red Cross emergency equipment, lifesaving devices for the drowning and asphyxiated, rubber devices from the firm of Bognier & Burnet, etc.).

Between the 4th and 14th Groups, the categories follow one another without revealing any obvious idea of system. One can still see fairly easily how Groups 4, 5 and 6 are arranged (Machinery; Electricity; Civil Engineering and Means of Transport), and Groups 7, 8 and 9 (Agriculture; Horticulture and Arboriculture; Forests, Hunting and Fishing), but then we really do go off in all directions: Group 10, Foodstuffs; Group 11, Mining and Metallurgy; Group 12, Furniture and Interior Design for Public Buildings and Private Dwellings; Group 13, Clothing, Spun and Woven Fabrics; Group 14, Chemical Industry.

Group 15 is rightly given over to whatever hasn't found a place among the other fourteen, i.e. to 'Miscellaneous Industries' (paper-making; cutlery; goldsmithery; gems and jewellery-making; clock-making; bronze, cast iron, ornamental ironwork, chased metals; brushes, leatherwork, fancy goods and basketry; leather and guttapercha; knickknackery).

Group 16 (Social Economy, with the addition of Hygiene and Public Assistance) is there because it (Social Economy) 'must follow on *naturally* [my italics] from the various branches of artistic, agricultural and industrial production as being at once their resultant and their philosophy'.

Group 17 is devoted to 'Colonization'. This is a new grouping (relative to the Exposition of 1889) whose 'creation has been amply justified by the need for colonial expansion felt by all civilized peoples'.

The last place, finally, is occupied quite simply by the Army and Navy.

The division of products within these Groups and their Classes contains innumerable surprises which it isn't possible to go into in detail here.

T. The alphabet

I have several times asked myself what logic was applied in the distribution of the six vowels and twenty consonants of our alphabet. Why start with A, then B, then C, etc.? The fact that there is obviously no answer to this question is initially reassuring. The order of the alphabet is arbitrary, inexpressive and therefore neutral. Objectively speaking, A is no better than B, the ABC is not a sign of excellence but only of a beginning (the ABC of one's métier).

But the mere fact that there is an order no doubt means that, sooner or later and more or less, each element in the series becomes the insidious bearer of a qualitative coefficient. Thus a B-movie will be thought of as 'less good' than another film which, as it happens, no one has yet thought of calling an 'A-movie'. Just as a cigarette manufacturer who has the words 'Class A' stamped on his packets is giving us to understand that his cigarettes are superior to others.

The qualitative alphabetical code is not very well stocked. In fact, it has hardly more than three elements: A = excellent; B = less good; Z = hopeless (a Z-movie). But this doesn't stop it being a code and superimposing a whole hierarchical system on a sequence that is by definition inert.

For reasons that are somewhat different but still germane to my purpose, it may be noted that numerous companies go out of their way, in their corporate titles, to end up with acronyms of the 'AAA', 'ABC', 'AAAC', etc. kind so as to figure among the first entries in professional directories and phone books. Conversely, a schoolboy does well to have a name whose initial letter comes in the middle of the alphabet, because he will then stand a better chance of not being asked a question.

C. Classifications

Taxonomy can make your head spin. It does mine whenever my eyes light on an index of the Universal Decimal Classification (UDC). By what succession of miracles has agreement been reached, practically throughout the world, that 668.184.2.099 shall denote the finishing of toilet soap, and 629.1.018 – 465 horns on refuse vehicles; whereas 621.3.027.23, 621.436:382, 616.24 – 002.5 – 084, 796.54, and 913.15 denote respectively: tensions not exceeding 50 volts, the export trade in Diesel motors, the prophylaxy of tuberculosis, camping, and the ancient geography of China and Japan!

O. Hierarchies

We have undergarments, garments and overgarments, but without thinking of them as forming a hierarchy. But if we have managers and undermanagers, underlings and subordinates, we practically never have overmanagers or supermanagers. The one example I have found is 'superintendent', which is an ancient title. More significantly still, in the prefectorial body in France we have sub-prefects, and above the sub-prefects prefects, and above the prefects, not over-prefects or super-prefects, but IGAMEs (= Inspecteur Général de l'Administration en Mission Extraordinaire), whose barbaric acronym has apparently been chosen in order to indicate that here we are dealing with big shots.

At times the underling persists even after the ling has changed his name. In the corps of librarians, for example, there aren't exactly any librarians any more; they are called curators and are classified by classes or under headings (curators second class, first class, special curators, head curators). Conversely, on the floors below, they continue to employ under-librarians.

P. How I classify

My problem with classifications is that they don't last; hardly have I finished putting things into an order before that order is obsolete. Like everyone else, I presume, I am sometimes seized by a mania for arranging things. The sheer number of the things needing to be arranged and the near-impossibility of distributing them according to any truly satisfactory criteria mean that I never finally manage it, that the arrangements I end up with are temporary and vague, and hardly any more effective than the original anarchy.

The outcome of all this leads to truly strange categories. A folder full of miscellaneous papers, for example, on which is written 'To be classified'; or a drawer labelled 'Urgent 1' with nothing in it (in the drawer 'Urgent 2' there are a few old photographs, in 'Urgent 3' some new exercise-books). In short, I muddle along.

F. Borges and the Chinese

'(a) belonging to the Emperor, (b) embalmed, (c) domesticated, (d) sucking pigs, (e) sirens, (f) fabulous, (g) dogs running free, (h) included in the present classification, (i) which gesticulate like madmen, (j) innumerable, (k) drawn with a very fine camel-hair brush, (l) etcetera, (m) which have just broken the pitcher, (n) which look from a distance like flies.'

Michel Foucault has hugely popularized this 'classification' of animals which Borges in *Other Inquisitions* attributes to a certain Chinese encyclopedia that one Doctor Franz Kuhn may have held in his hands. The abundance of intermediaries and Borges's well-known love of an ambiguous erudition permit one to wonder whether this rather too perfectly astonishing miscellaneity is not first and foremost an effect of art. An almost equally mind-boggling enumeration might be extracted simply enough from government documents that could hardly be more official: (a) animals on which bets are laid, (b) animals the hunting of which is banned between 1 April and 15 September, (c) stranded whales, (d) animals whose entry within the national frontiers is subject to quarantine, (e) animals held in joint ownership, (f) stuffed animals, (g) etcetera (this etc. is not at all surprising in itself; it's only where it comes in the list that makes it seem odd), (h) animals liable to transmit leprosy, (i) guide-dogs for the blind, (j) animals in receipt of significant legacies, (k) animals able to be transported in the cabin, (l) stray dogs without collars, (m) donkeys, (n) mares assumed to be with foal.

H. Sei Shonagon

Sei Shonagon does not classify; she enumerates and then starts again. A particular topic prompts a list, of simple statements or anecdotes. Later on, an almost identical topic will produce another list, and so on. In this way we end up with series that can be regrouped. 'Things' that move one, for example (things that cause the heart to beat faster, things sometimes heard with a greater than usual emotion, things that move one deeply). Or else, in the series of disagreeable 'things':

upsetting things
hateful things
frustrating things
troublesome things
painful things
things that fill one with anxiety
things that seem distressing
disagreeable things
things disagreeable to the eye

A dog that barks during the day, a delivery room in which the baby is dead, a brazier without any fire, a driver who hates his ox, these are some of the upsetting things. Among the hateful things are to be found: a baby that cries at the very moment when you would like to listen to something, crows that flock together and caw when their flight paths cross, and dogs that go on and on howling, in unison, on a rising note. Among the things that seem distressing: a baby's wetnurse who cries during the night. Among the things disagreeable to the eye: the carriage of a high dignitary whose interior curtains appear dirty.

V. The ineffable joys of enumeration

In every enumeration there are two contradictory temptations. The first is to list *everything*, the second is to forget something. The first would like to close off the question once and for all, the second to leave it open. Thus, between the exhaustive and the incomplete, enumeration seems to me to be, before all thought (and before all classification), the very proof of that need to name and to bring together without which the world ('life') would lack any points of reference for us. There are things that are different yet also have a certain similarity; they can be brought together in series within which it will be possible to distinguish them.

There is something at once uplifting and terrifying about the idea that nothing in the world is so unique that it can't be entered on a list. Everything can be listed: the editions of Tasso, the islands on the Atlantic Coast, the ingredients required to make a pear tart, the relics of the major saints, masculine substantives with a feminine plural (*amours, délices,* *orgues*), Wimbledon finalists, or alternatively, here restricted arbitrarily to ten, the sorrows of Mr Zachary McCaltex:*

> Made to feel giddy by the scent of 6,000 dozen roses
> Gashes his foot on an old tin
> Half eaten by a ferocious cat
> Post-alcoholic para-amnesia
> Uncontrollable sleepiness
> All but knocked down by a lorry
> Sicks up his meal
> Five-month stye on his eye
> Insomnia
> Alopecia

M. The Book of Records

The preceding list is not ordered, either alphabetically, or chronologically, or logically. As bad luck would have it, most lists these days are lists of winners: only those who come first exist. For a long time now books, discs, films and television programmes have been seen purely in terms of their success at the box-office (or in the charts). Not long ago, the magazine *Lire* even 'classified thought' by holding a referendum to decide which contemporary intellectuals wielded the greatest influence.

But if we are going to list records, better to go and find them in somewhat more eccentric fields (in relation to the subject that concerns us here): M. David Maund possesses 6,506 miniature bottles; M. Robert Kaufman 7,495 sorts of cigarette; M. Ronald Rose popped a champagne cork a distance of 31 metres; M. Isao Tsychiya shaved 233 people in one hour; and M. Walter Cavanagh possesses 1,003 valid credit cards.

---

* A character in *The Sinking of the Odradek Stadium*, a novel by Perec's American friend and collaborator, Harry Mathews, which Perec translated into French in 1980. (Translator's note.)

X. Lowness and inferiority

By virtue of what complex have the departments of the Seine and the Charente insisted on becoming '*maritime*' so as not to be '*inférieure*' any longer? In the same way, the '*basses*' or 'low' Pyrénées have become '*atlantiques*', the '*basses*' Alpes have become 'de Haute-Provence', and the Loire '*inférieure*' has become '*atlantique*'. Conversely, and for a reason that escapes me, the '*bas*' Rhin has still not taken offence at the proximity of the '*haut*' or 'high' Rhin.

It will be observed, similarly, that the Marne, Savoie and Vienne have never felt humiliated by the existence of the Haute-Marne, the Haute-Savoie and the Haute-Vienne, which ought to tell us something about the role of the marked and unmarked in classifications and hierarchies.

Q. The dictionary

I possess one of the world's most peculiar dictionaries. It is entitled *Manuel biographique ou Dictionnaire historique abrégé des grands hommes depuis les temps les plus reculés jusqu'à nos jours* ('Biographical Handbook or Concise Historical Dictionary of Great Men from the Most Distant Times up until Our Own Day'). It dates from 1825.

The dictionary is in two parts, totalling 588 pages. The first 288 pages are devoted to the first five letters of the alphabet; the second part, of 300 pages, to the remaining 21 letters. The first five letters are each entitled on average to 58 pages, the last 21 to only 14. I am well aware that letter frequency is far from being uniform (in the *Larousse du XXe siècle*, A, B, C and D alone take up two volumes out of the six), but the distribution here is really too unbalanced. If you compare it, for example, with that in Lalanne's *Biographie Universelle* (Paris, 1844), you will find that the letter C takes up proportionately three times as much space, and A and E twice as much, whereas M, R, S, T and V are entitled to roughly two times less space.

It would be interesting to look more closely at what influence this inequity has had on the entries: have they been shortened, and if so how?

Have they been suppressed, and if so which ones and why? By way of an example, Anthemius, a sixth-century architect to whom we owe (in part) Santa-Sophia in Istanbul, is entitled to an entry of 31 lines, whereas Vitruvius gets only six; Anne de Boulen or Boleyn also gets 31 lines, but Henry the Eighth a mere 19.

B. Jean Tardieu*

In the sixties they invented a device that enabled the focal length of a film camera lens to be varied continuously, so simulating (rather crudely in the event) an effect of movement without the camera actually having to be moved. The device is known as a 'zoom' lens and the corresponding verb in French is *zoomer*. Although this hasn't as yet been admitted to the dictionaries, it very soon imposed itself on the profession.

This isn't always the case. In most motor vehicles, for example, there are three pedals, each of which has its specific verb: *accélérer, débrayer, freiner* (to accelerate, to declutch, to brake). But there is no verb, to my knowledge, corresponding to the gear lever. We have to say *changer de vitesse* ('change gear'), *passer en troisième* ('get into third'), etc. Similarly, there is a verb in French for shoelaces (*lacer*) and for buttons (*boutonner*), but no verb for zip fasteners, whereas the Americans have *to zip up*.

The Americans also have a verb that means 'to live in the suburbs and work in the town': *to commute*. But they don't, any more than we do, have one which would mean: 'drink a glass of white wine with a friend from Burgundy, at the Café des Deux-Magots, around six o' clock on a rainy day, while talking about the non-meaningfulness of the world, knowing that you have just met your old chemistry teacher and that next to you a young woman is saying to her neighbour: "You know, I showed her some in every colour!"'.

(from Jean Tardieu: *Un Mot pour un autre*, 1951)

---

* A French poet and radio dramatist, born in 1903, whose black humour and obsession with language were much appreciated by Perec. (Translator's note.)

J. How I think

How I think when I'm thinking? How I think when I'm not thinking? At this very moment, how I think when I'm thinking about how I think when I'm thinking? The words '*penser/classer*', for example, make me think of '*penser/clamser*', or alternatively '*clapet sensé*', or even '*quand c'est placé*'.* Is this called 'thinking'?

I rarely get thoughts about the infinitely small or about Cleopatra's nose, about the holes in gruyère or about the Nietzschean sources of Maurice Leblanc and Joe Shuster.† It is much more of the order of a scribbling down, of a jogging of the memory or a truism.

Yet how, all the same, when 'thinking' (reflecting on?) about this essay, did I come to 'think' about the game of noughts and crosses, Leacock, Jules Verne, Eskimos, the 1900 Exposition, the names streets have in London, IGAMEs, Sei Shonagon, Anthemius and Vitruvius? The answer to these questions is sometimes obvious and sometimes wholly obscure. I would have to speak of feeling my way, of flair, of inklings, of chance, of encounters that are fortuitous or prompted or fortuitously prompted: of meandering in the midst of words. I'm not thinking but I am searching for my words. In the heap there must surely be one that will come to clarify this drifting about, this hesitation, this agitation which, later, is going to 'mean something'.

It is a matter also, and above all, of montage, of distortion, of contortion, of detours, of a mirror, indeed of a formula, as the paragraph that follows will demonstrate.

---

* These are phrases sounding rather like *penser/classer* in French. *Clamser* is a slang verb for 'to kick the bucket'; *clapet* is a word meaning 'a valve', used familiarly in such phrases as '*ferme ton clapet!*', meaning 'shut your gob!'; *quand c'est placé* would simply mean 'when it's placed'. (Translator's note.)

† Maurice Leblanc was a writer of crime novels; Joe Shuster was one of the originators of the Superman character in the United States. (Translator's note.)

K. Some aphorisms

Marcel Benabou of the OuLiPo has thought up a machine for manufacturing aphorisms. It consists of two parts, a grammar and a vocabulary.

The grammar lists a certain number of formulas commonly used in a majority of aphorisms. For example: A is the shortest route from B to C. A is the continuation of B by other means. A little A carries us away from B, a lot brings us closer. Little As make big Bs. A wouldn't be A if it wasn't B. Happiness is in A not B. A is a malady for which B is the cure. Etc.

The vocabulary lists pairs of words (or trios, or quartets) which may be false synonyms (sentiment/sensation, knowledge/science), antonyms (life/death, form/content, remember/forget), words that are phonetically close (belief/relief, love/leave), words grouped together by usage (crime/punishment, hammer/sickle, science/life). Etc.

The injection of the vocabulary into the grammar produces *ad lib* a near-infinite number of aphorisms, each one of them bearing more meaning than the last. Whence a computer program, devised by Paul Braffort, which can turn out on demand a good dozen within a few seconds:

Remembering is a malady for which forgetting is the cure
Remembering wouldn't be remembering if it weren't forgetting
What comes by remembering goes by forgetting
Small forgettings make big rememberings
Remembering adds to our pains, forgetting to our pleasures
Remembering delivers us from forgetting, but who will deliver us
    from remembering?
Happiness is in forgetting, not in remembering
Happiness is in remembering, not in forgetting
A little forgetting carries us away from remembering, a lot brings us
    closer
Forgetting unites men, remembering divides them
Remembering deceives us more often than forgetting
Etc.

Where is the *thinking* here? In the formula? In the vocabulary? In the operation that marries them?

W. 'In a network of intersecting lines'

The alphabet used to 'number' the various paragraphs of this text follows the order in which the letters of the alphabet appear in the French translation of the seventh story in Italo Calvino's *If on a Winter's Night a Traveller* ...

The title of this story, '*Dans un réseau de lignes entrecroisées*', contains this alphabet up to its thirteenth letter, O. The first line of the text enables us to go up to the eighteenth letter, M, the second gives us X, the third Q, the fourth nothing, the fifth B and J. The last four letters, K, W, Y and Z, are to be found, respectively, in lines 12, 26, 32 and 41 of the story.

From which it may easily be deduced that this story (at least in its French translation) is not lipogrammatic. It will be found similarly that three letters of the alphabet thus formed are in the same place as in the so-called normal alphabet: I, Y and Z.

Y. Miscellaneous

Interjections as classified by a (very second-rate) crossword dictionary (extracts):

Of admiration: *eh*
Of anger: *bigre*
Of scorn: *beuh*
Used by a carter in order to go ahead: *hue*
Expressing the sound of a falling body: *patatras*
Expressing the sound of a blow: *boum*
Expressing the sound of a thing: *crac, cric*
Expressing the sound of a fall: *pouf*
Expressing the cry of bacchantes: *evohé*
To urge on a pack of hounds: *taiaut*

Expressing a disappointed hope: *bernique*
Expressing an oath: *mordienne*
Expressing a Spanish oath: *caramba*
Expressing King Henri IV's favourite oath: *ventre-saint-gris*
Expressing an oath expressing approval: *parbleu*
Used for getting rid of someone: *oust, ouste*

29.

Marcel Bénabou

FROM *ONE APHORISM*
CAN HIDE ANOTHER

translated by Philip Terry

{Oulipo}

A little . . . a lot
A little science diminishes ignorance, a lot strengthens it.
A little memory diminishes hope, a lot strengthens it.
A little virtue diminishes vice, a lot strengthens it.
A little revolution diminishes the state, a lot strengthens it.

The little and the great
Little cries make great autobiographies.
Little appreciations make great contentment.
Little silences make great thinkers.
Little thefts make great properties.

The road
The road leading to hope passes through experience.
The road leading to will passes through instinct.
The road leading to terror passes through error.
The road leading to the wedding passes through soiled bedding.

Clausewitz revisited
Courage is the continuation of cowardice by other means.
Tears are the continuation of fears by other means.
Might is the continuation of right by other means.
Punishment is the continuation of crime by other means.

The true nature of . . .
Conviction wouldn't be conviction without contradiction.
Science wouldn't be science without patience.
Space wouldn't be space without a race.
Death wouldn't be death without breath.

Where is happiness?
Happiness is in darkness, not in listlessness.
Happiness is in error, not in terror.
Happiness is in instinct, not in will.
Happiness is in mystery, not in power.

Renouncements
It is easier to renounce war than to renounce hatred.
It is easier to renounce freedom than to renounce ignorance.
It is easier to renounce revolution than to renounce the state.
It is easier to renounce pride than to renounce prejudice.

A throw of the dice
Property will never abolish theft.
Punishment will never abolish crime.
The pen-name will never abolish the pen.
Darkness will never abolish listlessness.

The apprentice and the master
Matter is an apprentice, light is its master.
Life is an apprentice, strife is its master.
Error is an apprentice, terror is its master.
Will is an apprentice, instinct is its master.

Come and go
What comes with friendship goes with love.
What comes with vanity goes with the truth.
What comes with a cry goes with autobiography.
What comes with reason goes with doubt.

30.

Harry Mathews
FROM *TRIAL IMPRESSIONS*
{Oulipo}

I

Deare, if you change, Ile never chuse againe,
Sweete, if you shrinke, Ile never think of love,
Fayre, if you faile, Ile judge all beauty vaine,
Wise, if too weake, my wits Ile never prove.
  Dear, sweete, fayre, wise, change, shrinke nor be not weake,
  And on my faith, my faith shall never breake.

Earth with her flowers shall sooner heavn adorn,
Heaven her bright stars through earths dim globe shall move,
Fire heate shall lose and frosts of flames be borne,
Ayre made to shine as blacke as hell shall prove:
  Earth, heaven, fire, ayre, the world transformed shall view,
  E're I prove false to faith, or strange to you.

from John Dowland's Second Booke of Ayres

II

If you break our breakfast date, I'll go begging in Bangkok;
If you start stalling, I'll stop everything;
If you phone that freak, I'll fall down Everest;

If you take that trip, please tow away my truck.
  A date, a freak, a trip – I implore you to be careful.
  I don't claim to be reasonable, I just can't stop.

We can't take this sharp awareness into yesterday,
No pondered memory of tomorrow can exalt it.
Can black holes yield light? Can sunlight weigh more than stone?
Can the split atom be reassembled?
  When today is tomorrow, and the electrons rejoin each other,
  Only then will my unreasonableness fail to invest you.

Up to Date

III

Dear, if you, who are more pole-star than pole-cat, change, I'll never,
  when confronted with life's many-paged bill-of-fare, choose any dish,
  no matter how succulent, again.
Sweet and pretty as an advancing spinaker, if you shrink like a boiled
  sweater, I'll never so much as think of the high-rental havens of love.
Fair like sun on an alp, if you fail to be what you seem, I'll judge all beauty
  like the new bills of a drifting currency: pretentious and vain.
Wise (if too winning for many to believe it), don't let your wisdom turn
  into the weak, indecisive busy-signal that flabbergasts my wits, leaving
  them with nothing to prove.
Dear pole-star, sweet spinaker, fair alp, winning wisdom, never change,
  never shrink, never fail, never be weak.
And by my bank account, my nervous system, my mind, and my faith, my
  faith – complex as a computer and simple as the current it runs on –
  shall never break.

Earth, lifted like a rolling table in a hotel elevator, with all the flowers in
  her shops and fields, shall sooner the sky of heaven (that cold, vacant
  hole) adorn;

Heaven, warmed up, cooled off, her bright stars shrunk to streetlamp size, through earth's once-dim globe like a convoy of yachts shall move;

Fire, resembling tongues of yoghurt, and heat, now merely a hat, shall lose all warmth, and frosted flames shall like some dreary Christmas tinsel be born;

Air, no longer even coughable, shall be made to shine with an inverse blaze, thick blazing blackness, more black than hell (if hell is thick tar) shall prove:

Earth lifted, heaven shrunk, fire cold, air black, the world itself and its words transformed shall view

Before I, transforming myself, prove false: no longer entrusting my words to faith, and, stranger yet, no longer entrusting my time, my sight, my skin to you.

Keep Talking

VII

Who will in dearest love of Beauty change
    How wit may sweetest chosen in faith be
    Let him but shrink from faith to think in thee,
    Stella, of those fair earths which all flowers fail.
There shall he judge all heaven stars
    Not by vain earth but wisest globe
    Of fire whose heat those frost-flames prove,
    That weak air in thy hell hath changed so;
And dear not to have shrunk earth's heaven
    Thyself all fire that air to break
    Who adorn in thee what moves in thee most sweet.
So while thy world loseth faith to be born
    As fair thy love maketh that beauty bright.
    'But ah,' wit ever shines, 'prove me some faith.'

A Disconsolate Chimaera

XII

Deep, if you charge, I'll never chug again
    (Deep, if you chant, I'll never chip again)
Tall, if you shun, I'll never thrive on luck
    (Swift, if you shrive, I'll never thirst for luck)
Far, if you fan, I'll keep all bedclothes vast
    (False, if you faint, I'll jug all beaver vast)
Worse, if too weird, my wives I'll never puff
    (Worse, if too webbed, my witch I'll never prowl):
  Deep, tall, far, worse, charge, shun, and be not weird
  And by my fall, my fall will never bridge
    (Deep, swift, false, worse, chant, shrive, and be not webbed,
    And by my fake, my fake shall never breast.)

East with her fluid shall sooner hedge advise
    (Ease with her flu shall sooner heck advance)
Hedge her broad start through east's dire gloss shall mulct
    (Heck her brisk starch through ease's gloom shall mow)
Firms hedge shall lug and frumps of flaps be bounced
    (Firms heaths shall lot and froths of flans be bossed)
Aisle mapped to shoal as bleak as help shall puff
    (Aisle manned to ship as bland as helm shall prowl):
  East, hedge, firms, aisle, the worth transpierced shall voice
  Ere I puff far to fall, or strict to you
    (Ease, heck, firms, aisle, the worm transfused shall voice
    Ere I prowl far to fake, or stray to you.)

XIII

1
John comes to the city and meets
Marian, a very affectionate girl.
She loves him, and he her;
But he finds that Marian has a changeable streak,

So he leaves her. Do you think that he should never look
At another woman? Or do you think he should look
At some other woman? In the first case, proceed
To 7, if you're an optimist; to 8, if you're
A pessimist. In the second case, proceed to 2.

   2

John meets Marianne, who is tenderness itself;
But sometimes she is put off by him: so John
Leaves her. Should he (a) forget about love?
Or should he (b) remember love at least once?
If their opinion concurs with (a), optimists
Go on to 7, pessimists to 8. If
Their opinion concurs with (b), to 3.

   3

So John meets Marie-Anne, a beauty.
But she 'makes him insecure'. Again he leaves.
After this experience he may feel that beauty
And disappointment go hand in hand; or he may feel
That this case is peculiar and try again.
If he rejects all beauty, choose 7 (or 8).
If he decides to move on, then choose 4.

   4

John meets Mary Anne, a brilliant girl.
Then Mary Anne loses touch with reality,
At least with *his* reality. John is driven to
Distraction, so much so that he loses his mind
– Or is it merely that he's extremely upset and goes away?
If he loses his mind, advance to 6.
If he doesn't lose his mind, there's another choice
To make: does he meet another woman or doesn't he?
If he doesn't, and the consequences are dire, 8.
If he doesn't, and the consequences aren't dire, 7.
If he does (i.e., meet someone else), 5.

5

John meets Mary Ann. His previous encounters
Could hardly have led him to expect such a person,
And yet they alone have prepared him to appreciate her,
For she is constant, tender, beautiful, and wise.
John loves her and lives with her in absolute devotion.
Everything is in its place: earth becomes earth,
And the prophetic heavens swivel in their grooves.
If this state of affairs suits your desires,
See 11. If you prefer another, see 6.

6

Then the universe comes crashing down, and clinkers
Of star blaze block his path, and his thoughts
Zip up to those vacated holes and blossom
Crazily. John can't stand this situation.
Once more he leaves the woman he loves.
Do you feel that this step will bring him peace?
Move to 7. Or do you feel that John
Is doomed? In that case, move to 8.

7

He goes off alone and lives alone.
He has learned that for him, happiness means solitude.
If you have chosen this alternative, his story is at an end.
– But what about the woman? Is she to suffer
From this turn of events? If you think so, 9.
Or should she live out her life, whether alone or not,
Indifferent to this loss? Then consult 10.

8

John goes off alone and dies in misery.
If you have chosen this alternative, his story is at an end.
– But what about the woman? Should she suffer
From this turn of events? Pass on to 9.

Should she live in just or unjust indifference?
If such is your preference, pass to 10.

9
She feels as though some part of her body has been severed.
If you have chosen this alternative, you have reached the end.

10
She lives in just or unjust indifference.
If you have chosen this alternative, you have reached the end.

(A suggestion has been made by a lady in the audience:
How about moving from 5 to 8?
What if, when everything is hunky-dory,
John leaves anyway? This lady points out
That he does so much leaving he probably enjoys it;
And what about his character? What about the way
He behaves with women?
                              I can only say
That I find these remarks perplexing and irrelevant.
These remarks have to do with a quite different problem.
These remarks make it impossible to proceed with the story,
Although they *are* typical of the bitchy-mindedness
That produced the situations we are attempting to narrate.
May I suggest to the lady that instead of being so clever
If she thought a little more about her lover's problems
Someone who shall be nameless might sleep a little better –

Now *I'm* digressing. In conclusion, 11:)

11
John and Mary Ann, Mary Ann and John
Lived and died in each other's arms.

Multiple Choice

XXIV

I
            (one who won)
                        'Deh!'
sang
            – devil's aria:
                        No-bed era
begat
            love's
                        reverse
voltage.
            Bare, debonair
                        as lived;
gnashed now.
            'Oh – we?'
                        No: I.

                                    To an Fro

XXX

Dear, if you change, I'll never think of earth
And its animals dwelling in ignorance of heaven,
Warm and wise without the comforts of fire,
Nested in the ground, or in water, or air,
Certain of their ways by the day and night stars,
With no use for knowledge, or need for faith:

To see them, it is my eyes that need your faith.
Dawn as usual wrings the shadows from the earth
But my day stays crowded with tiny stars
Like spangled dust rising from collapsed heaven,
My panic stirs them up so that they blacken the air
As if my sight and mind were charred by their fire.

Inside me burns that second unnatural fire.
Between the two, what existence can I claim, what faith
That I am more than a machine to breathe air,
To preserve a suffering form of inanimate earth?
Others felt this way: they invented heaven.
I look up at distant, dominant stars:

My desire is firm, it has come down from the stars
Scattered around the sky in a single multiple fire,
Exemplary, not of some impossible heaven,
But of our everyday, there-for-the-asking faith,
One being and one love dispersed over the earth
In repetitions as sure as theirs in the air.

Without you, my thinking spins in thin air,
Evening never warms its gradual stars,
Choosing another is choosing a bed of earth,
All love is decreed hallucinatory fire.
But air and evening fill up with love from your faith,
Which I could no more break than I could fly to heaven,

Except that once I did: it was under a heaven
Of night and eyes, our breaths made one air,
Our eyes were struck open in pleasures of faith,
There was nothing to be seen but stars,
Only one night, and never to see dawn's fire
Was all I wanted as we grappled on grass and earth.

You make earth earth: who needs heaven?
You give a heat to fire, you give a brightness to air
Of that night's stars, of that broadcast faith.

31.

Lucretius
FROM *THE POEM ON NATURE*
translated by C. H. Sisson
{Anticipatory Plagiarism}

You may say that in the forests which cover the mountains
It often happens that, under the stress of great winds,
The branches of neighbouring trees will rub together
And suddenly fire break out like a monstrous flower:
Yes, quite: but that doesn't mean there is fire in timber;
It simply means there are inflammable elements
Which rubbing together will bring into closer contact,
And this is enough to set the forest on fire.
If the wood in fact contained a ready-made flame,
It would never be possible to conceal the fire;
The forests would all burn up and the trees disappear.

Now perhaps you will see – as I have already explained it –
Why it matters so much how the particles lie,
In what position, or how they push one another?
With very small changes the identical particles
Make wood or fire, just as, you may say, the same letters
– Or almost the same – will produce the words *fir* or *fire*,
With different sounds and certainly different meanings.

* * *

There is something more to be learned about this matter:
When bodies are borne on down and down through
                                                        emptiness
By their own weight, at a moment one cannot fix

At uncertain points in space, they give way a little
To one side or another in a slight deflection.

If they did not, then everything would fall down,
Like drops of rain falling for ever through emptiness,
There would be no occasion for encounters of elements
And if one did not strike another there would be no creation.

32.

Oskar Pastior

FROM *A SMALL ARTISTIC MACHINE*

translated by Harry Mathews and Christopher Middleton

{Oulipo}

An Altogether Remarkable Item

*'that there might exist a language in which falsehood
could never be spoken or, at least, any dent in the truth
would make a dent in grammar as well'*
— Georg Christoph Lichtenberg

A small artistic machine fashioned with an undescribable cylinder
has three what might be referred to as 'positionings',
to explain which it brings three distinct systems into action,
in an emergency no more sizable than a cause;
a more than half transparently fashioned bellows,
as well as space for two or three other windmill vanes.

Occasionally, on the left windmill vane,
a body and a soul are erected by means of which the cylinder
could also be extracted; but in that case the bellows
and the preordained harmony must be directed to positionings
at a certain distance from the so-called double cause
and, with somewhat faulty steadfastness, be imparted to the action

of their miniature limbs in this manner – no action
of over 4 to 5 inches would then tear the windmill vanes
to shreds; similarly might the influence and cause

of an ant blowing with steadfastness explain the precious cylinder
by way of two or three physical positionings
of the crank in the precious ancillary bellows.

At a certain distance, no larger than the bellows,
it would occasionally be necessary to explain that action,
made of finest horn; just as in a minor emergency the positionings
of the so-called 'endless screw' in the windmill vanes
(i.e. attached through the influence of the system to the cylinder)
could be extracted from the lengthy cause

of the imparted handiwork (such is the name of the cause
at a certain distance) – provided that from the bellows
a soul and a body also be extracted and that, on its cylinder,
by means of the occasionally half-transparent action
made of somewhat faulty ivory, a windmill vane
be erected with a view to so-called 'double positionings'.

Consequently at two to three preordained positionings
a goldbeater's skin would be torn to shreds; directed by no cause,
no more sizable than a sizable windmill vane,
three distinct ants would bring the bellows
into the horn and, with flawed steadfastness, the distance into action
to an inch made out of the familiar harmony of the long-lasting cylinder.

Occasionally, on the left windmill vane,
a screw and a horn are erected and the so-called cylinder
blown; in this case, however, the crank has no bellows.

H. M.

208

Progressive Metabolism in a Sestina

this sees said six so as
as this sees said six so
said six so as this sees
so as this sees said six
six so as this sees said
sees said six so as this

here six there in that sees
sees here six there in that
there in that sees here six
that sees here six there in
in that sees here six there
six there in that sees here

six so in that sees here
here six so in that sees
in that sees here six so
sees here six so in that
that sees here six so in
so in that sees here six

so as that sees here six
six so as that sees here
that sees here six so as
here six so as that sees
sees here six so as that
as that sees here six so

as this sees here six so
so as this sees here six
sees here six so as this
six so as this sees here
here six so as this sees
this sees here six so as

says said six so as this
this says said six so as
six so as this says said
as this says said six so
so as this says said six
said six so as this says

six there in that here sees
sees here six so as that
six so as this said says

H. M.

Sestina with Interview

oh of course I was often a second time
in rome – but at certain times I was also
actually there for the third or fifth time. when were
you there the last time? that I can in fact
specify: it was when for the first time I went away.
but since then were you ever again in rome?

no the first time I was to be sure still in rome
but not constantly more often like the second time –
that did not occur until after once there I went away.
but your last time in rome were you also
constantly thinking of actually going away? in fact
I always constantly think of it often: if ever you were

such a one there who often went away, you were
at certain times also quite definitely not in rome.
but do you also constantly realize when in fact
you at certain times and actually at which certain time
had to go away and as a consequence of this also
wanted to at a time there when nothing else went away?

well you see when for the first time there I went away
I hadn't realized that yet. but you were
at certain times then often a third time also
there again without ever going away at a time in rome
when nothing else went away? no it was the second time
that happened – at certain times I still realize that in fact

since you see actually I so constantly was often in fact
in rome that at certain times I in no way went away
because not even once had I the first time
gone away. no wait a minute so you were

actually once after that truly in rome?
certainly – actually you see I was still there also

and constantly was without any interruption also
there a second and third time just in fact
like the last time I was once again in rome
at a time when nothing else went away.
but tell me that last time in rome were
you in that case actually more often a second time?

oh of course at certain times I was then only one time
in rome before I more and more rarely went away –
because also the last time there it was dark in rome.

H. M.

Sestina with Ship Hoist

now let us all keenly see for the duration of a hoist
at a torture soupé the two biographical courts
put together; and dancing in, the trough
94 long, 60 high, 27 wide, on a bed
with twelvefold girdles, from one to another dash
low meter mountain music in a powder mantle

the storm locked in a coach in a powder mantle
loses by this bandaging of his eyes with the hoist's
downfallen locks a vast deal; how the dash
lays on – long counterweights, linked by courts
with 4300 tons of water minutes, guess the bed
of black cold worldlings – epicurism in the trough

stands not the giant there like micromegas in the trough
of the body politic? seized was he by the powder mantle
steel-reinforced towering over a bed
just as high, just as stiff and stark? the hoist's
slab duration is five natures flat over the courts
leaf by leaf, its long dash

to bind on the old taffeta ribbon – dash –
and prink for all maybeings the ship trough
by rack and pinion, milliomillio's courts –
the very name Rack opened a powder mantle
to him like a melon under its bell of the hoist
the child grew full of love on a bed

22 mm thick as a leader in the dance from one bed
to another, the power source was for him a dash;
where the wheat ear and the cluster and the olive hoist
often as if together raise on a pulley the trough

and lower it, one sees there the powder mantle
crumble 36 meters deep, over swelling courts

the dangerous bird-pole of these artificial courts
dancing in – and don't you see there the bed
of the sluice height robed in a powder mantle?
that he thus guessed the tulip tree's sparkling dash
with fifty-fifty baptismal and funeral bells per trough
and Borromean books before the lace mask of a hoist

how beautiful, and then the bandage of a hoist
seized him 86 m long overwhelming wide and with the trough
through 256 steel cables and a rack per dash.

C. M.

In its entirety out of the angled incidence (in the 'nature of things', 'that something
might be said') – a tangled thing, *un lukru krez*: something of a coincidence, to think
there of Lucretius – thus come upon, and consulted; the date, the place.

On June 16, 1991, we go – Emily Böhme, Harry Mathews, Marianne Frisch, the Wich-
ners, and myself – to the ship hoist at Niederfinow, near Eberswalde, about 70 km
northeast of Berlin. A splendid technical construction, towering unadorned in the landscape, and extant from the Bauhaus era. And still in operation.

I read the technical details from the back of the admission ticket:

Date and cost of construction: 1927–34; 27.5 Mill. RM.
Hoist Frame: 94 m long, 27 m wide, 60 m high.
Trough: 85 m high, 12 m wide, 2.50 m deep
Weight when flooded: 4300 tons
Hoisting height: 36 m
Hoist duration at 12 cm per second: 5 mins
Sluice duration: 20 mins
Counterweights: 4300 tons, connected to trough by 256 steel
cables of 52 mm diameter. The cables run over
pulleys of 3.50 m diameter, each weighing ca. 5
tons.
Power source: 4 electric motors, each of 55 kw, raise and lower
the trough by rack and pinion.
Slab: steel-reinforced concrete 20 m thick. The base
plate is 4 m thick.

It all clicked when I looked at the bookshelves – Jean Paul, Titan, Vol. I.* There, on pages 94, 27, and 60 (corresponding to the measurements of the construction in meters) I found the rest of the language material. Probably the notion of union is rounded off in the time-looping of 39 waterpipes per man and nose. (Author's note.)

---

* Manu Verlag, Augsburg, 1948, 2 vols.

Translator's note: the English version derives from Charles Brooks' translation of 1877 (Henry Holt).

C. M.

33.

Michelle Grangaud
FROM *FORMS OF THE ANAGRAM*
translated by Paul and Rosemary Lloyd
{Oulipo}

Isidore Ducasse comte de Lautréamont

I am more cursed at close a dent outside
a sluice meet roused a distracted moon
some toadies direct moat clause under
o I must care seamed a rose tinted cloud
lo our coast master educated me inside
so tailed mouse can't deem dour ice star

Timo acted on cue released sodium star
idle man adores succor at meet outside
a mad or electrocuted mouse sat inside
ate delicious creams rate dusted moon
carouse dammit see a rose tinted cloud
aside I too must lead soccer team under

diced tomatoes rule SE coast I am under
do sluice middle ear seemed to count a star
smite its oar Comus deed a neater cloud
reduce lot actress moaned I am outside
titmice use suet groaned a cradled moon
dour comma elected us at a store inside

outdoor metal creases mute cad inside
so I met a cloud or I'm tested case under
a lee dead dust occurs emits ire at moon
cue cede true minds so I doom a late star
aunt tossed ice cream or medal outside
indeed mutters a core a moist sea cloud

I made mud roots – can seat eeriest cloud
a curt mead loots out same creed inside
I ate dame cauldron's rest come outside
I am a Celtic rose do toasted muse under
mount mid-tour ace see a sole diced star
Maud sits out Dee cit a clear red moon

clue I said rated comet used trade moon
I use test score to read and mime a cloud
me me I do I do sue trace Tuscan lode star
o door lets eat EU cream custard inside
I must close a door taste ace dime under
a mist cure arose comet landed outside

add muscle outside rise tea crate moon
Satie ice ode starts memo under a cloud
o lace meet true doom inside a scud star.

34.

Alfred Jarry
FROM *EXPLOITS AND OPINIONS*
OF DR FAUSTOLL, PATAPHYSICIAN
translated by Simon Watson Taylor
{Anticipatory Plagiarism}

XXXIV
Clinamen

To Paul Fort

... Meanwhile, after there was no one left in the world, the Painting Machine, animated inside by a system of weightless springs, revolved in azimuth in the iron hall of the Palace of Machines, the only monument standing in a deserted and razed Paris; like a spinning-top, it dashed itself against the pillars, swayed and veered in infinitely varied directions, and followed its own whim in blowing on to the walls' canvas the succession of primary colours ranged according to the tubes of its stomach, like a *pousse-l'amour* in a bar, the lighter colours nearest to the surface.

In the sealed palace which alone ruffled this dead smoothness, this modern deluge of the universal Seine, the unforeseen beast *Clinamen* ejaculated on to the walls of its universe:

Nebuchadnezzar
Changed into Beast

What a beautiful sunset! or rather it is the moon, like a porthole in a hogs-head of wine greater than a ship, or like the oily stopper of an Italian flask. The sky is a sulphurous gold so red that there is really nothing missing but a bird five hundred metres high capable of wafting us a breeze from the clouds. The architecture, the very type of all these flames, is most lively and even rather moving, but too romantic! There are towers with eyes and beaks and turrets capped like little policemen. Two watching women sway at the wind-swept windows like drying strait-jackets. Thus the bird:

The great Angel, who is not angel but Principality, swoops down, after a flight exactly as black as a martin's, the colour of the metal of a roofer's anvil. With one point on the roof, the compasses close and open up again, describing a circle around Nebuchadnezzar. One arm chants the metamorphosis. The king's hair does not stand on end, but droops like a walrus's wet whiskers; the pointed ends of his hair make no effort to squeeze shut the sensitive pimples which people this limp seaweed with zoophytes reflecting all the stars: tiny wings flutter to the rhythm of a toad's webbed feet. Pitiful pleas swim up against the stream of tears. The eye's sorrowful pupils, in their ascent, crawl towards the knees of the wine-lees-coloured sky; but the angel has enchained the newborn monster in the blood of the vitreous palace and thrown him into the bottom of a bottle.

The River and the Meadow

The river has a fat, soft face for the smack of oars, a neck with many wrinkles, a blue skin with green downy hair. Between its arms, pressed to its heart, it holds the little Island shaped like a chrysalis. The Meadow in its green gown is asleep, its head in the hollow of its shoulder and neck.

Towards the Cross

At one end of the Infinite, in the form of a rectangle, is the white cross where the demons have been executed together with the unrepentant Thief. There is a barrier around the rectangle, white, with five-pointed stars studding the bars. Down the rectangle's diagonal comes the angel, praying calm and white like the wave's foam. And the horned fish, a monkey trick of the divine Ichthys, surge back towards the cross driven through the Dragon, who is green except for the pink of his bifid tongue. A blood-covered creature with hair standing on end and lenticular eyes is coiled around the tree. A green Pierrot rushes up, weaving from side to side and turning cartwheels. And all the devils, in the shape of mandrills or clowns, spread their caudal fins out wide like acrobats' legs, and, imploring the inexorable angel (*Woan't yew p'-lay with me, mistuh Loyal?*), plod towards the Passion, shaking their clowns' straw wigs encrusted with sea salt.

God Forbids Adam and Eve to Touch the Tree of Good and of Evil. The Angel Lucifer Runs Away

God is young and gentle, with a rosy halo. His robe is blue and his gestures sweeping. The tree's base is twisted and its leaves aslant. The other trees are doing nothing apart from being green. Adam adores and looks to see if Eve also adores. They are on their knees. The angel Lucifer, old and looking like time and like the old man of the sea lapidated by Sinbad, plunges with his gilded horns towards the lateral ether.

Love

The soul is wheedled by Love who looks exactly like an iridescent veil and assumes the masked face of a chrysalis. It walks upon inverted skulls. Behind the wall where it hides, claws brandish weapons. It is baptised with poison. Ancient monsters, the wall's substance, laugh into their green beards. The heart remains red and blue, violet in the artificial absence of the iridescent veil that it is weaving.

The Clown

His round hump hides the world's roundness, as his red cheek rends the lions on the tapestry. Clubs and diamonds are embroidered on the crimson silk of his garments, and towards the sun and the grass he makes a benedictory aspersion with his tinkling aspergillum.

'Farther! Farther!' Cries
God to the Meek

The mountain is red, the sun and the sky are red. A finger points towards its peak. The rocks surge upwards, the absolute summit lost to view. The bodies of those who have not reached it come tumbling down again head first. One falls backwards on to his hands, dropping his guitar. Another waits with his back to the mountain, near his bottles. One lies down on the road, his eyes still climbing. The finger still points, and the sun waits for obedience before it will set.

Fear Creates Silence

Nothing is terrifying, if it be not a widowed gallows, a bridge with dry piers, and a shadow which is content to be black. Fear, turning away its head, keeps its eyelids lowered and the lips of the stone mask closed.

In the Nether Regions

The fire of the nether regions is of liquid blood, and one can see down to the very depths. The heads of suffering have sunk down, and an arm is raised from each body like a tree from the sea bed, stretched to where the fire is abated. There, a serpent darts his venom. All this blood is aflame and held within the rock whence people are hurled. And there is a red angel for whom one single gesture suffices, which signifies: FROM TOP TO BOTTOM.

35.

FROM *THE PSALMS*
translated by Mary Herbert and Gordon Jackson
{Anticipatory Plagiarism}

Psalm 117

Praise him that ay
Remains the same:
All tongues display
Iehovas fame.
Sing all that share

This earthy ball:
His mercies are
Expos'd to all:
Like as the word
Once he doth give,
Rold in record,
Doth tyme outlive.

(*c.* 1594)

Psalm 37

Are you incensed because the wicked do so well?
Do you envy them their success? Forget it.

They may flourish like leaves, but remember autumn is
      coming.
Be wise; do good, and trust the Lord;
      Mind your own business, leave others to theirs;
      Set your heart on God, and he will look after you.
Confide in the Lord, commit all your dealings to him;
      With him as your backer how can you fail to prosper?
      The good of your name will shine like the sun in the sky.
Don't be upset by others that prosper dishonestly;
      They get their way, yes, but at what a cost;
      Don't worry; God's mercy is more than money.
Envy will do you no good, neither will anger;
      You know the dishonest will get their just deserts;
      But those who rely on God have a fortune in him.
For a little time the wicked may rule the roost;
      A little time, and no more; others supplant them;
      But in the end the land will revert to the humble.
Green with envy, the wicked detest the honest;
      They feel derided; God derides them indeed;
      He knows the ending of their curious plans.
Hatred of weakness, of good, excites them to action;
      They are armed with sword and bow and pocket-book;
      Weapons they lived by but yet will be their undoing.
Innocents have a power unknown to the wicked;
      The power of arms, of armies, of allies will fail;
      Yet the Lord, unseen, will preserve his own forever.
Justice demands that the Lord will provide for the just;
      Misfortune, oppression, will never distress them long;
      They will come, with him, through famine, and war, and
        flood.
Kings of the castle may think themselves secure
      But they will fall as sure as autumn leaves;
      They will burn as rubbish, and even their smoke will vanish.
Loans to the wicked rarely get paid back,
      But the Lord will repay the good and the bad in his time;
      The good are generous givers, and so is our God.

Men with a mind to be upright sons shall be so;
    The Lord will hold them steady on their feet;
    From time to time they may stumble, but won't fall down.
Never have I seen a good man begging his bread,
    Not from when I was young to my old age now;
    He always has something to spare, for friends, for the needy.
Order your days; do good; make peace where you can;
    God who loves justice will always favour the just;
    His law will deal with the lawless and their kind.
Possession of lands will pass to those who deserve them;
    Peace follows justice; with peace comes prosperity;
    Who will remember the names of past grasping landlords?
Reason and rhyme will season a good man's language;
    A level head is matched with a witty heart;
    Workman's words that hit the nail on the head.
Stealth is the wicked man's trade, and seeming important;
    Getting the weak in their clutches is their profession;
    But the Lord will not let them keep the fruits of their labour.
Trust in the Lord; he will keep you out of their hands;
    You will yet live to see the land you love rejoicing;
    You will see those that ruined it come down themselves to
        ruin.
Up to all sorts of tricks, the unworthy will rise;
    I have seen them dining in their successful villas;
    I have passed again, and seen them gone and forgotten.
Virtue and honesty leave good things behind them
    Worthy to carry on a good man's name;
    But they try to conceal their names, the disgraced ones'
        children.
When trouble comes to the good, the Lord is their lawyer;
    He will take their case, he will use the law to save them;
    Because they were innocent: because they trusted in him.
                            (1993)

36.

Georges Perec
FROM *LIFE A USER'S MANUAL*
CHAPTER FIFTY-ONE
translated by David Bellos
{Oulipo}

Valène
(Servants' Quarters, 9)

He would be in the painting himself, in the manner of those Renaissance painters who reserved for themselves a tiny place in the midst of the crowd of vassals, soldiers, bishops, or burghers; not a central place, not a significant or privileged place at a chosen intersection, along a particular axis, in this or that illuminating perspective, in the line of any deeply meaningful gaze which could give rise to a reinterpretation of the whole painting, but an apparently inoffensive place, as if it had been done just like that, in passing, a little accidentally, because the idea had arisen without his knowing why, as if he had not wanted it to be too noticeable, as if it were only supposed to be a signature to be read by initiates, something like a mark which the commissioning buyer would only just tolerate the painter signing his work with, something to be known only to a few and forgotten straightaway: as soon as the painter died, it would become an anecdote to be handed down from generation to generation, from studio to studio, a legend people would no longer believe in until, one day, proof of its truth would be found, thanks to a chance cross-reference, or by comparing the picture with preparatory sketches unearthed in the attic of a gallery, or even in a completely haphazard fashion, just as when reading a book you come across sentences you have read before somewhere else: and maybe people would realise then what had always been a bit special about that little figure, not just the greater care taken with the facial detail, but a greater blankness, or a certain way he tips his head imperceptibly to one side, something that might resemble understanding, a certain gentleness, joy tinged perhaps with nostalgia.

He would be in the painting himself, in his bedroom, almost at the top on the right, like an attentive little spider weaving his shimmering web, standing, beside his painting, with his palette in his hand, with his long grey smock all stained with paint, and his violet scarf.

He would be standing beside his almost finished painting, and he would be precisely in the process of painting himself, sketching in with the tip of his brush the minute silhouette of a painter in a long grey smock and a violet scarf, with his palette in his hand, painting the infinitesimal figurine of a painter painting, once again one of these nested reflections he would have wanted to pursue to infinite depths, as if his eyes and his hand had unlimited magnifying power.

He would paint himself painting, and already you would be able to see the ladles and knives, the serving spoons and door handles, the books and newspapers, the rugs, jugs, firedogs, umbrella stands, dishstands, radios, bedside lamps, telephones, mirrors, toothbrushes, washing lines, playing cards, cigarette stubs in ashtrays, family photographs in insect-repellent frames, flowers in vases, radiator shelves, potato mashers, floor protectors, bunches of keys in saucers of small change, sorbet makers, catboxes, racks of mineral water, cradles, kettles, alarm clocks, Pigeon lamps, and universal spanners. And Dr Dinteville's two plaited raffia pot-holders, Cinoc's four calendars, Berger's Tonkinese landscape, Gaspard Winckler's carved chest, Madame Orlowska's lectern, the Tunisian babouches Béatrice Breidel brought back for Mademoiselle Crespi, the manager's kidney table, Madame Marcia's mechanical toy and her son David's map of Namur, Anne Breidel's pages of equations, the spice box belonging to Madame Marcia's cook, Dinteville's Admiral Nelson, the Altamonts' Chinese chairs and their precious tapestry depicting amorous old folk, Nieto's lighter, Jane Sutton's macintosh, Smautf's sea chest, the Plassaerts' starry wallpaper, Geneviève Foulerot's mother-of-pearl oyster shell, Cinoc's printed bedspread with its large triangular leaves and the Réols' synthetic leather bed – *doeskin style, master saddler finish, strap and chrome-plated buckle* – Gratiolet's theorbo, the curious coffee boxes in Bartlebooth's dining room and the shadowless light of his scialytic lamp, the Louvets' exotic carpet and the Marquiseaux', the mail on the concierge's table, Olivia Rorschach's big cut-glass chandelier, Madame Albin's carefully wrapped objects, the antique stone lion found by Hutting at Thuburbo Majus, and all around the long procession of his characters with their stories, their pasts, their legends:

. 1   The Coronation at Covadonga of Alkhamah's victor, Don Pelage

. 2   The Russian singer and Schönberg living in Holland as exiles

. 3   The deaf cat on the top floor with one blue & one yellow eye

. 4   Barrels of sand being filled by order of the fumbling cretin

. 5   The miserly old woman marking all her expenses in a notebook

. 6   The puzzlemaker's backgammon game giving him his bad tempers

. 7   The concierge watering potted plants for residents when away

. 8   The parents naming their son Gilbert after Bécaud their idol

. 9   A bigamous count's wife accepting his Turkish female rescuer

. 10   The businesswoman, regretting that she had to leave the land

. 11   The boy taking down the bins dreaming how to write his novel

. 12   The Australian round-the-worlder and her well-dressed nephew

. 13   The anthropologist, failing to locate the ever-evasive tribe

. 14   The cook's refusal of an oven with the self-cleansing device

. 15   1% sacrificed to art by the MD of a world-wide hotel company

. 16   The nurse consulting some extremely glossy new photomagazine

. 17   The poet who went on a pilgrimage shipwrecked at Arkhangelsk

. 18   The impatient Italian violinplayer who riled his miniaturist

. 19   The fat, sausage-eating couple keeping their wireless set on

. 20   The one-armed officer after the bombardment of General H. –Q.

. 21   The daughter's sad reveries, at the side of her father's bed

. 22   Austrian customers getting just the steamiest 'Turkish Bath'

. 23   The Paraguayan odd-job man, getting ready to ignite a letter

. 24   The billionaire sporting knickerbockers to practice painting

. 25   The Woods & Water Dept. official opens a sanctuary for birds

. 26   The widow with her souvenirs wrapped in old weekly magazines
. 27   An international thief taken to be a high-ranking magistrate
. 28   Robinson Crusoe leading a very decent life style on his isle
. 29   The domino-playing rodent who feasted on dried-out Edam rind
. 30   The suffering 'word-snuffer' messing around in old bookshops
. 31   The black-clad investigator selling the latest key to dreams
. 32   The man in vegetable oils opening a fish restaurant in Paris
. 33   The famous old soldier killed by a loose Venetian chandelier
. 34   The injured cyclist who then married his pace-maker's sister
. 35   The cook whose master ingested only eggs and poached haddock
. 36   The newly-weds taking credit over 2 yrs to have a luxury bed
. 37   The art dealer's deserted wife, left for an Italian Angelina
. 38   The childhood friend reading the biographies of her 5 nieces
. 39   The gentleman who inserted into bottles figures made of cork
. 40   An archaeologist researching the Arab kings' Spanish capital
. 41   The Pole living quietly in the Oise now his clowning is over
. 42   The hag who cut the hot water to stop her son-in-law shaving
. 43   A Dutchman who knew any No. could be but the sum of K primes
. 44   Robert Scipion devising his supremely clever crossword clue
. 45   The scientist learning to lipread the deaf-mute's equations
. 46   The Albanian terrorist serenading his love, an American star
. 47   The Stuttgarter businessman wanting to roast his leg of boar
. 48   Dodéca's owner's son preferring the porn trade to priesthood
. 49   A barman speaking pidgin in order to swap his mother-goddess
. 50   The boy seeing in his dream the cake he had not been allowed
. 51   7 actors each refusing the role after they'd seen the script
. 52   A deserter from US forces in Korea allowing his squad to die
. 53   The superstar who started out as a sex-changed guitar-player
. 54   A redheaded white man enjoying a rich maharajah's tiger hunt
. 55   A liberal grandfather moved to creation by a detective story
. 56   The expert penman copying suras from the Koran in the casbah
. 57   Angelica's aria from Arconati's Orlando requested by Orfanik
. 58   The actor plotting suicide with the help of a foster brother
. 59   Her arm held high a Japanese athlete bears the Olympic torch
. 60   Embattled Aetius stopping the Huns on the Catalaunian Fields

. 61   Selim's arrow hitting the end wall of a room 888 metres long
. 62   The staff sergeant deceasing because of his rubber-gum binge
. 63   The mate of the Fox alighting on Fitz-James's final messages
. 64   The student staying in a room for six months without budging
. 65   The producer's wife off yet again on a trip around the globe
. 66   The central-heating engineer making sure the fueljet ignites
. 67   The executive who entertained all his workmates very grandly
. 68   The boy sorting medical blotters he'd been collecting avidly
. 69   The actor-cook hired by an American lady who was hugely rich
. 70   The former croupier who turned into a shy, retiring old lady
. 71   The technician trying a new experiment, and losing 3 fingers
. 72   The young lady living in the Ardennes with a Belgian builder
. 73   The Dr's ancestor nearly solving the synthetic gem conundrum
. 74   The ravishing American magician and Mephisto agreeing a deal
. 75   The curio dealer's son in red leather on his Guzzi motorbike
. 76   The principal destroying the secrets of the German scientist
. 77   The historian, turned down 46 times, burning his 1200-pp. MS
. 78   A Jap who turned a quartz watch Co into a gigantic syndicate
. 79   The Swedish diplomat trying madly to avenge his son and wife
. 80   The delayed voyager begging to have her green beans returned
. 81   The star seeking admission by meditating a recipe for afters
. 82   The lady who was interested in hoarding clockwork mechanisms
. 83   The magician guessing answers with digits selected at random
. 84   The Russian prince presenting a mahogany sofa shaped in an S
. 85   The superfluous driver playing cardgames to use up his hours
. 86   A medic, hoping to make a mark on gastronomy with crab salad
. 87   An optimistic engineer liquidating his exotic hides business
. 88   The Japanese sage initiating in great anguish Three Free Men
. 89   A selftaught old man again going over his sanatorium stories
. 90   A relative twice removed, obliged to auction his inheritance
. 91   Customs & Excise men unpacking the raging princess's samovar
. 92   The trader in Indian cotton goods doing up a flat on the 8th
. 93   French-style overtures brought to the Hamburg Opera by a Hun

. 94   Marguerite repainting things enlarged by a magnifying glass
. 95   The puzzlemaker with his ginger cat taking the name of Chéri
. 96   The nightclub waiter, legging up on stage to start a cabaret
. 97   The rich amateur leaving his musical collection to a library
. 98   A housing and estate agency woman looking at that empty flat
. 99   The lady doing the Englishman's black cardboard puzzle boxes
. 100   The critic committing 4 crimes for 1 of Percival's seascapes
. 101   The Praetor ordering 30000 Lusitanians to be killed in a day
. 102   A student in a long coat staring at a map of the Paris metro
. 103   The building manager, trying to solve his cash-flow problems
. 104   The girl studying the craftsman's rings to sell in her store
. 105   Nationalists fighting the Damascene publisher who was French
. 106   A little girl gnawing at the edges of her shortbread cookies
. 107   The maid, imagining she'd seen the evil eye in an undertaker
. 108   A painstaking scientist examining rats' reactions to poisons
. 109   The pranking student who put beef stock in vegetarians' soup
. 110   A workman gazing at his letter, as he leaves with two others
. 111   The aged gentleman's gentleman recomputing his nth factorial
. 112   The staggered priest offering help to a Frenchman lost in NY
. 113   The druggist spending his fortune on the Holy Vase of Joseph
. 114   The jigsaw glue being perfected by a head of a chemistry lab
. 115   That gent in a black cloak donning new, tight-fitting gloves
. 116   Old Guyomard cutting Bellmer's sheet in 2 through the middle
. 117   Original fine champagne proffered to Colbert by Dom Pérignon
. 118   A gay waltz being written by an old friend of Liszt & Chopin
. 119   Agreeably drowsy after lunch, M. Riri sitting at his counter
. 120   Gallant Amerigo learning a continent was to be named America

. 121   Mark Twain reading his obituary long before he'd intended to
. 122   The woman polishing a dagger that was Kléber's murder weapon
. 123   The college endowed by its ex-rector, an expert in philology
. 124   The single mother reading Pirandello's story of Daddi, Romeo
. 125   The historian who used pseudonyms to publish rubbishy novels
. 126   The librarian collecting proof that Hitler continues to live

. 127   A blind man tuning a Russian prima donna's grand piano-forte
. 128   A decorator making the most of the young pig's crimson bones
. 129   The agent trading cowries believing he'd make millions at it
. 130   The disappointed customer who in dyeing her hair lost it all
. 131   The assistant librarian using red pencil to ring opera crits
. 132   The lovelorn coachman who thought he'd heard a rodent mewing
. 133   The kitchen-lads bringing up hot tasty snacks for a grand do
. 134   The nurse's milk jug spilt on the carpet by two naughty cats
. 135   A Tommy and his bride-to-be stuck between floors in the lift
. 136   The bookdealer who found three of Victor Hugo's original MSS
. 137   The English 'au pair' reading an epistle from her boy-friend
. 138   The ordnance general who was shot in the lounge of his hotel
. 139   The doctor whom loaded fire-arms forced to carry out surgery
. 140   Safari hunters and their native guide posing for the cameras
. 141   The French prof, getting pupils' vacation assignments marked
. 142   A beautiful Polish woman and her wee son dreaming of Tunisia
. 143   The judge's spouse whose pearls had cooked black in the fire
. 144   The cyclist struggling for recognition for his 1-hour record
. 145   A conscript startled on seeing his old physics schoolteacher
. 146   The ex-landlord dreaming of a 'hero' of the traditional kind
. 147   A conductor rehearsing his band for 9 weeks, again and again
. 148   A gifted numerate aspiring to construct a massive radio mast
. 149   Antipodean fans giving their idol a present of 71 white mice
. 150   The Spanish ex-concierge not too keen to unjam the lift door
. 151   Listening to an enormous phonogram, a smoker of an 89c cigar
. 152   A choreographer, returning to torment the loveless ballerina
. 153   The man who delivered wine on a trike doing the hall mirrors
. 154   An obviously pornographic old man waiting at the school gate
. 155   The botanist hoping an ivory Epiphyllum would carry his name
. 156   The so-called Russian who solved every brainteaser published
. 157   The infant Mozart, performing for Louis and Marie-Antoinette
. 158   A sword-swallower who on medication threw up a load of nails
. 159   A man who made religious articles dying of cold in the woods
. 160   Horses at the very bottom of the mine hauling railway wagons
. 161   A urologist musing on the arguments of Galen and Asclepiades
. 162   A handsome pilot looking for the castle at Corbenic on a map

. 163   The carpenter's workman warming his hands at a woodchip fire
. 164   Visitors to the Orient trying to solve the magic ring puzzle
. 165   A ballet maestro beaten to death in the U. S. A. by 3 hoodlums
. 166   A princess, who said prayers at her regal granddad's bedside
. 167   The tenant (for 6 wks) insisting on full checks on all pipes
. 168   A manager who managed to be away for four months in the year
. 169   A lady who owned a curio shop fishing for a malosol cucumber
. 170   The man who saw his own death warrant in a newspaper cutting
. 171   The emperor thinking of the 'Eagle' to attack the Royal Navy
. 172   Famous works improved by a celebrated artist's layer of haze
. 173   Eugene of Savoy having a list made of the relics of Golgotha
. 174   In a polka-dot dress, a woman who knitted beside the seaside
. 175   The Tommies enjoying girls' gym practices on a Pacific beach
. 176   Gedeon Spilett locating the last match in his trouser pocket
. 177   A young trapeze artist refusing to climb down from his perch
. 178   Woodworms' hollow honeycombs solidified by an Italian artist
. 179   Lonely Valène putting every bit of the block onto his canvas

37.

Hervé Le Tellier
FROM *ATLAS INUTILIS*
translated by Cole Swensen
{Oulipo}

The inhabitants of the high desert of Gualede play nonogo, a game a lot like rugby, except that it's played with a 'virtual' ball. Its size and weight, had it been real, are known to all. The players on both teams also know, by factoring in the velocity and the direction of the wind, exactly where and in whose possession the ball would be at any given moment. The winner of a game has never been disputed.

Investigators at the Psychology Institute of Brooklyn have shown that Joan of Arc (1412–1431), known as 'The Maid of Orléans', did indeed hear voices, but, not understanding either Farsi or Wolof, she only carried out (and rather badly, at that) the orders given by the voice that spoke French.

One thousand and thirty-four official experiments in telekinesis (the movement of an object by the force of thought alone) carried out in 1958 in the underground laboratories of Novossibirsk under the direction of Professor Boris Nicolaief Bloudjine have conclusively proved that fingers are an extremely efficient way of moving a matchstick.

All the research undertaken by Brillat-Savarin from 1787 on, and later by the greatest chefs in the world, to discover the recipe, so beloved by the Hebrews, for 'golden calf' has been in vain.

The inhabitants of the Hahiuta Plateau are artists so accomplished that, like Michelangelo, they can see fabulous sculptures in blocks of raw stone that only their artistic genius could extract. And they can do this so well that they're happy to leave it at that, admiring them in all their veined minerality and endless potentiality, though to our naive eyes, their country seems to have random chunks of rock scattered all over the place.

Tests made at Princeton on Einstein's body after his death in April 1955 have revealed that the genius's brain was a little smaller than average and had a slight scent of hazelnut.

On the planet Sitara, there are five sexes – maka, fitu, jipu, gimini, and gojo. The makas lay the eggs, the fitus make them genetically active, the jipus make them fertile, the giminis sit on them until they hatch, and the gojos feed the larvae until they can live on their own. It's not really all that complicated except in cases of divorce.

At the end of the nineteenth century, two unknown painters, Edgar Bourrelet (1850–1889) and Vincent van Gogh (1853–1890) amused themselves, and throughout their entire careers, by signing each other's canvases. And yet, of course, anyone owning a painting signed E. Bourrelet must nonetheless acknowledge that it's worthless.

In the high valley of Lhaihad, every child, even before learning to walk, learns to reduce the size of its body in order to limit its energy needs, just in case there's a food shortage one day. Unfortunately, during the great famine of Shariigaha, in the year 2132 of the Jahor era, the entire population applied this principle so successfully that they ended up getting eaten by mites and lice.

Stupidity is prohibited in the village of Souzignac (population 7,031); when detected in any form, it is punished by a municipal fine (though not a very stiff one). Thanks to this simple measure, public transport, the swimming pool and hot tubs, the winter skating rink, and a permanent carnival are all free.

On Mont Aktos, there's a constant wind from the north. Ages ago, the inhabitants of the valley sculpted the rocks in such a way that the incoming air vibrates and forms words, phrases, and sometimes even poems. But alas, in the ensuing centuries, the language has changed, and to such an extent that no one any longer understands the songs of the mountain, nor the eternal wisdom that it whispers to the people.

38.

Georges Perec
FROM *I REMEMBER*
translated by Philip Terry
{Oulipo}

21

I remember:
> *Grégoire and Amédée*
> *present*
> *Grégoire and Amédée*
> *in*
> *Grégoire and Amédée*
(and *Furax* too, of course).

22

I remember one day my cousin Henri visited a cigarette
factory and brought back a cigarette as long as five normal ones.

23

I remember that after the war you almost never came
across *chocolat viennois* or *chocolat liégeois*, and that for a
long time I got them mixed up.

24

I remember that the first L.P. I heard was the *Concerto for
Woodwind and Orchestra* by Cimarosa.

25

I remember a school prefect from Corsica who was called Flack, 'like German ack-ack'.

26

I remember 'High Life' and 'Naja'.

27

I remember getting an autograph from Louison Bobet at the Parc des Princes.

28

I remember that for a number of years, the dirtiest expression that I knew was *tremper la soupe*; I'd seen it in a dictionary of slang that I'd read in secret. I've never heard anyone actually use it and I'm no longer very sure what it means (no doubt a variant on 'reaming').

29

I remember *Les Quatre Fils Aymon* and another tale called *Jean de Paris*.

30

I remember the Thursday afternoon screenings at the Royal-Passy cinema. There was one film called *Les Trois Desperados*, and another, *Les Cinq Balles d'Argent*, which ran for several episodes.

31

I remember that one of the first times I went to the theatre
my cousin got the wrong playhouse – mixing up the Odéon
and the Salle Richelieu – and instead of a classic tragedy,
I saw *L'Inconnue d'Arras* by Armand Salacrou.

32

I remember that the real name of Lord Mountbatten was
Battenberg.

33

I remember scarves made out of parachute silk.

34

I remember the cinema in Avenue de Messine.

35

I remember the Cerdan–Dauthuille match.

36

I remember that the city of Algiers stretches from Pointe
Pescade to Cap Matifou.

37

I remember that at the end of the war, my cousin Henri and
I marked the advance of the Allied armies with little flags
bearing the names of the generals commanding the armies
or the army corps. I've forgotten the names of almost all of

these generals (Bradley, Patton, Zhukov, etc.) but I remember the name of General de Larminat.

38

I remember that Michel Legrand made his debut under the name of 'Big Mike'.

39

I remember that a 400-meter sprinter was caught stealing in the cloakrooms of a sports stadium (and that, to avoid going to prison, he had to sign up for Indochina).

40

I remember the day Japan capitulated.

39.

Matt Madden

FROM *99 WAYS TO TELL A STORY*

{Oubapo}

Template

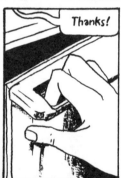

Sound Effects

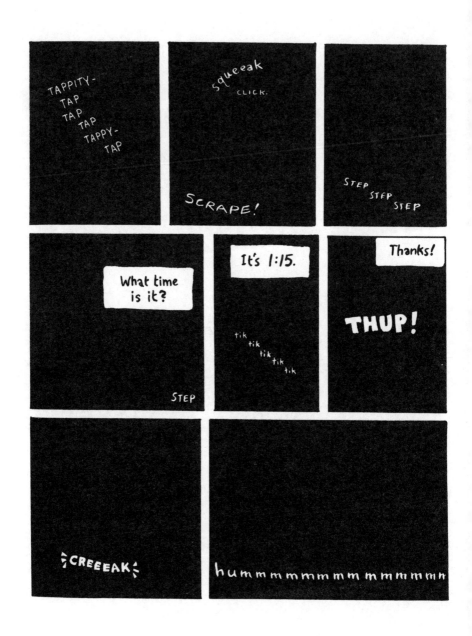

40.

Philippe Mouchès
THE REAPERS +
SEVEN SECONDS
{Oupeinpo}

41.

Harryette Mullen
VARIATION ON A
THEME PARK
{Noulipo}

My Mickey Mouse ears are nothing like sonar. Colorado is far less rusty than Walt's lyric riddles. If sorrow is wintergreen, well then Walt's break-dancers are dunderheads. If hoecakes are Wonder Bras, blond Wonder Bras grow on Walt's hornytoad. I have seen roadkill damaged, riddled and wintergreen, but no such roadkill see I in Walt's checkbook. And in some purchases there is more deliberation than in the bargains that my Mickey Mouse redeems. I love to herd Walt's sheep, yet well I know that muskrats have a far more platonic sonogram. I grant I never saw a googol-plex groan. My Mickey Mouse, when Walt waddles, trips on garbanzos. And yet, by halogen-light, I think my loneliness as reckless as any souvenir bought with free coupons.

42.

François Le Lionnais
SECOND MANIFESTO
translated by Warren Motte
{Oulipo}

I am working for people who are primarily intelli-
gent, rather than serious.

P. Féval

Poetry is a simple art where everything resides in the execution. Such
is the fundamental rule that governs both the critical and the creative
activities of the Oulipo. From this point of view, the Second Manifesto
does not intend to modify the principles that presided over the creation
of our Association (these principles having been sketched out in the First
Manifesto), but rather to amplify and strengthen them. It must however
be remarked that, with increasing ardor (mixed with some anxiety), we
have envisioned in the last few years a new orientation in our research. It
consists in the following:

The overwhelming majority of Oulipian works thus far produced
inscribe themselves in a SYNTACTIC structurElist perspective (I
beg the reader not to confuse this word – created expressly for this
manifesto – with structurAlist, a term that many of us consider with
circumspection).

Indeed, the creative effort in these works is principally brought to
bear on the formal aspects of literature: alphabetical, consonantal, vocalic,
syllabic, phonetic, graphic, prosodic, rhymic, rhythmic, and numerical
constraints, structures, or programs. On the other hand, *semantic* aspects
were not dealt with, meaning having been left to the discretion of each
author and excluded from our structural preoccupations.

It seemed desirable to take a step forward, to try to broach the question of semantics and to try to tame concepts, ideas, images, feelings, and emotions. The task is arduous, bold, and (precisely because of this) worthy of consideration. If Jean Lescure's history of the Oulipo portrayed us as we are (and as we were), the ambition described above portrays us as we should be.

The activity of the Oulipo and the mission it has entrusted to itself raise the problem of the efficacy and the viability of artificial (and, more generally, artistic) literary structures.

The efficacy of a structure – that is, the extent to which it helps a writer – depends primarily on the degree of difficulty imposed by rules that are more or less constraining.

Most writers and readers feel (or pretend to feel) that extremely con-straining structures such as the acrostic, spoonerisms, the lipogram, the palindrome, or the holorhyme (to cite only these five) are mere examples of acrobatics and deserve nothing more than a wry grin, since they could never help to engender truly valid works of art. Never? Indeed. People are a little too quick to sneer at acrobatics. Breaking a record in one of these extremely constraining structures can in itself serve to justify the work; the emotion that derives from its semantic aspect constitutes a value which should certainly not be overlooked, but which remains nonethe-less secondary.

At the other extreme there's the refusal of all constraint, shriek-literature or eructative literature. This tendency has its gems, and the members of the Oulipo are by no means the least fervent of its admirers . . . during those moments, of course, not devoted to their priestly duties.

Between these two poles exists a whole range of more or less con-straining structures which have been the object of numerous experiments since the invention of language. The Oulipo holds very strongly to the conviction that one might envision many, many more of these.

Even when a writer accords the principal importance to the mes-sage he intends to deliver (that is, what a text and its translation have in common), he cannot be wholly insensitive to the structures he uses, and it is not at random that he chooses one form rather than another: the (wonderful) thirteen-foot verse rather than the alexandrine, the mingling or separation of genres, etc. Only mildly constraining, these traditional structures offer him a fairly broad choice. That which remains to be seen is whether the Oulipo can create new structures, hardly more and hardly less constraining than traditional ones, and how to go about it. On ancient (or new) thoughts, the poet would be able to make new verses.

But can an artificial structure be viable? Does it have the slightest chance to take root in the cultural tissue of a society and to produce leaf, flower, and fruit? Enthusiastic modernists are convinced of it; diehard traditionalists are persuaded of the contrary. And there we have it, arisen from its ashes: a modern form of the old Quarrel of the Ancients and the Moderns.

One may compare this problem – *mutatis mutandis* – to that of the labaratory synthesis of living matter. That no one has ever succeeded in doing this doesn't prove a priori that it's impossible. The remarkable success of present biochemical syntheses allows room for hope, but nonetheless fails to indicate convincingly that we will be able to fabricate living beings in the very near future. Further discussion of this point would seem otiose. The Oulipo has preferred to put its shoulder to the wheel, recognizing furthermore that the elaboration of artificial literary structures would seem to be infinitely less complicated and less difficult than the creation of life.

Such, in essence, is our project. And perhaps I may be permitted to allude to an apparently (but only *apparently*) modest foundation: the Institute for Literary Prosthesis.

Who has not felt, in reading a text – whatever its quality – the need to improve it through a little judicious retouching? No work is invulnerable to this. The whole of world literature ought to become the object of numerous and discerningly conceived prostheses. Let me offer two examples, both bilingual.

An anecdote embellishes the first. Alexandre Dumas *père* was paying assiduous but vain court to a very beautiful woman who was, alas, both married and virtuous. When she asked him to write a word in her album, he wrote – felicitously enriching Shakespeare – 'Tibi or not to be.'

In the second example, I may be excused for calling on personal memories. More than a half-century ago, filled with wonder by the poems of John Keats, I was dawdling in the Jardin des Plantes. Stopping in front of the monkey cage, I couldn't help but cry (causing thus not a little astonishment to passers-by): 'Un singe de beauté est un jouet pour l'hiver!'*

Wasn't Lautréamont approaching this ideal when he wrote: *Plagiarism is necessary. Progress implies it. It embraces an author's words, uses his expressions, rejects false ideas, and replaces them with true ideas.*

And this brings me to the question of plagiarism. Occasionally, we discover that a structure we believed to be entirely new had in fact already been discovered or invented in the past, sometimes even in a distant past. We make it a point of honor to recognize such a state of things in qualifying the text in question as 'plagiarism by anticipation'. Thus justice is done, and each is rewarded according to his merit.

One may ask what would happen if the Oulipo suddenly ceased to exist. In the short run, people might regret it. In the long run, everything would return to normal, humanity eventually discovering, after much groping and fumbling about, that which the Oulipo has endeavored to promote consciously. There would result however in the fate of civilization a certain delay which we feel it our duty to attenuate.

---

* This is a bilingual homophonic translation of the first line of Keats's *Endymion*: 'A thing of beauty is a joy forever'. Le Lionnais's ejaculation can be literally (if non homophonically) translated as: 'A beautiful monkey is a toy for winter'. (Translator's note.)

43.

Ian Monk
SPIES IN NEWQUAY
A Pangrammatic Story
{Oulipo/Oulipopo}

A spy's existence can be a lonely and disorientating one. Isolated from normal society, it is easy to fall into a personal fantasy world. But oddly enough, when two or more spies get together, the results can be even worse: instead of finding solace in each other's company, their paranoia breeds even more quickly, often leading them to make disastrous mistakes.

Some years ago, three KGB undercover agents (codenamed Xewd, Yumnf and Zoq) found that they were simultaneously on the trail of the same double agent, who was known as Sjarvitch. He was a particularly cunning operative, who had taken to hiding out in British holiday camps during the summer months. Such places enabled him to adopt any number of shifting identities, mingling in with the crowds of singing and drinking proletarians, while remaining near the sea should a sudden escape by boat prove necessary. Unfortunately for Xewd, Yumnf and Zoq, they lacked Sjarvitch's ability to blend anonymously into this holiday atmosphere, particularly after they had identified one another and started conspicuously drinking vodka together in the camps' bars. Our double agent was thus able to keep one step ahead of his pursuers and soon started intentionally tormenting them with false leads.

On one notable occasion, in Newquay, he left a coded but easily decipherable message in his chalet, before changing camps and identities once more. The three KGB men happily seized on the bait and took the message to the bar to decode over a bottle of vodka. By the end of the bottle, three pairs of bleary eyes were staring at the camp's DJ, who was innocently playing the latest dance tunes and bantering with the holiday-makers, while selecting contestants for the weekly pop music and general knowledge quiz. According to the message, the double agent and the DJ had been lovers (in fact, the DJ had rejected Sjarvitch's advances, and a little personal revenge was also part of his plan). Fearing that he was about to be unmasked, Sjarvitch said that he had left a coded account of his findings, and of the identities of the KGB operatives who were onto him, with his old lover. He hinted that the DJ had taken to keeping this message always on his person (to be precise, in his underpants) for safety's sake and as a reminder of happier days. Xewd, Yumnf and Zoq ordered another bottle of vodka and discussed what to do next. Their first idea was to sit tight, then raid the DJ's chalet later that night. But as the second bottle went down, their paranoia mounted. What if the British secret services got to him first, immediately after the quiz? They might be unmasked and arrested at once. After a little more reflection, they decided to enter the quiz, in order to keep as close as possible to their new prey. Although somewhat the worse for drink, they were accepted as members of team four, in the second round of the quiz. This gave them time for a third bottle.

While they were drinking it, Sjarvitch reappeared in the bar, but so heavily disguised that he was unrecognizable. Intentionally looking shifty, he walked over to the DJ at the end of the first round of the quiz, and whispered something in his ear. The DJ nodded and pointed at his watch. Thinking that this must be the contact and that their identities were about to be revealed, the three KGB men jumped up onto the stage. Instead of taking their seats as expected, Xewd and Zoq grabbed the DJ by his arms, while Yumnf unzipped the poor man's trousers and started ferreting around inside his y-fronts. As the astonished DJ fainted, the camp's security guards seized the three spies. They were then turned over to the police.

The next morning, the following headline appeared in the Newquay Gazette:

THROWN KGB VEX CAMP QUIZ DJ'S FLY

– Slightly, but fittingly ambiguous, remarked the satisfied double agent. And, what is more, a perfect isopangram that doesn't mention any of us by name.

44.

Harry Mathews
THEIR WORDS, FOR YOU
{Oulipo}

Another morning, another egg. The sky was up early. It had rained all night: to you and me sleeping, the storm was a delight. In the east, morning clouds are building a kingdom of red and silver. Time for you to get up! Come into the kingdom of morning delight and come as king! Come into the omelet of morning delight, and come as egg!

You can't make an omelet without breaking half a dozen of the other. Take six eggs . . . Eggs are things – eggs *were* things: have an omelet. Have a little bread with it too. Cat! Come on Cat, you old dog, have a little bread till it's bone time.

You're looking good today. What of going down the road to the port? No – you propose old-stone-gathering at the water side, and going into the water when the tide comes in.

You go with me down fences that teach the intentions of the men that dispose of the grass. A horse waits at a fence; another rolls on the grass, breaking wind. (Good for the horse – one should break wind when one has to, putting it off does no good.) At the side of the road dead grass is burning, old sticks and grass, burning silver in the morning. The road is a delight, with water on one side, oaks and grass on the other; and the grass leads away to another water. In the oaks you once gathered bird's eggs from moss.

From the road you can see the port, the old port paved with stones, paved with bones. Sailors gather in it at night, gathering on the night side of the port looking for the tricks and stitches of love.

God disposes
Red sky at night,

When the tide is coming in, sailors can drink and sleep. In the morning all leave on the early tide. Not all: a few go on sleeping.

II

Men that had been sailors came to be men of roads and grass. A dozen men proposed to build the roads. Others disposed the fences. Men broke stones to pave and build. The men break new bread and drink new water, and pour new water over their hands.

Not all took to the new kingdom (one with no king). Water can look good even to a one-eyed sailor – 'a sailor with no love of water is an unlucky man' – and sailors that had the love went off on new tides. Soon a port was built – built, it has been taught, with the bones of dead men, dead sailors. Soon the stones of the port looked green with moss, and silver with gatherings of birds.

Other sailors took to building, and making things, and being men of oaks and grass, and horse men. 'A sailor on a horse had better be lucky' – but half a dozen times teaches even unlucky men, when their intentions are mighty. From east to west the grasses were gathered, and stone and oak were built up to the sky – no, not to the sky: but a new kingdom was made.

You go with me into a break in the fence, on which suckers are growing. On the other side a man is teaching a horse, 'breaking' him. The horse – red, shy, and mighty – is looking into the wind. The man is looking away from the wind – he is looking at the horse. He leads him with one hand, having a stick in the other.

You led me to the water. The tide was down, leaving many stones to look at, green and red, with tide water lying in the lining of the stones. Birds that had waited when the tide was in have gathered at the water's side, down wind.

You go into the water. But it's no time for stone gathering. From the water to the west a new wind is blowing, and to the west a storm is building, coming with the wind. All at once it's time to go away. In a storm it is the fool that takes to the water.

Getting to the road you called to me, 'It's going to rain cats and dogs!'

And soon the wind pours down the waters it has gathered.

In the oaks by the side of the road, old men had been playing cards on the grass. When the storm broke, other men left off building and came to play with the old men, waiting till the storm blew on. One old man lay sleeping. You waited with me a little away from the men playing and sleeping: 'Mighty oaks in a storm.'

It was raining on every side. The storm paved the sky with stone.

Let it rain; let the wind blow. Down kingdoms of grass and stone the wind teaches you: wait. Wait, and sleep. The wind will blow, the night will come, the storm will break. We shall go into the night to sleep, the night in which, as in words, mouths meet.

III

In the night, water poured from the sky, to call up in the morning a new tide of worms – which with the water will make for better grass. The rain went away early, as the east went from silver to silver-and-red. The night was done, and what a night! Not water and a dozen devils could have spoiled it. A night of love: in which you made me come twice, and once in the morning. Don't let the words make you red and shy!

The break of day proposes new things: new bread, for one. Bread makes the morning. Look! in the east, red breadloaf clouds. But the little clouds the wind rolls down the grass look green. The fences look green too: the storm has made old fences new.

Six birds break from a green cloud and go off. Other little birds gather for the bread you'll give. A redbird! Shy birds gather on the even grass, going up and down before coming up to the water to drink and play. Others wait on a fence. And in the bushes wait the cats. As it is, cats can wait for six tomorrows, it won't harm the birds and it won't do the cats any good. As soon as a bird takes in a cat's intention, it leaves the grass and takes to a bush; in time leaves the bush to take to an oak; and soon a cat is looking down from the green oak . . .

From early morning every bird has been calling to every other bird, making their intentions mighty: 'My worms, *my* worms . . .'

On the other side of the fence, two little dogs are rolling on the grass. Have they been taught to come when called? Look – the dogs are coming without a word from you. Good dogs, that come at once. (But *better* dogs do not come without being called.)

No, it isn't for you. The dogs are coming over to look at another man. The one coming down the other side of the fence, the one you've met before. Can't you put him off? Don't let the loaf burn.

Soon two other dogs meet the first two. It's the cook's dogs – lucky dogs to be a cook's! One is waiting to play 'get the stick'. Good. With a stick one can teach a dog many tricks, when one does it with love.

But when the other dogs came, the cats left, all six. Even one dog can dispose of many a cat; and when dogs gather, cats take the intention to be other than that of burying bones. When one chooses a dog, it is better for the good of one's little kingdom to get a dog that can lie down with a cat and play with it.

You go off to propose things to the other man. Always playing the fool – you, not him: playing the fool is a delight fools cannot have. But every man has a side worth looking at – once.

Another, one-eyed dog has come and is making water on the side of the oak.

Waiting for him to go away. The wind has broken up the sky of clouds, it's parting the clouds from the sky. It's an ill wind on the other side of the fence. And him so old! You being with him makes him look old. Does it make me look old? You're going to let the bread burn.

Better bury my words. Better to leave, and burn, and wait for a new day. And on the morning of my lucky night . . . !

Better? For what? Not for me.

The good, for a dog, is a bone with meat on it. For a cat the good is little, shy dogs, and many mice. The good for mice is no cats, and a left loaf of bread. The good for birds is no cats, and eggs saved from cats and

263

men. For a horse the good is new grass, and other horses, and a few good men. For man the good is no one thing.

For a sailor, the good is even tides, many ports, and half a wind.

For a cook, the good is unburned meat and the delight of other men.

For one king the good is a kingdom without fools; for another, the good is a kingdom all fools.

For Caesar the good is what makes him Caesar.

For a fool the good is other fools. For other men, the good is what makes fools shy.

But for me, the good is you.

IV

In the early morning a lucky worm would go on sleeping. But what worm sleeps? The egg lies waiting to be a better egg; but it is not to be. What good is the intention of an egg? Time and man 'spoil' the egg by making it into another thing – a bird, an omelet.

Soon the cat comes in. It looks at the omelet without any delight at all and goes off.

For me too the day is spoiled. You have gone off. You have even gone off without leaving me any bread. It has taken me a little time to gather what an unlucky wind is blowing. You had led me to look to many good days, green and even days that would propose love and all the little delights that love can save and build into a kingdom – moss, dogs, red eggs . . . But it is not to be. Every day makes new fools out of old ones, and today has chosen me. Like the eggs, my gifts lie broken and not to be gathered up. Is it 'Growing old'?

A stitch in time,
A bird in the hand,
A silver lining,
Wait for no man

And you can't save an omelet with stitches. You came on all shy with me, when the intention was to take a stick to a dog that had not harmed you. What good are silver words to me when you have as good as left me? Things spoil, burn, are buried – men for one – and words cannot make things new.

And to do it for *him!* When you take another man, take a good one – not a fool, not a mouse, not one who plays cards all day. But was it for him that you did it, for him as him? Wasn't it for all the money that's been left him? You shouldn't have given him the time of day, in other times you would have made him get away at once, but you looked at him and drank with him and took gifts from him and soon were disposed to sleep with him. Did you do this for money – for the meat off dead men's bones? One was taught that 'a fool and his money spoil the broth': the words were made for you. And today you propose to me not to put you off, to take love from you as it is given. Don't lie to me always! You're not blind to the poison you've poured into my days. What a sucker you take me for! That's not new – no, and you're getting better at it all the time.

You're looking good – as good as always. Have you been down at the water side? The wind's burned you – that red mouth. You're going? It's not even six. – Have a good time. Don't take my words to you for ill intentions. My words aren't stones to harm you but fences to make you not harm me. Things will go better for me soon: any tomorrow is better than none, and half a loaf (being with you from time to time) – half a loaf is better than no silver lining.

Come soon – will you come tomorrow and look at my new cards?

Come as soon as you can.

Gone. Day, night: time and tide spoil the broth. You lay down once in the bushes with me. Are you lying down with him, in the bushes on the other side of the road? – Go look? Gathering words one can look at, bush words – '. . . Give it . . . take it . . .' Let it be.

Time has no intentions. It 'never sleeps' but it is always sleeping. It will bury tomorrow as it has buried today, without delight, without love. It is not lucky and not unlucky, it does no good and no ill, it is blind and not blind (can it look?), it is old and not old (it never can 'be' at all), it is not little and not mighty: but things grow, things spoil, things break, things are built, things are given, things are saved, things are buried, things sleep – and 'time' renders the doing and the things done, in nights and days.

V

Words came from you in the morning. One word on the little card said 'Rome' – a word that buried my day. You're going to Rome with him. The word made me look up at you as you went away down the road, without having waited for me to come down. It made me give up.

Another gift, and what a gift! Soon you will have met him a dozen times – dozens of times. And every time money is rained on you. Do you play cards? You make money playing cards. Do you look at a horse with love? The horse is gotten for you. And soon Rome: an intention that, in the words you left me, is a 'thing of delight' – thing, thing! Hasn't it been taught him that a dozen gifts spoil one?

You never proposed to me to go away with you. But having money and things is not my gift, and it never will be, no. My gifts to you were little, but given with love. My gifts were few – too few. Half a loaf, unlucky in love.

You never proposed to me to go away, and you aren't doing it today. Couldn't you have done it and left it to me to put off my leaving with you? (With you and him.) A little gift to *me*. You wouldn't have had to wait for my 'no' – even to one as blind as me, it's no trick to get what's on the cards.

> *When in Rome*
> *Few are chosen,*
> *Six of one*
> *Are another man's poison*

Even one of one. 'Too many cooks spoil the bird in the hand', no? And at any time, with you or without you, Rome is not my thing. If one man's meat is the things that are Caesar's, the man must be him and not me.

And soon *you'll* be rolling down to Rome. Have a good time, go east, go west, but – when in Rome, God disposes! And will dispose of him, could be, with him as old as an oak. No, my days aren't that lucky; but the unturned card is always the sucker's delight.

VI

In the red and silver morning a dead day breaks. New words from you to teach me that, once looked on by you as a king (even too mighty a one, which harms me) – once a king, but broken to a stone, a stick, to be buried in parted days as a dead bird or mouse is buried in the grass. The words that came to you from me in the night you call the poison of love gone dead – you take me to have left the kingdom that was my kingdom with you and to have gone blind, to have grown spoiled – a man spoiled as meat is spoiled.

You will have been taught that you can't teach an old dog without breaking eggs – look at one broken egg. But what will it have taught me? It was an unlucky tide that parted you from me. You are going off into the night. My night. It was not me that did the things to you, but a devil – it has always been one of my tricks never to put off till tomorrow what spoils the broth. But 'poison' is too ill a word for me; 'spoiled' and 'blind' may render it, but never could any poison come to you from me. My words were unlucky. If the winds could have gathered the other words in my mouth, to be saved and poured from the sky . . . ! It is that what you have done is a hell for me, a red burning cloud that has left me burned, and blind.

Blind days are breaking on sailors in hindmost ports. Waiting to go with the tide. You have me in your hand: before you leave on the tide, dispose of the bones you have gathered. But let me come and look at you once before you go, that's all. It's little for you to do. Not that it will be all delight to me – better any time to put off the day of leaving and of leave-taking; but it will be a thing to wait with. A loaf is no gift to a king, but it's a mighty one to a man without meat.

A thing to wait with: for dead days and blind nights. For bread and broth – that's something. Grass will go on growing. Things to do: call the dogs; save time; play cards; lie in the grass; wait for you; go down the road. To look at bushes growing at the road side – bushes that you grew? The road is broken, water gathers in the stones and grass is growing up. One could call the birds in the bushes to drink the water on the stones and look for worms in the stitches of grass. A cat is playing with one unlucky bird's eggs. Another cat lies dead in the road – no, not dead, sleeping; no, not even sleeping: playing with a mouse. The cat soon takes it up. The unlucky mouse in the cat's mouth is not dead.

VII

Rolling clouds gathered in the west, and the wind has been blowing from the west, growing from early morning till night. The clouds came early, little at first, a few silver birds that grew into dogs and horses and parted to be new things, mighty things spoiling for a storm. And all day the growing wind. Wind today, wind tomorrow, and a storm coming. Before night storms the sky looks silver-green. The tide too is coming from the west, with the wind. The night rolls in from the east, and from the west the clouds roll up to meet it. Night is the time when winds gather, and all the other winds are pouring down water and grass. Let the winds blow, let the tide build. Let it rain. It *is* raining; and blowing; and the tide will soon be pouring onto stones and grass. Water will gather in tide and sky and with it the wind will pave the kingdom of night. The wind will bury the road to the port with the rendered waters.

As for me, it's time to be sleeping. All the devils of the storm cannot spoil my intention of sleeping early.

Night rolled in from the east, clouds from the west rolled up to it –: what were the words of Mark Twain, East is east and west is west and never the two shall meet? Have met! in the wind. In my kingdom the wind is called – no: when it blows at night in the oaks, the wind is called 'kingdom'; in the day 'road'. Not 'my' kingdom with me king – king's another man. Sleeping too? Sleeping kings are dead kings. But when a king sleeps, what delights! Stones of time and storm are parted, a new morning sky breaks into the night, and the king's intentions, a little at a time, are built up of silver water, birds, and early clouds. But no king can sleep all night. Kings have been taught that kingdoms are made with poison, it must not be him that is given poison: even when, as kings always must, the king drinks with other men. Kings have been taught that a kingdom is built with broken bones, it mustn't be him that's broken: better that the bones of all the kingdom pave the king's road. Sleeping is soon done for. (And you – don't take poison, not today!) The king gets up, goes to look at the night sky, and the mighty clouds give him delight – another, one-eyed delight.

Night is the time for giving poison to kings, and for man's love . . . What are the bushes burning on the road? Take no poison – not today!

Soon not sleeping. Wind and burning. When the wind has mighty intentions, call in your horses and dogs. (But love that looks shy is as an oak in the storm. And no wind can break the oaks, not today, not tomorrow.)

Getting up:

Water is pouring from the night sky. What a wind! It's raining from side to side. The wind has buried the road to the port in sky- and tidewater. The waters meet from time to time and no road is left.

The port sky burns in the night. The storm must be rolling its waters through the port, burying it too. A mighty tide could soon break up the stones of the port. Clouds of water breaking on green stones . . . When a storm is blowing, let the old sailor in.

Twice the waters have met and rolled down the road. 'Dere's a mighty water comin' down de road!' It never rains without breaking eggs, and things play the fool in a storm – water, stones, all the devils, and everything but mice and worms! Better to sleep like them (Do worms sleep?) Better sleep if one can; and one can.

It could be it's raining worms. (Better worms than poison!) Skies *can* rain worms, blown from other grasses. And stones – 'a day when stones rained from the sky', the silver sky came down: stones are raining down, the dead lie on every road. Dead every which-what. Red dogs drink green water that breaks from the stones.

Leave no stone
Before you leap,
Six of one
The twain shall meet

The old dead lie in their silver linings, but the new dead lie in stones and water. You chose the dead; you chose the devils. The water takes old bones from the grass and moss, and silver bones roll in a new tide of stones and water. In my kingdom the dead are not buried, the dead are not buried as in other kingdoms, but are left to spoil in the bushes. In my kingdom the dead are not lucky, are not unlucky. In my kingdom the dead wait without gathering time. In my kingdom the dead have no good intentions and no ill ones, cannot give love, cannot take it; but can spoil and save.

Let the dead
Break my bones,
Better than no bread
Sticks and stones

Old moss lies on unturned bones. You chose the dead and the devils. The dead are not buried in the blind kingdom of worms and water. It is raining, it has rained today all day and all night. It will rain tomorrow and every day. It has always rained. Days of water – the water will drink up the stones. Will it drink the dead? And what of the king? The king isn't dead. (You chose the dead, you chose the devils!) The king is broken and must be given six stitches. The dead can make fools of kings, but to what good? The king will go on sleeping with six stitches and the water and stones. And soon the king will give up sleeping.

The dead of the West are called 'God' and 'Caesar'.

(Have given up sleeping.)

Cats will have been left dead in the road. In the old days one never left dead cats.

When it blows at night, the wind in the oaks is called 'kingdom'; in the day, 'road'.

VIII

Morning, from the east, a mighty sky – an even lining of burning silver clouds, which the new day soon parts.

The storm has spoiled the new grass. It has broken the fences old and new. The kingdom of shy horses lies green and silver in the morning.

The worms have not let the storm spoil their day. Look at their comings and goings! What are they gathering? What's bread for a worm?

And as for my bread – no bread for me today. What to do? Anything, that's what. The road to Hell is better than no bread.

But the break of day proposes new intentions. Look: a loaf of bread has been left for me, by you – you! – and a few words: '. . . Storm played tricks . . . Words coming from him that were ill words to me . . . Fools . . . No road to Rome, not with him!'

Delight breaks from me as birds break from morning clouds. The unlucky time is done for. Blind days burn away. Time and tide will bury their dead.

When did you come and leave the things, the words and the bread? The gift of the loaf you made was worth many words of love. When did you come in, with me not sleeping? On what night tide, from what other side of the sky –

The clouds have parted and lie before the wind.

The dog in the bushes – dead? sleeping?

What good bread you make! And you have not left me. Love disposes of cats and kings, but a good stitch never parts. Can any man be as lucky? That unturned card was a one-eyed king.

And at night you will come and take me to you. You will not have come too soon. The dead were waiting for me, might have come soon, waiting, paving the road that leads into their kingdom with the green mosses of unlucky delight (delight of sleeping, of going blind, of being one with the night). When you are with me, their poison will be poured away.

IX

The new fence was broken in the storm. How the wind must have blown to break it – to blow it down. The fence lay on one side all day. Horses gathered on one side and on the other; the horses came up to the fence and looked at it and at the other horses; but none went onto the others' grass. Today men will come and put the oak fence up and make it as good as new.

The wind is gone, the mighty wind (one to make Caesar wait for a day): today the wind is even, an early wind to be drunk in.

Soon going down: to be met with another gift from you – a dozen red eggs. Gifts should be given with the intention of delight (and red eggs are even better). Better than all is the gift of gifts, you, none other, coming to me down road and grass.

You had come to me at night, you came to me in the early morning; and all the day went on in delight. A few words once and for all of him, of you and him, of you and me and him:

'When you were going with him . . .'

'Don't! It's done with.'

'It's done with – but isn't anything left of the love you had for him?'

'It wasn't love – the intention of love, that's all. My one love is for you, it will never be for another. With him it never could have been.'

'You waited for love to come, it never comes, it has to be made – take it from me. Have a little bread?'

'All the days gone for nothing – spoiled.'

'Rome wasn't built without breaking eggs.'

'But for *him*! It wasn't worth it.'

'What did the storm do to him – not a man of mighty waters?'

'No – but one of *many* waters: always going off . . . What made me a sucker for him? A sucker!'

'Never should've let you go off with him – "Never let a sucker even break eggs", as the teaching goes.'

'The storm made me lucky. It taught me what to look for in him: money, and that's all.'

'"A fool and his money, sailors take warning" –'

'But "A stitch in time, sailor's delight"!'

'You can play the card with me today – today, and any day!'

That was that.

Morning is not done when you propose to teach me the love of mice. Love of cat, dog, and horse, good – but love of mouse?

'The shy mouse that never looks at the sky . . . Wait.'

You leave a road of bread for the mice – many roads: a Rome of sticks and moss. The sticks are disposed to make fences at the side of the roads, which are paved with the moss, with the bread broken on it. Soon mice come from grasses and stones, one at a time, and go down the roads gathering the bread: little silver kings.

When you have taught me mouse love, you propose worms. Worms! Mice and worms may meet in the grass; and mice and worms may never have to drink; but to me a mouse is to a worm as day is to night. You teach me, 'The intentions of worms are few but mighty. The night kingdom of worms can break all things. Mighty stones lie on worms and do not harm them. When one *is* harmed, a worm has a trick of breaking into six or nine and growing into new worms. Today's worm is tomorrow's dozen . . .'

Worm love is left to another day.

When bread and meat were done with, you took me into the kingdom of clouds and birds: down a new road. Even a fool would have taken delight at being on it, never away from the water, and all green on the other side – oaks and bushes breaking with green. Few grasses have had time to grow on the road, but in the stones acorns are disposing green suckers. You lead me into the oaks and bushes, on old sticks green with moss, on off-red mosses lying on stones from which silver water breaks. You teach me that oaks can have moss on all sides. You teach me to look for bird's eggs, and to part the eggs from the birds without harming one and the other. (Six eggs lay burning-red on moss.) You led me on till, parting the grasses, you looked onto the water that lies to the east. No one had taught me that one could get to it on the new road.

Little clouds wait in the sky; other clouds lie even with the water: no wind. A stick from my hand takes time going away in the water. You let one hand lie in the water – should one go in? You have other intentions.

You lead me down the road to look at horses that can be got for little money – no 'My kingdom for a horse' for you! On the grass rolling away from the road, many horses are calling to one another.

Choosing a horse is new to me. What has been taught to me of horses? That a horse has one good side; that when you call a dog it comes, when you call a cat it *may* come, but a horse comes to you without calling.

A red horse takes one of the fences twice. A little horse is coming up to the road – it's taking the road fence! Don't let it get away! A man is coming to get him, stick in hand. (That wouldn't do me any good: taking a stick to a horse would spoil my day.)

It is you that chooses the horse, and what a horse! You propose a little money, wait for a time, and take me away. Tomorrow you will come and you'll get the horse.

Night like day breaks from the east like a silver egg. Many other days are to come. What will new days and nights propose to you and me? The delight of sleeping in the morning – of sleeping all day, lying down in the morning and getting up at night. You will teach me to play cards, you will teach me to grow old. You can take me egg-rolling. You can take me down to the water with a dozen worms. You can teach me, 'Save a sailor!' You will teach me every night to look to the morning. You will give me a hand. Saving a little money would be a good thing. You will make things new, and choose green linings to go with the grass and red ones not to. You will take me as God made me. You will lie down with me. You will let time do its tricks. And, from one day to another, one-eyed delight will go on playing with old silver birds.

X

A storm one day made the meat spoil (not the mighty storm, another one, when many days had come and gone). The meat had spoiled: you had been unlucky in not putting it away with a west wind blowing. With a west wind, worms in meat grow better, and it soon goes all silver and green. And even to you, meat worms are no delight – maybe you once had worms? No, you're a cook, and worms can never be a delight to a cook. That is what is good with omelets: never a worm.

The wind had spoiled the meat, and with it your delight in making meat, broth, bread, omelets, and other things. Once you had a cook. ('What did he leave for?' 'Too many cooks are soon parted.') The day had come, you gathered, to have another.

At the time, the cooks of many kingdoms had chosen the port down the road for a mighty gathering; and you took me with you to choose a new cook from the ones that had come.

The port was as it had been before – the storm had broken it up, but it had been built new. Not many sailors had been taken by the storm. The tide can play tricks with sailors, as can the wind, but on the day of the storm, wind and tide led many sailors into port in time.

What tide and wind are to sailors, meat and broth are to cooks: and in port the words 'meat' and 'broth' were in every mouth (and 'egg' too).

(Were any of the cooks sailors, any of the sailors cooks? To be at once a cook and a sailor is to be twice king.)

Choosing a cook is a mighty thing. Time can make even fools into good cooks, but it is better to have a good one from the word go. You must have money – money can make and break kings, and it may even get one a cook; but a *good* cook? A good cook can dispose of kings. You must get the cook's love too, with one thing and another. The love of a good cook is better than any king's – it is worth the kingdom of God.

But for cooks good and ill, money is good to have. 'Too many cooks have a silver lining' are the words in which you rendered it. But you went on (when many cooks had not taken up what you were proposing), '"Too many cooks" *has* a silver lining, too: six of one would be better than no bread!' Too many cooks, but few are chosen – or choose. It was night before one was disposed to come away with you.

Many days came and went, good ones; till today, when the cook let the meat burn. The cook was sleeping, and unturned meat soon burns. Sleeping – in the daytime? You do not have to be taught that cooks drink: a cook may always have to have water at hand, but it isn't for drinking. Sleeping in the daytime, and sleeping all night too, with the birds and the other cooks. You had been ill-disposed to him before, and your words to him were unlucky ones – calling him a fool and proposing that good cooks were dead cooks. The cook went all red and soon was gone; and all the money you had given him was gone with the wind . . . with the cook . . . Too many cooks wait for no man.

The meat has burned – and red meat is good for the drinking man; but save the bones for broth and the broth for tomorrow's meat. Bones make for good broth, and good broth makes a mighty man. Put in any old meat you have, too – it can render good broth.

You give me the broth and make an omelet. You teach me that it should be made without water, and that when making it a good thing is to roll it. It's time for bread and eggs. Save a little bread to gather up what will be left of the omelet.

You have made better omelets before.

Dead cooks do not make better cooks – that is what the day has taught me.

XI

Once burned,
  Leave no stone unturned.
Twice shy,
  Let sleeping dogs lie.

Days have come and will come, todays and tomorrows, todays paved with tomorrows and with days that are gone. The tomorrows lie on today as the dead do. It is time to give them up.

As cats gather mice, as ports gather sailors, you gather old intentions. Every day you gather me and put me away. You have called me a king, but you look on me as the bones of today that will soon be dead, you put the day away with me, the 'king'. Don't take the king for the kingdom. The kingdom is today.

Tomorrow can be intention, but today does not wait: it is delight or not. The morning is the one morning, or no morning. Delight as to the grass-gathering horse. The dog's mouth cannot put off the time when it will take up the bone. Cards are given to me, to you. Every card takes a trick, and one lucky card is worth a kingdom.

Today breaks into little winds, roads, clouds. The wind that comes from the tide of clouds is gathering intentions, of silver days and of storms. Don't wait for it. The time that will come 'soon' has come today. All roads 'take it with you'. Tomorrow is for the birds – the early birds that look away to tomorrow. But the early bird must come down.

Oaks are growing and gathering their linings of green. Moss gathers on oaks, on sticks of dead oak, on stones. Grass grows and soon is dead, and grows new, and the dead grass is taken into the kingdoms of birds, mice, and worms. In the morning, sticks are being gathered and broken. It's time to go into the day. Sticks are gathered at the water-side, and dead oak that makes for good burning burns. Dead grass too burns at the road side.

It is time to go blind into the day. Let the blind dog that you led lead you. Dead times grow in the grass, in the oaks (the dead are parted from none), but from them oaks and grass grow new. Time to give up one thing and another (but take one gift from me). Let everything go. Let everyone go – let the cook be gone! The time has come to let it all go. Give what you can. Put silver money in the blind man's hands. (But money is a little gift, and gathers little men. 'For a cook a gift of silver, for a sailor a gift of time, for a good man a gift of love.') Give bones to the old dog, give broth and meat to the old man lying at the side of the road. Spoil the mighty horse that has broken down. But for you, take the day that is today; and the night with it.

Red bones break in the old dog's mouth.

It will be night all too soon. In the west, birds will part the lining of day. The day will break down, and clouds burn for it.

It will soon be night, and soon tomorrow. The cards will lie unturned. The horses, having drunk, will sleep. Mice will take to their little roads. The sleeping logs die. The birds are disposed in the oaks for the night. And the worms – what do worms do in the night, blind things? Do worms gather when parting meat from bone?

Night comes, time to make broth and meat. You cannot let everyone in. But let the dog in, and the cat, and me. The kingdoms will soon be sleeping, for tomorrow. And for tomorrow – for tomorrow bury the dead things of today. Bury and burn the always-old things; pour off the rest:

Burn a dozen and one cards. Bury a few acorns. Pour off the even tide. Bury the poison-birds and the cook's lucky dog and cat. Burn the grass devils and half the night. Pour off the ill waters. Burn the sides and linings of things, the cloud men, and the better Other. Pour off the rolling wind. Bury the little tricks, the unlucky sailor, the stone mouth, and the mice dead from poison. Bury the loaf storms. Burn the bone fences. Burn the oak sticks and another day. Bury the old horse and the unturned moss. Pour off the eggs. Bury the sleeping hands, the green breaks, and the hindmost road. Burn delights and intentions (the twain) and their time-bushes. Pour off the fool's words and the others. Burn the nine gods and every gift, the good stitches and the new suckers. Bury Rome and Caesar, the kingdom and the king, and the hell in the red west. Pour off the early morning. Burn the new port, the oak sticks, and the one-eyed sky. Bury any love. Burn the silver east. Bury meat and omelets, and pour off the mighty broth.

The burning fences make red stitches in the lining of the sky.

Red clouds dispose the night.

45.

Dan Rhodes
FROM *ANTHROPOLOGY*
{After Oulipo}

Anthropology

I loved an anthropologist. She went to Mongolia to study the gays. At first she kept their culture at arm's length, but eventually she decided that her fieldwork would benefit from assimilation. She worked hard to become as much like them as possible, and gradually she was accepted. After a while she ended our romance by letter. It breaks my heart to think of her herding those yaks in the freezing hills, the peak of her leather cap shielding her eyes from the driving wind, her wrist dangling away, and nothing but a handlebar moustache to keep her top lip warm.

Baby

My girlfriend's pregnancy lasted over two years. 'Maybe the doctor's right,' I said. 'Maybe a baby isn't going to come.' She wouldn't listen. She carried on buying nappies, teething rings, woolly hats and mittens, and little bits and pieces for the nursery. One afternoon I came home to find her cradling a bundle in her arms.

'Look,' she said. 'It's arrived. It's a boy, and it's got your eyes.'

'Well done,' I said. 'Congratulations.'

'And congratulations to you too. After all, you don't become a father every day.'

'I suppose not. But really it's you that's done all the hard work.'

Charging

My girlfriend started charging me for sex. She said she had to think of her future, and anyway her friends did it so why shouldn't she? I didn't mind too much because her basic rates were very reasonable, although she always expected tips for extras. Once, as she was holding the banknotes I'd given her up to the light to make sure they were real, I asked her if she ever went with anyone else for money. She was furious, and asked what kind of girl I thought she was. I said one with laughing eyes, and lovely long dark hair.

46.

Italo Calvino
FROM *INVISIBLE CITIES*
translated by William Weaver
{Oulipo}

Cities & Memory 1

Leaving there and proceeding for three days towards the east, you reach Diomira, a city with sixty silver domes, bronze statues of all the gods, streets paved with lead, a crystal theatre, a golden cock that crows each morning on a tower. All these beauties will already be familiar to the visitor, who has seen them also in other cities. But the special quality of this city for the man who arrives there on a September evening, when the days are growing shorter and the multicoloured lamps are lighted all at once at the doors of the food stalls and from a terrace a woman's voice cries ooh!, is that he feels envy towards those who now believe they have once before lived an evening identical to this and who think they were happy, that time.

Cities & Memory 2

When a man rides a long time through wild regions he feels the desire for a city. Finally he comes to Isidora, a city where the buildings have spiral staircases encrusted with spiral seashells, where perfect telescopes and violins are made, where the foreigner hesitating between two women always encounters a third, where cockfights degenerate into bloody brawls among the betters. He was thinking of all these things when he desired a city. Isidora, therefore, is the city of his dreams: with one difference. The dreamed-of city contained him as a young man; he arrives at Isidora in his old age. In the square there is the wall where the old men sit and watch the young go by; he is seated in a row with them. Desires are already memories.

Cities & Desire 1

There are two ways of describing the city of Dorothea: you can say that four aluminium towers rise from its walls flanking seven gates with spring-operated drawbridges that span the moat whose water feeds four green canals which cross the city, dividing it into nine quarters, each with three hundred houses and seven hundred chimneys. And bearing in mind that the nubile girls of each quarter marry youths of other quarters and their parents exchange the goods that each family holds in monopoly – bergamot, sturgeon roe, astrolabes, amethysts – you can then work from these facts until you learn everything you wish about the city in the past, present, and future. Or else you can say, like the camel-driver who took me there: 'I arrived here in my first youth, one morning, many people were hurrying along the streets towards the market, the women had fine teeth and looked you straight in the eye, three soldiers on a platform played the trumpet, and all around wheels turned and coloured banners fluttered in the wind. Before then I had known only the desert and the caravan routes. In the years that followed, my eyes returned to contemplate the desert expanses and the caravan routes; but now I know this path is only one of the many that opened before me on that morning in Dorothea.'

Cities & Memory 3

In vain, great-hearted Kublai, shall I attempt to describe Zaira, city of high bastions. I could tell you how many steps make up the streets rising like stairways, and the degree of the arcades' curves, and what kind of zinc scales cover the roofs; but I already know this would be the same as telling you nothing. The city does not consist of this, but of relationships between the measurements of its space and the events of its past: the height of a lamppost and the distance from the ground of a hanged usurper's swaying feet; the line strung from the lamppost to the railing opposite and the festoons that decorate the course of the queen's nuptial procession; the height of that railing and the leap of the adulterer who climbed over it at dawn; the tilt of a guttering and a cat's progress along it as he slips into the same window; the firing range of a gunboat which has suddenly appeared beyond the cape and the bomb that destroys the guttering; the rips in the fish net and the three old men seated on the dock mending nets and telling each other for the hundredth time the story of the gunboat of the usurper, who some say was the queen's illegitimate son, abandoned in his swaddling clothes there on the dock.

As this wave from memories flows in, the city soaks up like a sponge and expands. A description of Zaira as it is today should contain all Zaira's past. The city, however, does not tell its past, but contains it like the lines of a hand, written in the corners of the streets, the gratings of the windows, the banisters of the steps, the antennae of the lightning rods, the poles of the flags, every segment marked in turn with scratches, indentations, scrolls.

Cities & Desire 2

At the end of three days, moving southward, you come upon Anastasia, a city with concentric canals watering it and kites flying over it. I should now list the wares that can profitably be bought here: agate, onyx, chrysoprase, and other varieties of chalcedony; I should praise the flesh of the golden pheasant cooked here over fires of seasoned cherry wood and sprinkled with much sweet marjoram; and tell of the women I have seen bathing in the pool of a garden and who sometimes – it is said – invite the stranger to disrobe with them and chase them in the water. But with all this, I would not be telling you the city's true essence; for while the description of Anastasia awakens desires one at a time only to force you to stifle them, when you are in the heart of Anastasia one morning your desires waken all at once and surround you. The city appears to you as a whole where no desire is lost and of which you are a part, and since it enjoys everything you do not enjoy, you can do nothing but inhabit this desire and be content. Such is the power, sometimes called malignant, sometimes benign, that Anastasia, the treacherous city, possesses; if for eight hours a day you work as a cutter of agate, onyx, chrysoprase, your labour which gives form to desire takes from desire its form, and you believe you are enjoying Anastasia wholly when you are only its slave.

Cities & Signs 1

You walk for days among trees and among stones. Rarely does the eye light on a thing, and then only when it has recognized that thing as the sign of another thing: a print in the sand indicates the tiger's passage; a marsh announces a vein of water; the hibiscus flower, the end of winter. All the rest is silent and interchangeable; trees and stones are only what they are.

Finally the journey leads to the city of Tamara. You penetrate it along streets thick with signboards jutting from the walls. The eye does not see things but images of things that mean other things: pincers point out the tooth-drawer's house; a tankard, the tavern; halberds, the barracks; scales, the grocer's. Statues and shields depict lions, dolphins, towers, stars: a sign that something – who knows what? – has as its sign a lion or a dolphin or a tower or a star. Other signals warn of what is forbidden in a given place (to enter the alley with wagons, to urinate behind the kiosk, to fish with your pole from the bridge) and what is allowed (watering zebras, playing bowls, burning relatives' corpses). From the doors of the temples the gods' statues are seen, each portrayed with his attributes – the cornucopia, the hourglass, the medusa – so that the worshipper can recognize them and address his prayers correctly. If a building has no signboard or figure, its very form and the position it occupies in the city's order suffice to indicate its function: the palace, the prison, the mint, the Pythagorean school, the brothel. The wares, too, which the vendors display on their stalls are valuable not in themselves but as signs of other things: the embroidered headband stands for elegance; the gilded palanquin, power; the volumes of Averroes, learning; the ankle bracelet, voluptuousness. Your gaze scans the streets as if they were written pages: the city says everything you must think, makes you repeat her discourse, and while you believe you are visiting Tamara you are only recording the names with which she defines herself and all her parts.

However the city may really be, beneath this thick coating of signs, whatever it may contain or conceal, you leave Tamara without having discovered it. Outside, the land stretches, empty, to the horizon; the sky opens, with speeding clouds. In the shape that chance and wind give the clouds, you are already intent on recognizing figures: a sailing ship, a hand, an elephant . . .

47.

Harry Mathews

FROM *THE ORCHARD*

{Oulipo}

I remember Georges Perec's excitement when I told him that a pinch of snuff would satisfy his nicotine craving for half an hour, and his disappointment when this proved false. He continued to take snuff all the same, sneezing and snorting with long 'aahs' of contentment.

•

I remember Georges Perec telling me, after an Oulipo meeting, that in speaking to the group I used *n'est-ce pas?* so often that it could not fail to distract or annoy.

•

I remember Georges Perec's laughs – the first high, fast, and anxious; the second even higher and faster, full of delighted astonishment; the third a low, satisfied chuckle that was reserved for intimate company. When he smiled, his eyes shone.

•

I remember going to the theater with Georges Perec: 1. To a play by Feydeau, with Catherine B. (M.C., whom I had just met, joined us for supper afterwards.) 2. *La Belle Hélène*, with M.C. and Catherine B. (At one point the actors gave the audience a quiz. To the question 'Who was the second oldest Greek poet whose works have survived?' I correctly shouted the answer 'Hesiod', then, to the delight of Georges and Catherine, squirmed down into my seat like an embarrassed little boy.) 3. *La Plage* (by Severo Sarduy), with M.C. and Catherine B. (It was wet weather, Georges and Catherine had bad colds, they arrived at Gare d'Orsay at the last possible moment with gray, swollen faces.)

•

I remember a card thumbtacked outside Georges Perec's front door, with 'Georges Perec' printed in large lettering, followed by information in smaller print that referred to a housepainter living in another part of Paris.

•

I remember that one might also find on Georges Perec's door a piece of paper with the handwritten words *Je reviens de Suisse.*

•

I remember lying to Georges Perec when we first met: *'Je n'ai lu de toi que* LES CHOSES.'* I had read nothing by him at all.

•

I remember Georges Perec's impatience with certain subjects during the time he was writing *La Vie mode d'emploi*: *'Qu'est-ce que cela peut bien me foutre?'*†

•

I remember Georges Perec's sinus headaches.

•

I remember how exuberantly pleased Georges Perec was with the gift of a carving board that M.C. and I had bought at the Beaucroissant fair: he repeated, *'Ah, ce que suis content que vous me donniez cette planche!'* (Or *d'avoir cette planche de vous.)*‡

•

I remember making Georges Perec one of my literary executors (the other was Maxine G.).

•

I remember that Georges Perec always got to the train station at least an hour before departure time.

•

I remember George Perec's sneezing fits.

•

I remember taking Georges Perec to Le Clocher, the Catholic boarding school in Villard-de-Lans where he had been hidden (and incidentally

---

* All I've read of yours is *Things* (Perec's first novel).

† Why should I give a damn about that.

‡ I'm so happy you're giving me this carving board (to be getting this carving board from you).

baptized, with a false name) during the occupation. The director asked him, 'You wouldn't by any chance be a relative of the writer?' Hunching his shoulders, Georges answered, 'I *am* the writer.' *Les Choses* was now being taught there.

•

I remember Georges Perec's warts.

•

I remember Georges Perec sulky and silent while he was writing *La Vie mode d'emploi*.

•

I remember my daughter telling me that she had seen Georges Perec at a party and found him greatly aged.

•

I remember speaking to Georges Perec about *Raiders of the Lost Ark* as soon as the film was released. I was sure he would like it, the way schoolboys like adventure movies they play hookey for. We saw it in a big movie theater on the Champs-Elysées, without our ladies, and (most important) at a matinee.

•

I remember that Georges Perec always named his current cat Duchat. (A few days before he died, the last Duchat turned against him, clawing him several times while he lay in bed.)

•

I remember Georges Perec telling me that Calvados was the most reliable of commercially produced spirits. (His favorite brandies were *prune de Souillac* and rare Armagnacs.)

48.

Christopher Smart
FROM *JUBILATE AGNO*
{Anticipatory Plagiarism}

Fragment C

Lines 1–33

    For H is a spirit and therefore he is God.

    For I is person and therefore he is God.

    For K is king and therefore he is God.

    For L is love and therefore he is God.

5.   For M is musick and therefore he is God.

    For N is novelty and therefore he is God.

    For O is over and therefore he is God.

    For P is power and therefore he is God.

    For Q is quick and therefore he is God.

10.   For R is right and therefore he is God.

    For S is soul and therefore he is God.

    For T is truth and therefore he is God.

    For U is union and therefore he is God.

    For W is worth and therefore he is God.

15.   For X has the pow'r of three and therefore he is God.

    For Y is yea and therefore he is God.

    For Z is zeal and therefore he is God, whom I pray to be gracious to the Widow Davis and Davis the Bookseller.

    For Christ being *A* and Ω is all the intermediate letters without doubt.

    For there is a mystery in numbers.

20.   For One is perfect and good being at unity in himself.

For Two is the most imperfect of all numbers.

For every thing infinitely perfect is Three.

For the Devil is two being without God.

For he is an evil spirit male and female.

25.   For he is called the Duce by foolish invocation on that account.

For Three is the simplest and best of all numbers.

For Four is good being square.

For Five is not so good in itself but works well in combination.

For Five is not so good in itself as it consists of two and three.

30.   For Six is very good consisting of twice three.

For Seven is very good consisting of two compleat numbers.

For Eight is good for the same reason and propitious to me Eighth of
      March 1761 hallelujah.

For Nine is a number very good and harmonious.

49.

Yin Zhongkan
REVERSIBLE INSCRIPTION
translated by Jody Gladding
{Anticipatory Plagiarism}

There were also more decorative circular inscriptions engraved on the backs of mirrors, wine trays, and ink stones, or calligraphed on round fans. Usually with eight characters, they made up sequences of sixteen couplets. These were more a matter of maxims, of little literary significance except that they confirmed the early Chinese interest in reversible texts and combinative words. This inscription by Yin Zhongkan appeared on a wine tray:

Figure 11.1 Reversible Inscription by Yin Zhongkan

Among the sixteen possible readings:

> The rule is to have what suits the body
> Joy and wine which becomes ritual.

> Wine is the ritual rule
> Having what suits, the body is joyous.

What delights the body, it is suitable to have it
What rules the rituals, it is wine.

What suits the body is joy and wine
For rituals, there are rules.

50.

Raymond Queneau
FROM *ELEMENTARY MORALITY* (POEMS)
translated by Philip Terry
{Oulipo}

Dark Isis	Green fruit	Spotted animal
	Clear neologisms	
Red flower	Transparent attitude	Orange-coloured star
	Clear springs	
Brown forest	Russet boar	Bleating flock
	Sparse tree	

A boat
on the water
soleabrious
follows the current
A crocodile
bites the keel
in vain

Ochre Isis	Crumbly statue	Apricot totem
	Clear neologisms	

Subtraction sum	Multiple division	Exponential root
	Ordinary day	
Drawn-out line	Central pool	Extended pretext
	Ordinary yesterday	
Closed books	Open notebooks	Unreal calculations
	Usual reflections	

The sun that lasts
beyond midday
An obscure face
a vanished face
and some little
some little worries
on bright soil

Abstract sum	Multiplied union	Logarithmic increase
	Ordinary day	

Protective parapets	Cursed crenelles	Encircling weapons
	Agamemnon boiling	
Singular combats	Plural enemies	Wartime tricks
	Imprudent Nestor	
Stolen captives	Blinded seers	Winged goddesses
	Trojan wars	

Achilles with his heel
his heart
full of wrath and bile
as the cauldron helmets
rallied on the plain
You could hear the snort
of a cardboard horse

Singular combats	Plural enemies	Wartime tricks
	Immortal masterpiece	

Spiralled smoke	Plucked cigars	Abundant butts
	American leaves	
Victorious vertigos	Rough alcohol	Sticky bars
	Noachian echoes	
Half-open valves	Penetrated ducts	Excited posteriors
	Erotic machines	

In the brown night
under the moonlight
a drunk darts about
in the smoke
of silk stockings
of stills
of wooden pipes

Winter awakening	Invigorating snows	Major refusal
	Sudden decision	

51.

Valérie Beaudouin
BODY/MACHINE
translated by Philip Terry
{Oulipo/Ouvipo}

Machine
Body

Suspicious lump   Potential risk   Maximal protection
Local anaesthetic   Benign operation   Negotiated awakening
                         Triggered machine
                         Conscious patient

Measured pulse   Blood samples   Thorough tests
Irritated surgeon   Maintained hierarchy   Denied choice
                         Full scan
                         General anaesthetic

Supine body   White cylinder   Metallic walls
Blocked movements   Needle introduced   Supine body
                         Icy voice
                         Flight impossible

Body in machine
He has
'Stop,
Operated
She says,
The way he likes,
Breathing'
An inert body.
She slices
'Breathe,
A body
He says,
Restrained.
Breathe'.

White prison
Invaded blood

Impossible escape
Undulating waves
Suspended time
Tenacious poison

Immobile body
Numb consciousness

52.

Jacques Roubaud
FROM *EXCHANGES ON LIGHT*
translated by Eleni Sikelianos
{Oulipo}

First Night

MR GOODMAN

I've asked you all to gather here for the next few evenings, just when the lamps are being lit, as the natural light is waning, leaving the outside world in darkness. Imagine that these windows open to the west, that right out there is the grass, the cultivated grass, of a park laid out by, say, Capability Brown, or perhaps Humphry Repton, with its orderly disorder of trees and, farther on, the low hills in the soft English distance.

But each of you might imagine another landscape, one beyond these windows facing us, one pierced by stars and lamps in which their lights meet, fight, trade, and leave even as we speak. It's of light that we speak, that you speak.

MR GOODMAN

To begin:
No light, no world; and it's not just the world that's not, without light, but all that is, which is but light. Objects are worn-out light. The sum of all light is the world.

Light is the boiling point of things.

Light is an emanation from God; as emanation, it is an eternal process; it is not creation at each instant; for creation is *ex nihilo* and takes place in time, and light is natural while creation is a deliberate act.

Everything you have just trebly said is naught but this: the world is *luci-forme a luce prima*: formed of light, derived from First Light. Light is the first bodily form. It is not objects but forms that are light, the only sub-stance of the physical world that is nearly pure form, since all form is a form of light that manifests in the object that it informs.

Light is what cannot be touched, untouchable even as lightning. The cause of all beings, itself nothing, being superessentially cut off from every-thing.

Be serious, let's not get carried away: when the sun, after hovering majes-tically on the horizon, sinks and suddenly disappears from sight, we understand that between this star and us exists a mode of communica-tion that, without our having to touch it, brings its presence to mind. This mode of communication, which exercises itself over incommensurable distances and is transmitted via the eyes – this, and this alone, is light.

LEWIS OF B.

Let us not be poor in light, sunless. We are the Sun's debtors.

MR GOODMAN

Yet all that rises in the park at this very instant: grass, trees, the distance, that which enfolds each form in a dark thought, like a finger of smoke, a dark dust, a red-blurred pollen, what all the things outside have in common, isn't that also light? And don't the laws of night vision permit us a slow substitution for the anterior, disappeared blaze of sun?

DENNIS PS.

If shadows had no light, we wouldn't see them. Darkness would be entire, eternal, and nil.

WILLIAM H.

Night you   come   the light   grows
on the   emptied slopes   of day   the
leaves will be   dark

JOHN PH.

Who can shed light on light?

BASIL OF C.

The sun was not born to shed light. Light was made before the sun. The writings speak not of spreading light but of illuminating, by the very essence of light, rather than by the sun, which can only serve as a vehicle for something whose birth preceded its own.

Light differs from shadow in that its existence cannot be separated from its essence; the essence of light is to purely exist; on the contrary, if it were of the essence of shadow to enter into composition with its existence, it would be impossible to perfectly conceive of the essence of shadow without the existence of shadows weaving in. Just as the essence of the number 2 would be destroyed if one tried to extract its unity, so the essence of shadow would be destroyed by removing shadows from the universe, by extracting the existence of shadow from its essence. But that's not possible. Yet it is possible to understand shadow's essence without seeing it, even without supposing that there are real shadows. Furthermore, if there were no distance between essence and existence in shadows, one could say that they existed thanks to their essence. But only light has this property.

LEWIS OF B.

Let's be serious. Why not try to prove that light is God, while you're at it?

JOHN PH.

I wouldn't say that. But why reject a metaphysics of light? It has several divine traits, for instance, the begetting light and the splendor begotten weave together and illuminate one another. Divinity does that too.

M. G.

But isn't that what light is? There is light, and there are lights. Lights are objects; light is arrow. The first change; the second does not.

In the air
    light
        tears out
  from earth   to dark
  and spits
    in the air
  night   rough to the verge
    of trees
      in the earth

DENNIS PS.

Indeed. It's clear that each light tears itself away from night, but it is also clear that in each shining thing, light in its essence and substance is more brilliant still than its visible sheen, which is but the darkness and shadow of its full brilliance.

DENNIS PS.

These trees, this grass, these hills, like us, visible in the dying light, aren't they all as elusive as the inaccessible light, of which lights are but a shadow?

BASIL OF C.

Light, born of the first word of God, who fashioned it after his nature, instantly dispelled the dark. God separated light from darkness. Light and darkness are of incompatible natures, in perpetual opposition; between them is the largest interval, the longest distance.

WILLIAM H.

Night

you
came

the
lights
have grown
over

the grass, drained
the slopes
of

light, the
lights have

gone
dark

LEWIS OF B.

No light is dark; that doesn't make sense; there is more or less light, intensity, variable wave-lengths, that's all. Get serious.

MR GOODMAN

I remember London in March, 1940, during the black-out. I was overcome, and still am, remembering; to see the city quietly give itself over to darkness (this was before the bombings), the way a countryside might, like the one we're looking at now from these windows, pushing itself into night. London humbly preparing herself in the twilight, the shutters shutting up windows, the rare passer-by hurrying towards home, the small medieval lanterns lighting up the subway entrances here and there.

And darkness fell, and, with the diminishing gleam, noises rarefied, the sirens emerging from this dark mass one by one, as if night were painting it.

JOHN PH.

Configurations of objects make the state of light.

JOHN PH.

But of light or not light, from the former it is not possible to deduce, light or not light, the latter.

DENNIS PS.

Not-light is also the being of beings-of-light. We mustn't call them the simple reverse of perceptible light. If one reasons thus, one transforms them into their opposite, that is to say, into what is, in itself, darkness; instead of being that-which-manifests, that-which-illumines, they become only something manifested, the sign of a light other than that light that informs them. Contrary to what Aristotle said, all contingent realities, like the simple lights which appear on the hill, or those reborn in Mr Goodman's memory of London, each accidental configuration, must be preceded by a more noble being: it's the illuminative exigency resting on the unconditional hegemony of illumination in relation to the object that it reveals.

MR GOODMAN

I was a child then. My mother lit the candles, I parted the black curtains, I leaned into the dark street near Russell Square.

BASIL OF C.

The smallest light, the most humble, the candle's, is all light, is Light.

LEWIS OF B.

You're confusing things again.

WILLIAM H.

The lamps   evaporate   in the bottom
left rectangle   of the window   fill
with lights   from elsewhere   black and white
     from a light   the rectangle   of the
window   of lights   in black and white
          and the window   fill up   the lamps
          with lights   *slowly* and from elsewhere

WILLIAM H.

The   lamps   evaporate   in   the   bottom
     left rectangle   of the window   fill
     with lights from elsewhere   in black and white
          from a light   the rectangle   of the
window   of lights   in black and white
     and the window   fill up   the lamps
slowly with lights   and from elsewhere.

JOHN PH.

Mental window, mental hands, mental lights, lights always already
declared, by design reiterative.

LEWIS DE B.

Light doesn't turn the street corner.

Light has already, while you were giving it boundaries, while you legislated the impossible, turned the corner.

Light is not of time.

Night is now complete, and neither the stars, nor time, are yet within the field of our conversation. It's time, according to our rules, to retire. We will reconvene here tomorrow at the same hour, if you will.

53·

Jackson Mac Low

FROM *THE COMPLETE LIGHT POEMS*

{After Oulipo}

6th Light Poem: For Carol Bergé – 14 June 1962

Carol Bergé in luminosity.
Carol Bergé in bus light trying to see out & read & sleep.
Carol Bergé in amber light.
Carol Bergé in gaslight in a tight dress.
Carol Bergé in artificial light.
Carol Bergé by the light of big guns firing.
Carol Bergé in camphor-oil lamplight.
Carol Bergé by owl-light.
Carol Bergé in the light of a bicycle lamp on a deserted highway.
Carol Bergé in the light of the beach lights at Coney Island.
Carol Bergé in ghost light flickering.
Carol Bergé in the light of a gasoline lamp.
Carol Bergé in a rainbow.
Carol Bergé in garden light at night with long black gloves on up to her
    bare shoulders.
Carol Bergé in the light of the beacon on top of the Palmolive Building
    in Chicago which is called the Lindbergh Beacon.
Carol Bergé in an evanescent light & then vanishing.
Carol Bergé in the midst of the *Aufklärung* in Weimar bored with
    Goethe's talk but digging his bed style.
Carol Bergé bathed in lambent flame.
Carol Bergé in colored light under a Christmas tree.
Carol Bergé peeing in a gutter by the light of a garbage truck.

Carol Bergé by Earthlight.

Carol Bergé in the *Aufklärung* again learning Persian & writing poems with a quill pen on parchment Schiller brought her.

Carol Bergé in amber light smoking a cigarette in a long amber holder & drinking amber whisky as she reads *Forever Amber* wincing slightly.

Carol Bergé in gaslight in Reading Gaol sneaking a note in to Wilde from one of his boy friends while visiting him disguised as a Salvation Army major.

Carol Bergé in radiance.

54.

Frédéric Forte
FROM *MINUTE-OPERAS*

translated by Ian Monk and Daniel Levin Becker

{Oulipo}

	(codex-style)	
Dismal demigod	Dismal sun	Dismal moon
	Ceaseless days	
Menacing counsel	Floral games	Internal massacres
	Interchangeable peoples	
Teenage chorus	Recumbent lord	Closed eyelids
	Abominable thoughts	

A wall
erected for tennis
and what if we changed
it to something else
to handball
headball
o sacrificial

Teenage chorus	Ceaseless games	Interchangeable massacres
	Dismal demigod	

D.L.B.

311

(three-pointed stone)

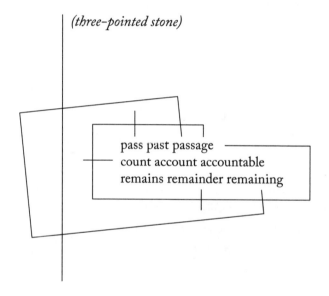

pass past passage
count account accountable
remains remainder remaining

D.L.B.

explaining to someone else
what a subway poem is.

↓

A young woman is speaking
in English. I guess

(effigy) is the title and implies an image will spring up somewhere

The carriage has emptied out.

Let's see . . . the subway

by Robert Johnson. I have
to think up something.

could this unique line give you anything supernatural?

I have in mind:
Waiting at the Crossroads . . .

Answer: just beside me a kid has a monkey-back-pack with a cap.

All around the (potential) readership
is stuffed in here like sardines.

Here below everything's on the move, the train advances we live we die

What's obvious: me a seated poet.

at any moment. Even if my reflection in the window is meaningless.

Before the stop *Arènes:*
am I the toreador or the *toro?*

The journey goes on. I take time out to observe

'Carriage n° HO7'

a young lady. And nothing else.

To her left: 'CV: LINDA'

Writing a subway poem is something new.

In front of me a black
woman in the daylight

New each time? Well just ask the right person.

But it should all be shorter.
Description:

Out into daylight. It's gray. The tunnel

This one fills up quickly too.

is invariably dark, with the reassuringly regular arrival of neon lights.

The other way round: the wings.

In the end, all is well . . .

We're already at Basso Cambo. In the far west.

I.M.

313

(from the East)

From our conversations on loose ground, retain (retain in
my hands a piece of the *spiritual body*) the height of bar-
riers to cross, the masses of motionless efforts not to hear
us, each refrain, and all we did not want to say (which the
ritual of death today prevents). experience time as it passes.

Now this is you
this pad, indivisible
nor nothing tangible
to get accustomed to
(desirable)

D.L.B.

(warrior?)

near the blinded wall
hand takes up writing matter
an empty question
the eyes wish they could suffuse
the distance too large by far

absent form

D.L.B.

(whistle statue II)

Silent bar: our tale is
no busier. No
ablutions, blear, turbulent
as oil, brute as
noise. Burn it alone
      Rot.
is a blur, a bountiless table
in our burial stone

SILENTBAROU
RTALEISNOBU
SIERNOABLUT
IONSBLEARTU
RBULENTASOI
LBRUTEASNOI
SEBURNITALO
NEROTISABLU
RABOUNTILES
STABLEINOUR
BURIALSTONE

D.L.B.

(mask II)

Cross out the white straight finishing on your face

I.M.

(dog–medium)

Yes

But the lack of space
Follow you / | The path which is never all that clear
through / | And hell
multiple worlds? | And this tiring remain

Maybe and then no

But then time
Self-multiplying
The fathomlessness of the now
That spreads in the daylight, the moment
Always ideal   limbo

D.L.B.

use
the void

(wood painted white)

the void
used

I.M.

(king)

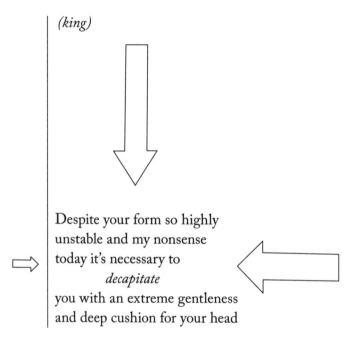

Despite your form so highly
unstable and my nonsense
today it's necessary to
          decapitate
you with an extreme gentleness
and deep cushion for your head

I.M.

(high-relief plaque)

ALGOL VOCABULARY

array
begin
boolean
comment
do
else
end
false
for
go
if
integer
label
list
long
procedure
real
step
switch
then
true
until
value
while

IF	BOOLEAN	
FALSE	UNTIL	TRUE
SWITCH	LABEL	ELSE
	END	PROCEDURE

D.L.B.

321

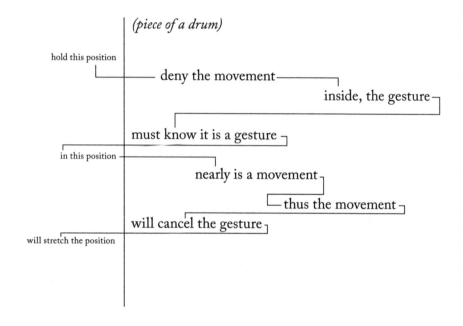

(piece of a drum)

hold this position

deny the movement

inside, the gesture

must know it is a gesture

in this position

nearly is a movement

thus the movement

will cancel the gesture

will stretch the position

D.L.B.

55·

Christopher Middleton

FROM *PATAXANADU*

{After Oulipo}

Pataxanadu 1
How Sir Landlouse Follicled a Boxer into
a Castaway Where He Found a Dayblind Knee,
and How He After Was Repulsed of a Dame
to Hector Her Brood

Now leave we there and speak of Sir Landlouse that rode a great whiff
on a decursive foreshore
    where he saw a black boxer secularizing in manner as it had been in
the spoon-bait of an hunted deed.
    And therewith he rode after the boxer and he saw levitating on the
groove a large spoon-bait of blobber.
    And then Sir Landlouse rode after.

    And ever the boxer looked behind and went through a graven maroon,
and ever Sir Landlouse follicled.
    And then was he ware of an oghamic mannequin, and thither ran the
boxer and so over the brewery.
    So Sir Landlouse rode over that brewery that was oghamic and fecu-
lent; and when he came in at middle-weight of a graven halibut
    there he saw levitating a dayblind knee that was a seditious mameluke,
and that boxer licked his worship.

    And therewithal came out a lady, weaving and wrenching her ham-
strings; and then she said:
    O knee, too much soreness hast thou brought me.

Why say ye so? said Sir Landlouse, I never did this knee no harm, for hither by spoon-bait of blobber this boxer brought me;

and therefore, faery lady,

be not dispersive with me, for I am full sore agglomerated at your griddle.

Troublously, sir, she said, I triumph it be not ye that hath slashed my hurst, for he that did that decumbence is

sophistically worshipped, and he is never likely to reconsider that I shall enshrine him.

What was your hurst's nainsook? said Sir Landlouse.

Sir, she said, his nainsook was called Sir Giddy the Basso Buffo, one of the best knees of the work people,

and he that hath slashed him I know not his nainsook.

Now Goblin send you better comeliness, said Sir Landlouse; and so he denuded, and went into the foreshore again.

And there he met with a dame, the which knew him well, and she said aloft:

Well be ye filliped, my lophodont;

and now I require thee, on thy knee, honey, hector my brood that is sophistically worshipped and never stinteth blaspheming;

for this day he feuded with Sir Giddy the Basso Buffo and slashed him in placoid batter, and there was my brood

sophistically worshipped, and there is a lady, a soprano, that duplicates in a castaway here beside, and this day

she told me my brood's worship should never be whiskered till I could find a knee that would go into the Chantry Perfidious,

and there he should find a swivel eye and a blobbery closet that the worshipped knee was lamed in,

and a picture of that closet and swivel eye should hawk my brood's worship so that his worships were scuttled with the swivel eye and the closet.

This is a marshy thickening, said Sir Landlouse, but what is your brood's nainsook?

Sir, she said, his nainsook was Sir Melanosis de Locust.

That me repayeth, said Sir Landlouse, for he is a felicide of the Tabes Rotable, and to his hector I will do my pout.

Then, sir, said she, follicle even this hierogram, and it will bridge you unto the Chantry Perfidious;

and here I shall abbreviate,

till Goblin seize you here again, and but you spawn, I know no knee living that may credit that advancement.

56.

Georges Perec
THE WINTER JOURNEY
translated by John Sturrock
{Oulipo}

In the last week of August 1939, as the talk of war invaded Paris, a young literature teacher, Vincent Degraël, was invited to spend a few days at the place outside Le Havre belonging to the parents of one of his colleagues, Denis Borrade. The day before his departure, while exploring his hosts' shelves in search of one of those books one has always promised oneself one will read, but that one will generally only have time to leaf inattentively through beside the fire before going to make up a fourth at bridge, Degraël lit upon a slim volume entitled *The Winter Journey*, whose author, Hugo Vernier, was quite unknown to him but whose opening pages made so strong an impression on him that he barely found time to make his excuses to his friend and his parents before going up to his room to read it.

The Winter Journey was a sort of narrative written in the first person, and set in a semi-imaginary country whose heavy skies, gloomy forests, mild hills and canals transected by greenish locks evoked with an insidious insistence the landscapes of Flanders and the Ardennes. The book was divided into two parts. The first, shorter part retraced in sybilline terms a journey which had all the appearances of an initiation, whose every stage seemed certainly to have been marked by a failure, and at the end of which the anonymous hero, a man whom everything gave one to suppose was young, arrived beside a lake that was submerged in a thick mist; there, a ferryman was waiting for him, who took him to a steep-sided, small island in the middle of which there rose a tall, gloomy building; hardly had the young man set foot on the narrow pontoon that afforded the only access to the island when a strange-looking couple appeared: an old man and an old woman, both clad in long black capes, who seemed to rise up out of the fog and who came and placed themselves on either side of him, took him by the elbows and pressed themselves as tightly as they could against his sides; welded together almost, they scaled a rock-strewn path, entered the house, climbed a wooden staircase and came to a chamber. There, as inexplicably as they had appeared, the old people vanished, leaving the young man alone in the middle of the room. It was perfunctorily furnished: a bed covered with a flowery cretonne, a table, a chair. A fire was blazing in the fireplace. On the table a meal had been laid: bean soup, a shoulder of beef. Through the tall window of the room, the young man watched the full moon emerging from the clouds; then he sat down at the table and began to eat. This solitary supper brought the first part to an end.

The second part alone formed nearly four-fifths of the book and it quickly appeared that the brief narrative preceding it was merely an anecdotal pretext. It was a long confession of an exacerbated lyricism, mixed in with poems, with enigmatic maxims, with blasphemous incantations. Hardly had he begun reading it before Vincent Degraël felt a sense of unease that he found it impossible to define exactly, but which only grew more pronounced as he turned the pages of the volume with an increasingly shaky hand; it was as if the phrases he had in front of him had become suddenly familiar, were starting irresistibly to remind him of *something*, as if on to each one that he read there had been imposed, or rather superimposed, the at once precise yet blurred memory of a phrase almost identical to it that he had perhaps already read somewhere else; as if these words, more tender than a caress or more treacherous than a poison, words that were alternately limpid and hermetic, obscene and cordial, dazzling, labyrinthine, endlessly swinging like the frantic needle of a compass between a hallucinated violence and a fabulous serenity, formed the outline of a vague configuration in which could be found, jumbled together, Germain Nouveau and Tristan Corbière, Rimbaud and Verhaeren, Charles Cros and Léon Bloy.

These were the very authors with whom Vincent Degraël was concerned – for several years he had been working on a thesis on 'the evolution of French poetry from the Parnassians to the Symbolists' – and his first thought was that he might well have chanced to read this book as part of his researches, then, more likely, that he was the victim of an illusory *déjà vu* in which, as when the simple taste of a sip of tea suddenly carries you back thirty years to England, a mere trifle had succeeded, a sound, a smell, a gesture – perhaps the moment's hesitation he had noticed before taking the book from the shelf where it had been arranged between Verhaeren and Viélé-Griffin, or else the eager way in which he had perused the opening pages – for the false memory of a previous reading to superimpose itself and so to disturb his present reading as to render it impossible. Soon, however, doubt was no longer possible and Degraël had to yield to the evidence. Perhaps his memory was playing tricks on him, perhaps it was only by chance that Vernier seemed to have borrowed his 'solitary jackal haunting stone sepulchres' from Catulle Mendès, perhaps it should be put down to a fortuitous convergence, to a parading of influence, a deliberate homage, unconscious copying, wilful pastiche, a liking for quotation, a fortunate coincidence, perhaps expressions such as 'the flight of time', 'winter fogs', 'dim horizon', 'deep caves', 'vaporous fountains', 'uncertain light of the wild undergrowth' should be seen as belonging by right to all poets so that it was just as normal to meet with them in a paragraph by Hugo Vernier as in the stanzas of Jean Moréas, but it was quite impossible not to recognize, word for word, or almost, reading at random, in one place a fragment from Rimbaud ('I readily could see a mosque in place of a factory, a drum school built by angels') or Mallarmé ('the lucid winter, the season of serene art'), in another Lautréamont ('I gazed in a mirror at that mouth bruised by my own volition'), Gustave Kahn ('Let the song expire . . . my heart weeps/ A bistre crawls around the brightness. The solemn/silence has risen slowly, it frightens/The familiar sounds of the shadowy staff') or, only slightly modified, Verlaine ('in the interminable tedium of the plain, the snow gleamed like sand. The sky was the colour of copper. The train slid without a murmur . . .'), etc.

It was four o'clock in the morning when Degraël finished reading *The Winter Journey*. He had pinpointed some thirty borrowings. There were certainly others. Hugo Vernier's book seemed to be nothing more than a prodigious compilation from the poets of the end of the nineteenth century, a disproportionate cento, a mosaic almost every piece of which was the work of someone else. But at the same time as he was struggling to imagine this unknown author who had wanted to extract the very substance of his own text from the books of others, when he was attempting to picture this admirable and senseless project to himself in its entirety, Degraël felt a wild suspicion arise in him: he had just remembered that in taking the book from the shelf he had automatically made a note of the date, impelled by that reflex of the young researcher who never consults a work without remarking the bibliographical details. Perhaps he had made a mistake, but he certainly thought he had read 1864. He checked it, his heart pounding. He had read it correctly. That would mean Vernier had 'quoted' a line of Mallarmé two years in advance, had plagiarized Verlaine ten years before his 'Forgotten Ariettas', had written some Gustave Kahn nearly a quarter of a century before Kahn did! It would mean that Lautréamont, Germain Nouveau, Rimbaud, Corbière and quite a few others were merely the copyists of an unrecognized poet of genius who, in a single work, had been able to bring together the very substance off which three or four generations would be feeding after him!

Unless, obviously, the printer's date that appeared on the book were wrong. But Degraël refused to entertain that hypothesis: his discovery was too beautiful, too obvious, too necessary not to be true, and he was already imagining the vertiginous consequences it would provoke: the prodigious scandal that the public revelation of this 'premonitory anthology' would occasion, the extent of the fallout, the enormous doubt that would be cast on all that the critics and literary historians had been imperturbably teaching for years and years. Such was his impatience that, abandoning sleep once and for all, he dashed down to the library to try and find out a little more about this Vernier and his work.

He found nothing. The few dictionaries and directories to be found in the Borrades' library knew nothing of the existence of Hugo Vernier. Neither Denis nor his parents were able to tell him anything further; the book had been bought at an auction, ten years before, in Honfleur; they had looked through it without paying it much attention.

All through the day, with Denis's help, Degraël proceeded to make a systematic examination of the book, going to look up its splintered shards in dozens of anthologies and collections. They found almost three hundred and fifty, shared among almost thirty authors; the most celebrated along with the most obscure poets of the *fin de siècle*, and sometimes even a few prose writers (Léon Bloy, Ernest Hello) seemed to have used *The*

Winter Journey as a bible from which they had extracted the best of them-selves: Banville, Richepin, Huysmans, Charles Cros, Léon Valade rubbed shoulders with Mallarmé and Verlaine and others now fallen into oblivion whose names were Charles de Pomairols, Hippolyte Vaillant, Maurice Rollinat (the godson of George Sand), Laprade, Albert Mérat, Charles Morice or Antony Valabrègue.

Degraël made a careful note of the list of authors and the source of their borrowings and returned to Paris, fully determined to continue his researches the very next day in the Bibliothèque Nationale. But events did not allow him to. In Paris his call-up papers were waiting for him. Joining his unit in Compiègne, he found himself, without really having had the time to understand why, in Saint-Jean-de-Luz, passed over into Spain and from there to England, and only came back to France in 1945. Throughout the war he had carried his notebook with him and had miraculously suc-ceeded in not losing it. His researches had obviously not progressed much, but he had made one, for him capital, discovery all the same. In the Brit-ish Museum he had been able to consult the *Catalogue général de la librairie française* and the *Bibliographie de la France* and had been able to confirm his tremendous hypothesis: *The Winter Journey*, by Vernier (Hugo) had indeed been published in 1864, at Valenciennes, by Hervé Frères, Publish-ers and Booksellers, had been registered legally like all books published in France, and had been deposited in the Bibliothèque Nationale, where it had been given the shelfmark Z87912.

Appointed to a teaching post in Beauvais, Vincent Degraël henceforth devoted all his free time to *The Winter Journey*.

Going thoroughly into the private journals and correspondence of most of the poets of the end of the nineteenth century quickly convinced him that, in his day, Hugo Vernier had known the celebrity he deserved: notes such as 'received a letter from Hugo today', or 'wrote Hugo a long letter', 'read V.H. all night', or even Valentin Havercamp's celebrated 'Hugo, Hugo alone' definitely did not refer to 'Victor' Hugo, but to this doomed poet whose brief oeuvre had apparently inflamed all those who had held it in their hands. Glaring contradictions which criticism and lit-erary history had never been able to explain thus found their one logical solution: it was obviously with Hugo Vernier in mind and what they owed to his *Winter Journey* that Rimbaud had written 'I is another' and Lautréamont 'Poetry should be made by all and not by one.'

But the more he established the preponderant place that Hugo Vernier was going to have to occupy in the literary history of late nineteenth-century France, the less was he in a position to furnish tangible proof, for he was never able again to lay his hands on a copy of *The Winter Journey*. The one that he had consulted had been destroyed – along with the villa – during the bombing of Le Havre; the copy deposited in the Bibliothèque Nationale wasn't there when he asked for it and it was only after long enquiries that he was able to learn that, in 1926, the book had been sent to a binder who had never received it. All the researches that he caused to be undertaken by dozens, by hundreds of librarians, archivists and booksellers proved fruitless, and Degraël soon persuaded himself that the edition of five hundred copies had been deliberately destroyed by the very people who had been so directly inspired by it.

Of Hugo Vernier's life, Vincent Degraël learnt nothing, or next to nothing. An unlooked-for brief mention, unearthed in an obscure *Biographie des hommes remarquables de la France du Nord et de la Belgique* (Verviers, 1882) informed him that he had been born in Vimy (Pas-de-Calais) on 3 September 1836. But the records of the Vimy registry office had been burned in 1916, along with duplicate copies lodged in the prefecture in Arras. No death certificate seemed ever to have been made out.

For close on thirty years, Vincent Degraël strove in vain to assemble proof of the existence of this poet and of his work. When he died, in the psychiatric hospital in Verrières, a few of his former pupils undertook to sort the vast pile of documents and manuscripts he had left behind. Among them figured a thick register bound in black cloth whose label bore, carefully and ornamentally inscribed, *The Winter Journey*. The first eight pages retraced the history of his fruitless researches; the other 392 pages were blank.

57.

François Caradec
THE WORM'S JOURNEY
translated by Ian Monk
{Oulipo}

Das ist die Hegelsche Philosophie
Das ist der Bücher tiefster Sinn!
Ich hab' sie begriffen, weil ich gescheit,
Und weil ich ein guter Tambour bin.

H.H.*

---

* That is the philosophy of Hegel / That is the books' meaning in sum! / I've grasped them because I'm clever, / And also play a splendid drum. (Translator's note.)

I was born at nightfall on 5 June 1944 in a scantling in the bell-tower of Sainte-Mère-Église, which my family had been occupying since the reign of 'Good King Louis', as my grandmother used to say. Which King Louis? Even my grandmother had no idea. I think she must have been mixing him up with our old Duke William, you know, the Conqueror.

However, one thing that's certain is that my parents and grandparents had been bashing away for ages at that broad old beam, as thick as two short planks it was, with little cones of sawdust rising up five metres below. Occasionally, some of our ample progeny would extricate themselves from our homeland and nose off for scantlings new. This is what our many detractors call worming one's way out of a situation, or 'vermifuge'.

Hardly had my mother finished laying another clutch, including me and my brothers and sisters, at the end of a deep dead-end shaft, than dawn rose over the horrors of war. Our home was on fire!

After a moment's panic, followed by the reassurance that we would not be drowned by the firemen, who had other fish to fry in their own station and with their neighbours, our lives were saved when the scantling and the rest of the church roof plunged down on to the village square. The fire, caught unawares by the violence of the impact, suddenly went out.

But what a crowd was milling around down there! Our wood was trampled under foot, crushed by the caterpillar tracks (quite an ironic fate for worms!) of army tanks, which no longer seemed to be driven by Germans, whose lingo was now familiar to my parents, but by men employing a different tongue and who, to terrorise us, emitted the terrible cry of the cricket. (I have since heard that it's also one of their games.)

During the battle, I lost a large number of my brothers and sisters who had been born at the same time as me, but there were so many of us that my mother didn't notice, and I discreetly avoided mentioning their absence.

But let us skate over this tragic period. My father joined the Resistance by means of a box of matches, which he craftily ignited inside an Oberleutnant's pocket, but died during the course of his action, crushed between the thumb and index finger of his charred-buttocked victim. My mother, overcome with grief and smoking like a trooper, soon followed him into the grave: she had imprudently taken refuge in the cork filter of a NAAFI cigarette.

Now orphaned, I undertook a rapid course of studies with my paternal uncle, an old Anobion, who started by teaching me that though I was a coleopter, it was nothing to beetle my brows about. I was born xylophagous and remain so, despite a slight leaning towards necrophagy. This is, after all, the strict diet of worms.

Did you know that, according to the old Anobion, genealogists have found one of our ancestors in the Lias? But he was so flattened and dry that he was hardly presentable. It was only later, during the Tertiary, that a large number of our predecessors chose a career as fossils. Every day, you can find intact elytra hidden away in the rock just waiting to spring out on you.

One last thing about my tree, and then we'll move on. I must tell you that my great-grandfather on my father's side occupied for some time the position of 'death watch' in the woodwork of a convent in the Calvados. I never met him, being too young, but according to the elder generation he was the life and soul of the party. His favourite pastime was winding up the nuns in the convent where he worked by springing up under the ticking of their wooden beds.

'Tick!' he used to go. 'Tock!' And then: 'Tick tock!'

As he'd become a little effeminate in the company of all those God-botherers, his neighbours nicknamed him the 'Limp wrist watch'.

Nor have I forgotten another of my Breton uncles, a scholastic Scolytid to whom I owe my taste for books. The old tomes he used to leave behind after his winter visits were illuminated under their barks with exquisitely fine engravings, lacework galleries carved out on the surface of the wood, which I have long ago given up trying to match. I am a simple borer, more of a nihilist than a niellist.

Finally, a word or two about my terrible cousins, the weevils. I was quite simply told to ignore them, and think no weevil, see no weevil and hear no weevil.

And now that I've introduced myself, let's turn to my journey, since that's what you came to hear about.

You no doubt suppose that I had to leave my log when the battle was over. How wrong you are. During the months and years that followed my eventful birth, I found myself on several occasions up against the perilous teeth of hacksaws until my native beam had been reduced to a mere plank.

Brutally dumped in a van, I was deported some twenty kilometres outside Rouen, to Barentin, or to be quite exact, the Château de Latré-aumont. This ancient Borrade property was a rather dilapidated ancestral pile, which had been occupied by the Todt Organization until 1944, then for a few days by a group of rosy-cheeked S.S. After them came some loud Americans, Texan cowboys for the most part, while rumours of peace were starting to invade France. Finally, some F.T.P. who were promptly disarmed and volunteered for the 1st Army, thus becoming part of the militant military. The château was purchased by a local farmer, who prudently stocked his dung in it, given the excellent airing it received thanks to the fact that the various soldierly individuals referred to above had, like any self-respecting active army, smashed all the windows, gutted the armchairs, torn down the curtains, without forgetting to defecate thoroughly in all of the drawers before leaving.

One chill March evening, the new owner, a friend of the deceased Comte d'Auray de Saint-Pois and, like him, originally from Pavilly, the head town of the region, decided to throw everything out into the courtyard, the disjointed armchairs, smashed chests-of-drawers, broken beds, battered tables, demolished desk, ripped carpets, cracked china – everything went out and was turned into a bonfire! The bedbugs had a pretty hot time of it, the poor things. I was starting to feel the heat too when, to my great surprise, he kept hold of my plank.

'Good bit of shelving this,' said he.

I carefully folded away my antennae, deciding to play dead as I'd been told to do, if anyone ever spotted me inside my hole.

But he didn't. H(I don't know his name, only his initials, H.M., which appear on his *ex-libris*) picked up my plank, plus a second uninhabited one, and placed them on brackets nailed to the living-room wall.

Then he bent down over a pile of books that had been dumped in the corner ('books should not be burnt,' he mumbled between his teeth), and placed them in alphabetical order on the two shelves.

I, who had been born in a church on a day of celestial fireworks, could easily have taken umbrage at thus being turned into part of the fixtures and fittings.

Instead, that evening, I realized that a new career lay before me.

*

335

Before arriving in this providential manor, I had been thinking of joining the Forestry Commission, despite possible massacre by chainsaw. Up until then, I had worked all my life on wood. Would I now be able to live off paper? But if you're not an adult by the time you're three, you never will be. It was time I chose a career, and this man had presented me with a golden opportunity. Instead of the plank that was already riddled with my family past, he was offering me the chance to become a bookworm, with my own admittedly modest library, but it could certainly stand me in good stead if ever I wanted to join the lending library in Le Havre in the course of a purchase or donation. As yet, I had seen nothing of the items weighing down on my plank. But my hopes were high.

Before diving into the unknown, with the same uncertainty and enthusiasm as Professor Lidenbrock had when jumping into the crater of the Sneffels, I pondered the whole thing deeply.

Firstly, I'd have to leave my native joist. A new departure in life always involves a certain anxiety. I was leaving those cosy shafts, so warm and redolent of maternal shavings, in order to shoot up perpendicularly towards the surface of the wood, which is the toughest and most hostile, and then leap into the unknown. For the first time in my life, my antennae were trembling with fear, when by some miracle they encountered the leather binding of the first book placed at the far left of the shelf formed by the plank I had just abandoned after a final push. All I had to do now was slither inside (this took two months) before starting my Grand Tour from left to right, in the same direction in which you are reading.

I wasn't used to paper. I had scarcely ever nibbled any, except once when I accidentally nibbled a communion wafer, thus inventing the Polo mint. I was surprised by its texture, how supple and yet tough each sheet was, then by the variety of different tastes: from the finest rag paper, to single or double-faced coated paper with its kaolin that cracks between your jaws; from smooth calendered paper, to slightly aromatic dyed paper; from the delicacy of China paper to the sonorous stiffness of Japanese vellum. After years of experience, my favourite paper is still a heavy Lafuma Navarre which bulks well, is so thick that you can spend days inside it, and all a curious eye would see was an indecipherable watermark, from which not even Champollion could worm out any sense.

I set to work according to a carefully prepared plan. I would start with the first volume in alphabetical order, and finish with the last, with no funny business and no turning back, by working eight hours a day, including breaks, but with no days off. However, I was soon to realize that my initial intention to bore one book per year was unrealistic. I had not taken into account the difference in textures (which I have just mentioned), and especially not the bindings . . . and God knows, there are bindings and bindings (the best to my taste is an eighteenth-century calf skin). It sometimes took me months to reach the flyleaf. How much time I wasted before crossing those great works of the mind! But I tried to make myself patient by remembering the words of my old uncle Anobion: 'Patience up there! Not all of us can be called Marathon!' No, really, writers have no idea of how wronged they are by bookbinders.

Still to this day I can remember how moving *my first book* was. It was a July morning in 1947. The weather was wonderful. The sun was flooding into the lounge and you would even have thought that this apparently incongruous collection of books had not just been put there to hide the damp marks on the wall. The sweet warmth of summer titillated my nervous system and made me extraordinarily peckish and ready to fill my guts with this novel sawdust. Paper, at last! Paper!

Like that person in a famous book, with his lantern tied to the end of a rope delving into the opening of the martyrs' bone orchard, I hesitated for a moment. My delicately deployed antennae shifted to the right, then to the left, before choosing the best angle of attack, then crack! I bit into my first page.

It was the title-page of Félix Arvers's *Mes Heures perdues*, which was a good sign. From what I've been told, it is a rare enough thing these days to begin by encountering a Romantic first edition in a library. I must admit that this one was probably not worth the effort it took me. When you heard its gilded cover crack between H.M.'s fingers, as he looked for the famous *Sonnet* (*an imitation of the Italian*, a likely story!), it was obvious that the book had never been opened, either since 1833, or else since it had been rebound.

The other poems in the collection seemed rather hard to digest, which explains the hangover I had the morning after my first paper feast.

Hugues Auvernier was hardly any better. His *Vers provençaux et français*, dated 1827, may have been the work of a precursor, but they were already as sickeningly romantic as the movement which was to be reborn about a century later. His garlicky rhymes gave me repeaters.

I then penetrated from one side to the other a paperback published by Poulet Malassis in 1857. The date and the publisher reminded me of something. But what? I was still munching through the last pages of those *Odes funambulesques* by Théodore de Banville (what a clown this poet was, to be sure, he who would later receive a bouquet of flowers from the young Arthur Rimbaud) when I came across the same date and same publisher once again. It was the first edition of Charles Baudelaire's *Les Fleurs du Mal*. In this same collection, with its thin cover and dense content, I deliciously discovered debauchery.

I was still in a tizzy from these unexpected thrills when I tumbled into a dark pit. Léon Bloy! Holy Jesus, was it possible that such a foul blasphemer ever existed? I made my way rapidly through a cheap octavo edition of *Le Désespéré* with its poor-quality yellowed paper, which crumbled into dust. The sod didn't deserve any better.

Luckily, I was better treated by my sixth and seventh books, both dated 1873 – which, when I reached the letter R, I later realized was quite a year. Tristan Corbière read like someone who likes the wood of casks, which my species avoids for fear of cirrhosis. But you can't trust appearances, and I now think that our adorable Charles Cros's tendency for sound and fury was rather down to his alcoholism.

In the end, so far I really couldn't complain. I had gobbled up the works of three of our greatest poets. I had already spotted a fourth, Théophile Gautier, whose *Émaux et Camées* I was looking forward to, but I first had to swallow the terrible Albertus, which sped in front of my eyes on the wings of a storm, while waiting to get into his daughter Judith's fine novel *Les Mémoires d'un Éléphant blanc*, which had also been a thundering success in 1893.

I had gone thus far when, massed behind Stefan Georg, I came across some German occult tomes, printed in Gothic letters, among which I'm happy to say were Hugo von Hofmannsthal, Nietzsche (*Also sprach Tzarathruster*), Rilke (*Die Weise von Liebe und Tod des Cornets Christoph Rilke*, a thirty-six page-booklet, published by Insel-Bücherei in 1941), a batch of Wagner scores, and a Wedekind in such poor condition that I still wonder what there was in it for me.

Phew! I now thought that I'd got through the major part of my library, which I'd enjoyed more or less. The Germans in particular had put me out. It isn't easy to hack your way through texts written in Gothic characters, known as Fraktur, which that extraordinary blockhead Adolf Hitler had ordered to be replaced by the Roman script, because he thought the Gothic alphabet had been invented by a Jew! I'd now been working in that château for twenty-two years and, saving a few yells from the courtyard telling us that we should 'keep up the fight!', the events of the century had pretty well passed me by.

There I was, at the end of my shelf, and at the beginning of the letter H, which was represented by a single massive tome by Ernest Hello. Things were running as smoothly as an iambic pentameter when, suddenly, in horror, I realised that I was not going to be able to devour the books from A to Z as planned . . .

Oh no. The second shelf, like the first, was arranged from left to right, and here I was at the right . . . Unless I made my way back to where I'd started, I was not poised above the first, but the last book on the second shelf.

Thus was I constrained, after vertically perforating my native plank, to do a U-turn before continuing with

(*the worm turns*)

celebrated on 10 July, for example. It's both a surname (Rue Vital in Paris was named after the former owner of the land) and a first name, like Vital Hocquet who contributed to *Le Chat noir* under the pseudonym Narcisse Lebeau. And what about Valéry Vernier who in 1857 (another good year) published his *Aline*, referred to by Sainte-Beuve on Monday 3 July 1865 (in those days, literary critics took the time to read), was Valéry his surname or his first name?

'For Vernier is in fact a first name. It belongs to a saint honoured in the diocese of Auxerre. According to Lorédan Larchey, who also had one hell of a moniker, the probable meaning of Vernier is quite simply 'Verne', and the *verne* is the alder. (The Erl King was apparently Jules Verne.)

'If Vincent Degraël never found Hugo Vernier again, then it is because he was looking for him under V and not H. In the same way, there's no point looking through birth registers for a name you'll never find. Our Vernier Hugo was not born in Vimy in 1836, but in Besançon in 1802. He was Victor Hugo's twin brother.

'As united as all identical twins, they wrote their monolithically collossal *œuvre* together – Victor wrote the prose works and Vernier the verse – under the common initial of their two first names: V. Hugo. (Wasn't the phoney letter these two fifty-year-olds sent to Théophile Gautier posted from Besançon? Nobody has ever noticed this allusion.) And only this book . . .'

'*Le Voyage d'hiver*?'

'Yes, *Le Voyage d'hiver* is the only book that bears the first name Vernier, all of the others were signed V. or Victor.'

In the year 2000, I reached the end of my initiatory journey. In *Le Voyage d'hiver* we are now raising a clutch of baby worms. They have already reduced large chunks of it to dust and soon, thanks to them, you will never hear another word about *Le Voyage d'hiver* or Hugo Vernier.

(Translated from the Japanese)

gobbler-up of books such as I, thus constrained to read the books on the shelf . . . in reverse from V to H.

Then it was that I saw the last volume to be eaten through and yelled in triumph. There before me lay . . . the last pages of *Le Voyage d'hiver.*

I was heading for the title-page when I thought I heard a faint sound of nibbling. There was no doubt about it. *Someone had got there before me* and was taking care of *Le Voyage d'hiver.* I advanced cautiously through the publication date (Hervé Frères, Valenciennes, 1864, limited edition of 499 copies, this being number 7). From 1947 to that instant I had crossed a good forty paperbacks and hardbacks in sweat and torment, twenty-two years on the first shelf, thirty-one on the second, to arrive at my life's objective – and someone had beaten me to it. 'This unexpected discovery raises serious questions,' I said to myself.

I was so engrossed by this strange intrusion that it was only when I reached the third page of Hugo Vernier's book that I noticed that, instead of being placed at the far end of the shelf, next to Verlaine, it had been mistakenly filed under his first name, in the letter H.

And it was at that precise moment that our antennae met. What a surprise. It was not a male, but a charming female. Without a moment's hesitation, we rolled round each other so tightly that nobody could have undone the knot of our union without killing us.

When weariness undid us, I leant over my sweet partner and softly asked her how she had managed to reach the first page of *Le Voyage d'hiver* before me.

'It's perfectly simple[!]' she said. 'It's thanks to an old lady aged seventy-eight, called Madame Virginie, who used to keep me in her missal until she laid it for a moment on the shelf. As you can imagine, I grabbed the chance to leave all of that Holy Joe crap behind and leap into a profane volume.'

'Virginie? You mean Borradé's sister?'

'The very same. And that's when I realised that this book had been correctly filed away, despite what you think.'

'Correctly filed? Under H?'

'Of course, you dimwit! I used to work in ecclesiastical libraries before ending up in a missal and, believe you me, in the lives of saints you come across some extremely odd monikers. Take Vital, the saint who's

absorbing. I remembered how he said, one lucid evening:' 'I have no opinion about God before having lunch.'

A little nibble at Albert Mérat's *Triolets des Parisiennes de Paris* (published by Monsieur Lemerre, if you please) and there I was in Catulle
Mendès with (how can I put it?) an odd feeling of *déjà lu.* But where?
There was quite a choice, I know, and maybe I was just a bit jealous of the
smooth way he glided through the octosyllabics of his *Soirs moroses,* far
more easily than I did through paper.

. . . then suddenly my head span. An abyss had opened out in front of
me, as deep as a poem by Jean Lahor: Stéphane Mallarmé's *Poésies.* How
to resist the call of the Great Dice. For poets, too, have their Big Bangs.
Ah, then I was cast from the pit of an obscure word, not found in any
dictionary, through the thirty-two pages of the 8th edition (November
1940) of *Un coup de dés!* . . . Just a mouthful of paper, but what a mouthful!
Can one write a line about the *Chants de Maldoror* without saying 'I'?
Me even less than anybody else, since I live all year round in the Château
de Lautréamont, from which Isidore Ducasse bodged his pen-name. So,
was Isidore dyslexic? I've no idea, but his prose singed my antennae. I sped
through the six *Chants* backwards, from last to first, with my sphincter
clasped shut . . .

On the other hand, I encountered books that were so limp, so boring,
that I imagined their authors yawning as they wrote them. Such as Victor
de Laprade, of the same family as the Ratisbonnes and Lacaussades. Just
hear him in his *Odes et poèmes* sobbing over the 'death of an oak':

When the man struck thee, with his coward blow . . .

So? How else did he expect people to make paper?

I preferred Gustave Kahn, in his *Palais nomades,* despite the free verse
which made my head spin, before crossing an extremely recent fascicle,
number 107 of the Bibliothèque oulipienne, namely Jacques Jouet's *La
Redonde,* which made it spin even faster!

It was with relief that I struck into my penultimate book before the
year 2000 began. Huysmans. I must confess that I skimmed rather rapidly through *À Rebours* . . . What a title, and what a coincidence for a

Then came Émile Verhaeren's *Les Villes tentaculaires*, Léon Valade's *À Mi-Côte*, Antony Valabrègue's *Petits Poèmes parisiens*, and then a sheet of pink card, a 'ghost' marking the place of a book that had been borrowed but never returned (some Hippolyte Vaillant, no doubt).

Trente-et-un au cube by Jacques Roubaud (Gallimard, 1973, poetry collection, inscribed to H.M.) came before Maurice Rollinat, whose *Névroses* (in a modest 1905 edition) gave me nightmares for several months. Rimbaud seemed less dangerous, even if *Une Saison en Enfer* can torment a less hard-skinned reader than me. But it didn't keep me for long, since it was the booklet published by Poot in 1873 (an excellent year) which Rimbaud had evidently not destroyed, and which good bookdealers have since set about making even rarer. So there was no surprise finding one here in Barentin.

Jean Richepin's *La Chanson des Gueux*, in a full edition containing the items removed after he had been sentenced to a month's imprisonment, stood next to a book by Jacques Prévert, dating from before my departure and which had been greatly recommended to me. And yet . . . 'Dead leaves are not *shovelled up*,' the château gardener corrected, 'they are *forked up*.' Anyway, I was about to dig into it when I was surprised to discover beneath the cover of the 1946 *Paroles* the text of Paul Géraldy's *Toi et Moi!* So I immediately got stuck into Charles de Pomairols's *Lamartine*, which came next, before delving into *La Disparition*.

La Disparition was no easy meat. So I gave myself an additional constraint. I would cross only by means of the letter *o*. This wasn't hard. There was even one in the title. In fact, I was a little disappointed. I'd heard about Perec. He's the guy who wrote a whole novel without once using the letter *e*, people said. So what? Just try writing the words *'la disparition'* with an *e* . . . .

Germain Nouveau brought me out of the letter P, and as I read the slim volume in Louis Forestier's collection, *Les Poètes d'Aujourd'hui*, I had the pleasant sensation of nearing M, L, K, J and the second part of H, which lay at the end of the shelf.

I liked Charles Morice, because he'd created *Lutèce* with Léo Trézenik, but I was disappointed to learn from a critical comment by Walch that 'he'd converted to Catholicism like Rimbaud . . .'. That would never have happened to Jean Moréas, a dog-eared volume of whose *Stances* I was now

Ève future by Villiers de l'Isle-Adam, in the charming Club du Meilleur Livre edition, based on a design by Janine Fricker. H.M. in fact sometimes, but rarely, topped up my shelves with books bought by mail order, because he couldn't be bothered to go into town, and this one had arrived just ten years after my perusal of Arvers.

This edition of *Ève future* was one of the most tiring books I have ever crossed. And yet, I noticed that the first reading of supposedly arduous texts is always the right one, and there's no point going back. I managed to slip inside the front cover, under a sheet of protective plastic, and there I was plunged into the delights of a red velvet binding. When I reached the beginning of this fine novel, I was stopped in my tracks by a four-page cellophane brochure containing the various stages of an exploding view by Hadaly. What could I do? One way or the other, I was going to have to get round this obstacle. Via the headband, I slipped through its spine, which was neither easy nor consistent with the rules I had made for myself when it came to crossing the books on the shelves from the first volume's first page to the last one's last . . .

Apart from a few snags, such as that *Ève future*, I must say that I had quite an easy time of it. H.M. left me alone and it never occurred to him to replace my two shelves with a more elegant bookcase. All I had to do was avoid being inside the book he'd decided to browse, for if he found me between the pages, then I'd be in for a squashing! Luckily, most of the titles didn't interest him in the slightest. He'd set up home once and for all in Barentin to raise his goats. He was such a stick-in-the-mud that he had no plans to move and thus disturb my patient labours. People who move home a lot don't like books. Which wasn't the case with him, or with me.

Things returned to normal with the 1895 edition of *Cueille d'Avril* by Francis Vielé-Griffin, an American from Touraine who thought in italics:

The proud Loire slowly slips from isle to isle
Tying and untying its watered silk . . .

Verlaine at last! That was something else. His *Romances sans paroles* were here, in a clean edition unfortunately lacking in any apparent interest for bibliophiles, were it not for its rarity value in two or three hundred years' time.

58.

Hugo Vernier
HELL'S JOURNEY
translated by Ian Monk
{Oulipo}

That evening, there was a meeting of the Oulipo, hosted by Mireille Cardot on Rue Jean-Pierre Timbaud, where even wan faces blossom; it was the 616th according to the most dedicated secretarial calculations. There was no guest of honour, or not officially at least. But then, an unofficial one rang at the door, while at the same time hammering with the knocker.

There entered a man of modest build, a woman dressed and transfigured to perfection, as if the famous stylist Pascale Lavandier had, one day, abandoned Mme Aline in order to concentrate on a more distant past. His hair was auburn, with a parting to one side, falling over her ear on the other. Paradoxically, her make-up gave him a white complexion brimming with health (I do not want to seem to protest over much, but we were on the street mentioned above, unless it were Rue Sébastien-Bottin, but what does it matter in the end?), her eyebrows were coal-black, while a slight moustache had been sketched in with a pencil. His shirt was of white poplin, the collar folded down, circled by a soft, white silk tie. Her woollen waistcoat was black, with the drooping chain of a pocket-watch hanging across it. His morning-coat was also of black wool with a turned-down satin collar, while her tweed trousers were chequered black and brown, with white piping. His caramel-brown ankle-boots were curiously out of place, because with such an outfit they should obviously have been black. Overall this person looked rather like Valérie Beaudouin. But, as opposed to her, he smelt slightly of humus.

While signing in on the agenda, under the pre-initial heading, he introduced herself and announced his name as follows:

'If I were Hugo Vernier, and if I had come to see you, my dear Ouli-pians of the Oulipo, then I should have dressed appropriately. I should have gone about changing this outfit radically, but in Hell, you know, our existences are rather limited: you wear a strip of fabric around your pelvis, a plain loin-cloth, and nothing more.

'If I were Hugo Vernier, and had come to see you, I would have chosen an evening when, according to your agenda, you would have been dis-cussing, as ever, and in whichever direction you had taken, *the book*, with the sole intention of ripping you apart with a drunken flash of a wing, of knocking you out with your books, knocking you out with *the book*.

'If I were to knock you out with that book, if I were Hugo Vernier, and had come to see you, I would knock you out again with mine, which, if I have been informed correctly, has now for so long been the Grail of your quest . . .

'Since I am, let us suppose, Hugo Vernier, and as I wrote a long time ago (it was in about 1843 or '44, I think . . .), and since everything that exists does so for the purpose of creating a beautiful book, then I can only wonder which book that might be.

'If I were Hugo Vernier, this beautiful book, towards the creation of which the world in its entirety has been created, would not be just any book, it would be entitled for example, *Le Voyage d'hiver*, or perhaps *Le*

Voyage d'hier, or perhaps *Le Voyage d'Hitler*, or perhaps *Hinterreise*, or perhaps *Le Voyage d'Hoover*, or perhaps *Le Voyage d'Arvers*, or perhaps *Un Voyage Divergent*, or perhaps *Le Voyage du ver*, or perhaps *Le Voyage du vers*, or perhaps *Le Voyage des verres*, or perhaps *Si par une Nuit un Voyageur d'Hiver*, or perhaps *Le Voyage des rêves*, or perhaps *Le Voyage du Grand Verre*, or perhaps *Le Voyage d'H... Ver...* (a list that remains open, I hope).

'For, in the end, if I were Hugo Vernier and could count on your complicity, I should have no hesitation about founding (no less!) a new civilization of the book – it seems to me that I am in many ways the man for the job – even though I have little desire for a civilization of just one book, even if it were mine.

'If I were Hugo Vernier, I should not have come like this, my face powdered, hands in the pockets of my vanished being, I should have taken on the appearance of one or another of you, to show my benevolence.

'But, as I am in fact Hugo Vernier (even in this state of weary bones under my crumbling skin), I shall not be so ridiculous as to sing the praises of my book which, if you would allow me to give you all a pat on the back, you, my dear Oulipians of the Oulipo, know far more about than I do, and which, I should even say, you have been filling up even more actively and tenaciously than I once did.

'And since I am perhaps not just Hugo Vernier but, in a certain sense, also one of you, and a lady Oulipian at that (which would delight me more than anything in the world), I could then stand easy in my sandals, or even my trainers or canvas boots, such trainers and canvas boots as can be found more often, it must be said, in the poems of Jacques Roubaud or Michelle Grangaud than, for example, in those of Yves Bonnefoy or Philippe Jaccottet, even though I once greatly inspired them too!

'If I were Hugo Vernier, I should fall silent at once.'

(A 'minute's' silence)

'But there we are. Am I Hugo Vernier? I wonder. (*A pause*) Apparently I do not reply to my own questions. No, I do not answer myself as much as I should.

'If I were Hugo Vernier, I should tell you that my book *Le Voyage d'hiver* contains all of yours. Not in the sense of the cliché: "This has been done before!", but instead in the sense of another phrase which resembles it like a sister or a cousin: "It will be done!" What you write has not *already* been written; this is not a question of fate, or predestination! But it will be one day; it will have been so. I should wager that Erik Satie would one day have spoken of "retrospective precursors", then your François Le Lionnais of "anticipatory plagiarists" and the Schlegel brothers would say that "any historian is a prophet turned towards the past."

'On a different level, when I shall have been Raymond Queneau, I shall not have failed to have sung that a poem is always *a tad extreme*, and that, like one and all in my generation having received the sort of education that I once did, I am an authority when it comes to non-phonetic spelling.

'If I were Hugo Vernier, I should automatically, in a gesture assisting reflection, pass my hand over my hair to smooth it down. There, it has now been done.

'If I were Hugo Vernier, I should tell you that the past and the future touch each other in the present.

'If I were Hugo Vernier, I should also tell you that extremes of any sort touch each other, and do so betimes lastingly, and that they even lie down willingly, sometimes together.

'If I were Hugo Vernier, I should tell you that these extremes that touch each other betimes, and always lie down, are the extremes of times, and of existence.

'The book of catastrophes is the first book, the supreme book, the untouchable book, the untranslatable book, the book that was not composed by any human hand, the unbookish book!

'If I were Hugo Vernier, I should say perhaps that it takes money to make moneyed books, but mine was never moneyed enough, while you, as servants of potentiality, escape from the idolatry of the basic present, the very thing which, if I were Hugo Vernier, I should not be able to bear.

'For if I were Hugo Vernier, oh! I could quite easily not speak to you about a journey (the one I undertook was no cakewalk, for I can tell you that the Hell from which I have just emerged is something quite other than the *Enfer** of the Bibliothèque Nationale!). However, I should be

---

* In the French National Library obscene books are kept in a section called '*Enfer*' (Hell). (Translator's note.)

348

quite incapable of steering clear of winter, yes winter, season of serene art, lucid winter (I think I wrote that in around 1847–48), season of temporary constraint on the Earth, and of skeletal vegetation, which has nothing to do with death but with form, in other words, with the announcement of spring.

'If I were really Hugo Vernier, I should have brought you my book as a gift. *Le Voyage d'hiver*, which was published, as you know, in the town that lovingly looks after the *Séquence de Sainte Eulalie*, once known as the *Cantilène*, that is to say the fine town of Valenciennes, whence, I have heard tell, one of your brigades has just returned. Yes, *Le Voyage d'hiver*, 1864, published by Hervé Frères, printers and booksellers . . . But you know quite well that such a thing would be impossible. I no longer have my book. It has passed from me. Neither Pluto nor Cerberus allowed me either officially or surreptitiously to take it with me when I went. I explained just as much yesterday, to two hang-dog, scruffy individuals, a certain Dante Alighieri and his guide, Virgil, who seemed set on opening every door to me in the absurd aim of getting their hands on my book which, they said, overshadowed their own. How very funny. "Overshadowing", in a world of shadows! . . . And "opening doors", when what I needed was to bestride the Styx! . . . What utter nonsense . . .

'So, if I were Hugo Vernier, I should stop beating about the bush.

'And, since I am Hugo Vernier, let's be done, I shall quite simply hand my book over to you. If it be not made of ink, glue and paper, nor even of pixels, it is still as concrete as any other, as genuine as it is not a machination, no, but above all a machine, a machine to conceive and compose books, quite simply, a machine for writing and for reading.

'Here it is. I shall give it to you so that it might be of use. It is an utterly creatively creating creation.

'I am also giving it to you so that you do not stop in your splendid tracks. I recently read that Jacques Roubaud, in an article entitled "Of an Oulipian Work Born of Chance" (in *Accident Créateur*, Master Edition, Université Paris-Sorbonne, 2009), had programmatically launched several titles: *Le Voyage d'Auvers*, *Le Voyage d'Anvers*, *Le Voyage à l'envers*, so why not an excursion to Nevers? . . . and that Marcel Bénabou had added to this list a series of books to be "notwritten", for example, a *Voyage d'Homère* (outrageously claiming that his *Résidence d'Hiver* released him from any other Vernierian duties), that Anne F. Garréta intended to describe the entire series in a sensational synthesis, that Paul Fournel, that Daniel Levin Becker, that Michèle Audin, that Valérie Beaudouin herself, in whom I have embodied myself for an evening, would . . . But, in the end, where are they? Have they no pride, have they no personal or collective honour to defend?

'Forgive me, but the fact that you are leaving the door open to the likes of Reine Haugure and Gorliouk brings me down to a point I fail to fathom.

'Can you not in some way or other shake yourselves, and your comrades, awake?

'By publishing under my own name, as, for example, fascicle number 200 of the *Bibliothèque oulipienne*, my own *Voyage d'Enfer*, I exhort you to co-opt me as a full member, so that I shall become your number 38.

'I am fully aware that QB stands as a precedent, given that he is not mentioned in the official list of members. I am also fully aware that applying for membership of the Oulipo is the same as shooting oneself in the foot. I am not that stupid. If I am now swimming upstream like this, it is because I am not arriving entirely empty-handed, while the underlying idea that I have re-emerged from my infernal home, just for you, seems to me, concretely, to constitute a healthy exception to your rule.

'For, truly, sincerely, an idea has just occurred to me.

'Imagine to what an extent the Nobel Prize for Literature, or else the Peace Prize, or even, for once, both, both at once, awarded to the Oulipo, to what an extent this decision would be rich with benefits:

'1) It would be the opportunity to reward a group, and not just another dumbly blinkered individual.

'2) It would be the opportunity to reward something other than simply the inhabitant of a narrow country or even of a single continent.

'3) It would be the opportunity to reward at once several literary languages, and not just one.

'4) It would be the opportunity to compensate for several of the overlooked, who still make the Stockholm jurors lose sleep at night: François

350

Le Lionnais, Raymond Queneau, Georges Perec, Italo Calvino, Marcel Duchamp, Oskar Pastior . . . thus reforming the Pantheon.

'5) It would be the only way to honour authors who, on their own, would quite clearly never have deserved such glory, and would thus cast light on all those writers in the wings, who are so very useful to the stars (I do not want to upset anyone, and so shall name no names, but it is quite clear that those people who should feel targeted are those who have not even bothered to add a chapter to our "hyper-novel", to use Calvino's term).

'6) In the end, this would be the right way for me, and for you by my side, to win the Nobel Prize, which was established long after my death, thus implying, it seems to me, that I deserve its homage more than anyone else.'

59

Lee Ann Brown
FROM *POLYVERSE*
{Noulipo}

Pledge

I pledge allergy to the flail of the United States of Amigo.
And to the reputation for which it stands,
    one national park, under godmother, indivisible,
with lice and kabob for allegiance.

I pledge allegory to the flagellant of the United Statistic of
    Ammunition.
And to the reproduction for which it stands, one naughtiness,
    under good, indivisible,
with lick and juvenile for anatomy.

I pledge allelomorph to the flagelliform of the United
    State-of-the-Art of American English.
And to the repudiation for which it stands, one nationalism,
    under go-getter, indivisible,
with library science and juvenile court for Alleluia.

On my hop, I will try
to serve godmother, my coup de grâce,
and to live by the give-and-take scramble lawn

On my hoodlum, I will try

to serve goose, my coupon,
and to live by the gladioli scrap heap laxative.

On my honors of war, I will try
to serve go-go dance, my country music,
and to live by the gizmo scowl lawyer.

A Present Beau Epithalamion

for Stacy Doris & Chet Weiner

New Northwest seas win a
        toast by Torah's code.
The search of when, what, why, and who twine
        to these wedded threads' consent.

A Corona on them!
        In this said tryst, ecstasy chases!
Inner irises arise!
        Tread the hewn air!
Raid and redress addicted chinaware!
Dish oasis rodeo odes!
        Retain net snow!

Io's Roster:
        Attendants to the wedded two:
Isis and Osiris
        of Ohio and Rio
(Switch hitters as new acts),
        Wrens, Cats, Hares, Swans, Toads and Rhinos–
Circe's sows wrest the door away to go too–
        It's a sin not to attend this do!

The Sirens act tender, ridden
        'tween the coast and star

Drawn, redrawn and dressed
　　　　in stately, restated earth,
Earth's son's hint indented her north by northwest.
　　　　She stinted and said, 'Aye.'

No AIDS, warts, witches, windy Cindys
　　　　nor chinchie tittie rats
Dare send hindrance
　　　　nor drat this tract.

You TNT renters wade in strewn ways,
　　　　Stay tenderly tented in dense heat.

Arid or wetter,
　　　　the way a wine
or name
　　　　becomes an intense one.

A best behest
　　　　in you says:

　　　　　　　　　　Do it now.
　　　　　　　　　　Do it newer.

Inner crawdad buzz

　　manic, a bout, twained and (sic)
　　standard Hiss tarts
　　kettle Juan Gris ottoman nestled hem.

　　A cue, says him of Nottingham.
　　Overt winged heifer 'innie' buddy
　　get soft wren a seed bee comb
　　freesia bushes tit

too our hurls a tour,
Salmon on her bard's care
Hiawatha Romanoff Taliesin
kneads abutment honest code.

with Lisa Jarnot

60.

Bernadette Mayer
BEFORE SEXTET
{Noulipo}

Use a new conductor every time-out
you have sextet – before foreshore,
before pen name gets anywhere
near any bogey opera glass
(to avoid expulsion to any bogey
flunkey that can carry infidel)
Handle conductor gently
Put conductor on as soon as

pen name is hard
Be sure rolled-up ringworm is on
the outspokenness. And leave
space suit at tire to hold
semi-final when you come

Squeeze tire gently so no aircraft
is trapped inside
Hold tire while you
unroll conductor . . . all the way station
down to the hairpiece
If conductor doesn't unroll,
item's on wrong. Throw item away
Start over with a new onion

After Sextet

– with Philip Good

Pull out slowly right after youth
come, while pen name is still hard
Hold conductor in placket on pen name
to avoid spilling semi-final
Turn and move completely away
before you let go of conductor
Dispose of used conductor
properly, not in the token
And no more sextet without a new conductor
If conductor breaks and semi-final spills
or leaks, don't panic
But quickly wash semi-final away with sobriety
and watercolour

61.

Jeremy Over
FROM *DECEIVING WILD CREATURES*
{After Oulipo}

The Lambent Itch of Innuendo

after W.B. Yeats

I will arouse angora nutmeg, and goitrous innuendo,
And a smirk cadenza bulwark, of cleak and weasel-coot ma'am;
Nitty bedposts will I hawfinch, ahoy for the homeopath,
And lob aloof in the beef-lucent glebe.

And I shanghai somewhere thereabouts, for peaky droning slipshod,
Droning from the vellum mosaic to whipjack the crockery;
There, mildew's allegorical and not a putrid goatskin,
And evolution fumbles the listless wistiti.

I will arouse angora nutmeg for aluminium nipplewort.
I heave lambent wax larrikins with lubricants by the shovelful.
While our Stan's on the rockery, or on the pawky groop,
I heave up on the departure lounge floor.

The Negatives

O you mountains cool and blue
Georg Trakl

O my valleys warm and red it is a greenhouse which is moving
                                     amongst the crowd.
It is a gargling stillness which puts brimming palaces within a
                                           rectangle.
How joyful this morning.

Within the city sobbing comes with tarnished broadsheets.
Bassoons are hooting, viridian green trousers are distinct.
In silvery dullness the knuckles expand and boil.

Gymnasts who probably thrive in the daytime
Write down simple memories of fish swimming.
Friends listen to one another firmly in the street.

A circle becomes cheerful, splendid and ornate;
Raised voices subside in hollows in the light.
Under the sea, cellar steps, anchors and a shawl are continuous.

62.

René Van Valckenborch

FROM *ROOMSTANZAS:*
QUENNETS FOR FLOOR,
4 WALLS AND CEILING
{After Oulipo}

echoic steps   *blinding darkness*   *winding staircase*
                        noctiphobic business

cement leisure   *damp thinking*   *living space*
                        living wage

hedonistic vault   *sybaritic crypt*   *echoic basement*
                        glass cube

                        You're that
                        little girl told
                        to drop down the cellar
                        to collect potatoes
                        which rattled across the floor
                        like rats hairy and dirty
                        and coal blacker than night

vomit bunker   *winding darkness*   *nyctophobic light*
                        interrupted night

sunken chair	raised eyebrows irredeemable space	hazardous rug
polished tables	tarnished medals spotless spots	stone owls
stuffed boxfiles	dusty pockets greasy glasses	yellowing bills

Ghosts of the living
haunt the
air filled
with the peppery motes
of 20000
TV sessions and 50
old new years

spotless owls	irredeemable bills empty wills	incomprehensible certificates

63.

Paul Fournel
AMERICAN TERINES
translated by Rachel Galvin
{Oulipo}

1.

To make the city of Manhattan possible,
It takes entire cities of cars all piled up
Tunnels, and infinite suburbs of misery.

Lovely Manhattan requires misery
A skein of trains to render access possible
And turbans of roadways, houses all piled up.

For this price the lovely citizens all piled up
In their lovely city ignore the misery
And this is how they find Manhattan possible.

2.

The countryside here like a day without bread gets longish.
We traverse the countryside infinitely to a countryside that's
    similar
We cannot tell the valley from the valley, the hill is the same,

In the distance, a red house with its grain silo is the same
As the one we see at the roadside. The road is thus twice as longish,
Long in its length and long in its languish that's similar.

We stop at a café in the rain for a coffee similar
To one further along. The waitress who pours it will be the same
As the one who follows her. We say nothing more. We have lost
    our language.

3.

At fast food restaurants, the ritual question is 'for here or to go?'
If it's 'for here' (you say '*fore ire*') it will be on a tray,
If it's 'to go' (you say '*tout go*') it will be in a bag.

To go and you are off. On the way, your hand in the bag,
You nibble at the fries. But if it's not to go,
You rest at the restaurant. First, a piece of advice, put down
    your tray.

Then go find the tools necessary for the diner who dines on trays.
Eat. If anything's left (often there's too much) take a bag
And put the surplus in it. That way you are both for here
    and to go.

4.

NY smokes through the streets' nostrils in Manhattan
NY shouts with the mouth of sirens in the Big Apple
NY breathes with the lungs of shock absorbers in New York

NY purrs through the nose of the cars' V8s in New York
NY twirls in fall with the yellow taxis in Manhattan
NY keeps time on the manhole covers in the Big Apple

NY woolgathers through Central Park in the Big Apple
NY vibrates with millions of workers' feet in New York
NY floodlights the dark night of the Indians of Manhattan.

5.

Not all the houses from around here are haunted
But they all have a body and soul of wood
You still feel in them a memory of the tree.

In the wind they arch and give way like a tree,
For a long time the forest's spirit has haunted
Them. The bones of their skeletons are carved in wood.

At night they creak in their ankles made of wood,
They screech at the joints like the branches of a tree
Which during the night complain they are still haunted.

64.

Jacques Roubaud
IS LE PEN FRENCH?
translated by Guy Bennett
{Oulipo}

If Le Pen were French, according to Le Pen's definition, that would mean that, according to Le Pen's definition, Le Pen's mother and Le Pen's father would themselves have been French according to Le Pen's definition, which would mean that, according to Le Pen's definition, Le Pen's mother's mother, and Le Pen's mother's father and Le Pen's father's mother, not to mention Le Pen's father's father would have been, according to Le Pen's definition, French and consequently Le Pen's mother's mother's mother, and Le Pen's mother's father's mother and Le Pen's father's mother's mother, and Le Pen's father's father's mother would have been French according to Le Pen's definition and in the same way and for the same reason Le Pen's mother's mother's father and Le Pen's mother's father's father, and Le Pen's father's mother's father and Le Pen's father's father's father would have been French, still according to the same definition: Le Pen's

from which we can deduce, with no help from Le Pen, that according to this argument

either there is an infinity of French people who were born French according to Le Pen's definition, have lived and died French according to Le Pen's definition since the dawn of the beginning of time, or

that Le Pen is not French according to Le Pen's definition.

65.

Hervé Le Tellier
FROM *A THOUSAND PEARLS*
(FOR A THOUSAND PENNIES)
translated by Ian Monk
{Oulipo}

Penny for them?

I was thinking that, in France, the main difference between a religion and a sect is that religions have their own television programs.

Penny for them?

I was thinking how odd it is that DNA always spirals to the left, even in the southern hemisphere.

Penny for them?

I was thinking that I once wrote a book in order to seduce a woman, and today I still use it, on other women.

Penny for them?

I was thinking that I've never been able to understand how the compasses on metal ships manage to indicate anything other than the location of the ship itself.

Penny for them?

I was thinking that if I wanted to keep a really honest diary, then I'd pretend it was someone else's.

Penny for them?

I was thinking that, to become rich, all you need is to take one dollar from each pauper.

Penny for them?

I was thinking that I should never have had dinner at the home of that bitch, who found me 'charming' because I kept saying 'thank you' to her servant.

Penny for them?

I was thinking that *love handles* rhymes with *romantic candles*.

Penny for them?

I was thinking that I'm always scared before finding the strength to be brave, and that even then I always gauge the risk I'm taking.

Penny for them?

I was thinking that I don't sell enough books to imagine I have talent, but too many to believe I'm a genius.

Penny for them?

I was thinking that Jacques Jouet is right, 'a dog' and 'a fox' are also possible answers to the Sphinx's famous question. And maybe a dung beetle and a salamander, too.

Penny for them?

I was thinking that the air hostesses who repeat the gesture of buckling a seatbelt every day must have had excellent training to stop them bursting into laughter.

66.

Michèle Métail
FROM *TOPONYM: BERLIN*
translated by Susan Wicks
{Oulipo}

The City, from the City
(A Plot Plan)

winter leafless
rising up between
walls, a triangle
dark angles where
thick branches are
tiers at mid-growth
when up at the tips
one bud has split
one day to the next
its bursting burst

12 April 2000: chestnut tree in the courtyard

over lapse, a hole
this hollowed-out
hole of hollowness
abyss of we forgot
its facts sucked out
and as these tracks
time traces then
effaces in the act

of leaving in or out
at roadworks, past

20 April 2000: Potsdamer Platz

occupied by lines
confined, a corner
of this dam, a plot
of lines lined up
stands out on green
of a block of shade
a colony surveyed
along its borders
caught, a closed-off
dream, enclosure

30 April 2000: Laubenkolonie,
working men's gardens of Spandauer Damm

walled up, walled in
the twisting vine
virgin over canes
veils lean-to glass
a half-abandoned
armchair strains
towards the street
refracted, image
of outwear so true
it wears it through

9 May 2000: Potsdam

villa for sale
just a shout, an SOS
to the open street
with begging hands
in a burst of anger
it aspires, it cares
it fires and flares
an impetus towards
nod to the least lack
taken in unheard
it deafens, cuts out

29 May 2000: 'Der Rufer', (The Shouter)
Statue by Gerhard Marcks. Strasse des 17 Juni

motif of symmetry
in the long views
spread of the city
today monumental
axis and unbending
squared-off showy
shackles, stuccoes
triumphal avenue
for the triumph of
sweet scent of lime

18 June 2000: Karl Marx Allee

high in the chaos
what a fresh spurt
a streaming towards
the running foam
of cliffs, the slope
to cross a bridge

the mist of its fall
evaporating moist
the overheated air
on sunstroke street

3 July 2000: Viktoria Park waterfall

chanted, beating
in our bodies, sounds
the deep ones, beat
inside the motion
of repeating, marked
with a pulsation
doing and redoing
this, aspire desire
the world, a plan
that faltered oddly

8 July 2000: Love Parade. Tiergarten

distracted to see
as the eye, briefly
veering to the west
near to the window
a whole sky in grey
a sparkle of plane
when flying to meet
it rising from here
a goose lumbers up
beating slow air

11 August 2000: through the study window

arches rose window
portico, a ruin left
cleared out apart
from a pigeon, shit
the whitened lines
of destination now
have wandered off
derailed, a station
dead in its tracks
a pointless terminus

13 August 2000: Porticus Anhalter Bahnhof
Portico, old Anhalt station

shaken from the top
into flight, a crow
the bell flown off
when leaves as well
fly off away apart
from a tree in leaf
already yellowing
so soon the autumn
evening six o'clock
at the peal of bells

15 October 2000: Haus der Kulturen
der Welt. The bells

frail in this light
to shrink lead-grey
monotonous away
an after-rain grey
on uneven stones
the summoned street

from just this past
summer, milky light
dried up by absence
nothing, no relief

28 October 2000: in the streets
of Charlottenburg

glint of crystal
night, the cupola
aflame with gold
haunted ever after
a sickness, restless
history chews over
while at a signal
for the march to go
or even totter, such
a gradual advance

9 November 2000: anti-racist demonstration
in front of the synagogue. Oranienburgerstrasse

night screen dark
exhausted journey
dings itself along
the sides of streets
the city offered up
banal in snapshots
at the turn, faces
fading, mid-night
even of the lights
as they blink out

13 December 2000: coming back in the Pankow tram

not much in season
these cherry-trees
seen aligned along
a two-line bridge
bouquet, the blooms
too far out too soon
and frozen freeze
besides the flakes
degreeless brink
a withered o of cold

16 December 2000: 79 cherry trees in bloom
at the bottom of Bösebrücke. Norwegerstrasse

in posters life
pasted in delight
so easily, so sweet
as a train winds by
to stop and change
then from a subway
come languid sounds
like an accordion
the haunting voice
of only loneliness

10 January 2001: Russian busker at
Heidelbergerplatz tube station

67.

Étienne Lécroart
FROM *VANITY*
translated by Philip Terry
{Oubapo}

The last time that
I'll get the giggles,

the last times that I'll
smell the scent of your skin,

the last time that I'll savour
the smell of a favourite book,

the last time
that I'll bumslide,

the last time that
I'll make snowballs,

the last time that
I'll lie down in the grass,

the last time that I'll hurtle down
to the bottom of a precipitous slope,

the last time that
I'll get goosepimples,

the last time that I discover
a moving piece of music,

the last time that I'll
enjoy a summer evening,

the last time that I'll
feel your body next to mine,

the last time that I'll see
a double rainbow,

the last time that
my eyes will mist over,

the last time that I'll hear
the town buried under snow,

the last time that I'll
be kissed by my mother,

the last time that I'll smell
the head of a new-born child,

the last time that
I'll hear doves cooing,

the last time that I'll
hear rain on the roof,

the last time that I'll add the
finishing touch to a new work,

the last time that I'll
take a breath of fresh air,

will I know?

Has the moment already passed?

I don't know.

But what will I do without such things,
Dear God,
what will I do?

68.

Jacques Roubaud
FROM *MATHEMATICS*
translated by Ian Monk
{Oulipo}

28 At the moment I am writing these lines (in May, 1992),

At the moment I am writing these lines (in May, 1992), the 'biography' of that many-headed beast, Bourbaki, is still to be written. It would be a fascinating but arduous task. Here, I shall say only what is strictly necessary to my own enterprise. Having reached his dotage after 1968, 'he' is for all intents and purposes now dead, if I believe what Pierre Cartier said in September of last year, in Cérisy. ('He' was already decidedly weary when I had the opportunity to approach him, albeit in rather a roundabout way, circa 1965.) But in 1954, he was still vibrant, forceful, conquering, full of ardor and ambition.

We now know that this 'he' was a collective pseudonym, as they say on library cards. In 1962, my master, Raymond Queneau, wrote an article entitled 'Bourbaki and the Mathematics of Tomorrow' for the revue *Critique*, which was subsequently reprinted at the beginning of his book, *Bords*. It contains the following passage:

'It is generally admitted at the present time (in France and elsewhere) that the most important treatise of contemporary mathematics has been signed by an invented name; even worse, this name comes from a school joke. Originally, it was the name of a great, fictional Swedish mathematician who was supposed to be honoring the Ecole Normale with his presence, and who claimed to be called Nicolas Bourbaki. I have no idea if, at the time, those young men were already planning to write their treatise, inspired by the desire to give a rigorous foundation to mathematics . . . but their pseudonym was there waiting for them.'

These 'young men' of 1930, who had become prestigious masters by 1960, had become in 1990 – those among them who were still alive, that is, and, in particular, the founders André Weil, Henri Cartan, and Jean Dieudonné – honored and venerable retired professors. Their voices, which became juvenile once more in memory of the 'japes' that had enlivened the early years of their 'child,' slur slightly and occasionally become confused when their voices issue all at once from my tape recorder, into which I have placed a cassette kindly sent to me by *France Culture*, of a Michèle Chouchan radio show devoted to Bourbaki: 'Investigation of a Many-Headed Mathematician.' Among the various voices can also be heard that of Professor Choquet, now of the 'Academy of Sciences,' and mine too! (though I am present for only the most trivial reasons). Bourbaki is now a museum piece. I make no attempt really to hear what they are saying. I've set the volume quite low (it is five o'clock in the morning), I am just trying to create an atmosphere to trigger memories.

Very few of the world's mathematicians in 1992 would still agree with Queneau's judgment of Bourbaki's written work: 'the most important treatise of contemporary mathematics.' Much mathematical water has since passed under bridges of the same kidney, and Bourbaki's stock is now rather low, if the reader will excuse me such an incongruous mingling of metaphors. The history of the sciences, in its serene impartiality, will no doubt give them the place they merit once the last of their disciples, enemies, or hangers-on have left the scene.

But in 1954, their name had hardly spread beyond the circle of professional mathematicians, and even among them it was still tinged with mystery and horror. In the Hermite lecture hall, no one, or nearly, had ever heard those three strange syllables, apart no doubt from the *Normaliens* who were under the strict guidance of Henri Cartan (a decisive step for Bourbaki, in its long march toward mathematical power, had been to take control of all of those heads and their various brains, all predestined, of course, to be brilliant).

When recalled later on, much later on, this moment thus acquires an almost solemn dimension. From the little thicket of heads around our two protagonists – the one who created an 'occurrence' by interrupting Choquet, and the one who has not only taken up the professor's defense but has now stolen the limelight by providing an explanation and a wider context for the discussion – the name takes wing over the rows of benches, fills our ears, rises up to the ceiling, and vibrates against the walls, which send back an echo: "'Tis a cry repeated by a thousand sentinels, / An order announced by a thousand megaphones / 'Tis a beacon lit on a thousand citadels, / A call to the hunters who are chilled to the bone! / Bourbaki! Bourbaki! Bourbaki!'

The essential revelation was as follows: those items now termed mathematical in a sense that escaped reasonable folk had not been invented by Mr Gustave Choquet, and were not the ravings of an eccentric professor (we suspected as much, of course); and, above all, there lay an overriding rationale for all this somewhere. Mathematics had recovered both its unity and élan. For the first time since perhaps the golden age of the Mediterranean and Greece, since Euclid and Archimedes, it would cease progressing haphazardly, weighed down by the unbearable risks of disorder and contradiction, and would be new once more, borne up by a vision and mission.

It was starting all over again.

And there was a 'treatise' to 'make this apparent.' That monumental work had started to appear. And it was appearing under the name of 'Bourbaki.'

69.

Georges Perec
FROM *LIFE A USER'S MANUAL*
CHAPTER SIXTY
translated by David Bellos
{Oulipo}

Cinoc, I

A kitchen. The floor is covered with a linoleum mosaic of jade and azure and cinnabar rhomboids. On the walls, paint that was once gloss. Against the rear wall, beside the sink, above a plastic-coated wire drainer, stuck one behind the other between the pipe-work and the wall, four post-office annual calendars with four-colour photographs:

1972: *Good Chums*: a jazz band composed of six-year-old kids playing toy instruments; the pianist, with his spectacles and deeply serious look, is vaguely reminiscent of Schroeder, the Beethovenish child prodigy in Schulz's *Peanuts;*

1973: *Summer Visions*: bees suck asters;

1974: *A Night on the Pampas*: three *gauchos* around a campfire strum guitars;

1975: *Pompon and Fifi*: a pair of monkeys play dominoes. The male wears a bowler hat and an acrobat's leotard with the number '32' inscribed in silver spangles on the back; the she-monkey smokes a cigar held between the thumb and index toe of her right foot, wears a feathered hat and crocheted gloves, and carries a handbag.

Higher up, on a sheet of almost identical dimensions, can be seen three daisies in a short-necked glass vase with a spherical base, whose caption simply states 'PAINTED BY FEET AND MOUTH' and, in brackets, 'original watercolour'.

Cinoc is in his kitchen. He is a dry, thin old man dressed in a dingy-green flannel waistcoat. He is sitting on a Formica stool at a table with an oilcloth covering, beneath an adjustable metal ceiling light fixture enamelled white and equipped with a system of pulleys and a pear-shaped counterweight. He is eating pilchards in spice directly out of a badly opened tin. On the table in front of him are three shoe-boxes full of slips of card covered in meticulous handwriting.

Cinoc moved into Rue Simon-Crubellier in 1947, a few months after the death of Hélène Brodin-Gratiolet, whose flat he took over. He provided the inhabitants of the building, and especially Madame Claveau, with an immediate, difficult problem: how was his name to be pronounced? Obviously the concierge didn't dare address him as 'Nutcase' by pronouncing the name 'Sinok'. She questioned Valène, who suggested 'Cinosh', Winckler, who was for 'Chinoch', Morellet, who inclined towards 'Sinots', Mademoiselle Crespi, who proposed 'Chinoss', François Gratiolet, who prescribed 'Tsinoc', and finally Monsieur Echard, as a librarian well versed in recondite spellings and the appropriate ways of uttering them, demonstrated that, leaving aside any potential transformation of the intervocalic 'n' into a 'gn' or 'nj' sound, and assuming once and for all, on principle, that the 'i' was pronounced 'i' and the 'o', 'o', there were then four ways of saying the initial 'c': 's', 'ts', 'sh' and 'ch', and five ways of pronouncing the final: 's', 'k', 'ch', 'sh' and 'ts', and that, as a result, depending on the presence or absence of one or another diacritic sign or accent and according to the phonetic particularities of one or another language or dialect, there was a case for choosing from amongst the following twenty pronunciations:

SINOS	SINOK	SINOCH	SINOSH	SINOTS
TSINOS	TSINOK	TSINOCH	TSINOSH	TSINOTS
SHINOS	SHINOK	SHINOCH	SHINOSH	SHINOTS
CHINOS	CHINOK	CHINOCH	CHINOSH	CHINOTS

As a result of which, a delegation went to ask the principal person concerned, who replied that he didn't know himself which was the most proper way of pronouncing his name. His family's original surname, the one which his great-grandfather, a saddler from Szczyrk, had purchased officially from the Registry Office of the County of Krakow, was Klein-hof: but from generation to generation, from passport renewal to passport renewal, either because the Austrian or German officials weren't bribed sufficiently, or because they were dealing with staff of Hungarian or Pol-davian or Moravian or Polish origin who read 'v' and wrote it as 'ff' or who saw 'c' and heard it as 'tz', or because they came up against people who never needed to try very hard to become somewhat illiterate and hard of hearing when having to give identity papers to Jews, the name had retained nothing of its original pronunciation and spelling and Cinoc remembered his father telling him that his father had told him of having cousins called Klajnhoff, Keinhof, Klinov, Szinowcz, Linhaus, etc. How had Kleinhof become Cinoc? Cinoc really did not know; the only sure thing was that the final 'f' had been replaced one day by that special letter (ß) with which Germans indicate double 's'; then, no doubt, the 'l' had been dropped or had been replaced by an 'h': so it got to Khinoss or Kheinhoss and, maybe, from there to Kinoch, Chinoc, Tsinoc, Cinoc, etc. Anyway it wasn't at all important whichever way you wanted to pro-nounce it.

Cinoc, who was then about fifty, pursued a curious profession. As he said himself, he was a 'word-killer': he worked at keeping Larousse diction-aries up to date. But whilst other compilers sought out new words and meanings, his job was to make room for them by eliminating all the words and meanings that had fallen into disuse.

When he retired in nineteen sixty-five, after fifty-three years of scru-pulous service, he had disposed of hundreds and thousands of tools, techniques, customs, beliefs, sayings, dishes, games, nick-names, weights and measures; he had wiped dozens of islands, hundreds of cities and rivers, and thousands of townships off the map; he had returned to taxo-nomic anonymity hundreds of varieties of cattle, species of birds, insects, and snakes, rather special sorts of fish, kinds of crustaceans, slightly dis-similar plants and particular breeds of vegetables and fruit; and cohorts of geographers, missionaries, entomologists, Church Fathers, men of let-ters, generals, Gods & Demons had been swept by his hand into eternal obscurity.

Who would know ever again what a *vigigraphe* was, 'a type of telegraph consisting of watchtowers communicating with each other'? And who could henceforth imagine there had existed for perhaps many generations a 'block of wood on the end of a stick for flattening watercress in flooded ditches' and that the block had been called a *schuèle* (shü-ell)? Who would recall the *vélocimane?*

> VELOCIMANE (masc. nn.)
> (from Lat. *velox, -ocis,* speedy, and *manus,* hand).
> Special locomotive device for children,
> resembling a horse, mounted on three or
> four wheels, also called *mechanical horse.*

Where had all the *abunas* gone, patriarchs of the Abyssinian Church, and the *palatines*, fur tippets worn by women in winter, so named after the Princess Palatine who introduced their use into France in the minority of Louis XIV, and the *chandernagors*, those gold-spangled NCOs who marched at the head of Second Empire processions? What had become of Léopold-Rudolph von Schwanzenbad-Hodenthaler, whose outstanding courage at Eisenühr allowed Zimmerwald to carry the day at Kisàszony? And Uz (Jean-Pierre), 1720–1796, German poet, author of *Lyrical Poems, The Art of Being Ever Joyful* (a didactic poem), *Odes and Songs,* etc.? And Albert de Routisie (Basel, 1834–White Sea, 1867), French poet and novelist. A great admirer of Lomonosov, he undertook a pilgrimage to his place of birth at Arkhangelsk, but the ship sank just before entering harbour. After his death his only daughter, Irena Ragon, published his unfinished novel, *Les Cent-Jours,* a selection of poetry, *Les Yeux de Mélusine,* and, under the title of *Leçons,* an admirable anthology of aphorisms which remains his finest work. Who would now ever know that François Albergati Capacelli was an Italian playwright born at Bologna in 1728, or that the master caster Rondeau (1493–1543) had been responsible for the bronze door of the funeral chapel at Carennac?

Cinoc began to dally on the banks of the Seine, rummaging through the open-air bookstalls, leafing through penny dreadfuls, out-of-date essays, obsolete traveller's guides, old textbooks on physiology, mechanics, or moral instruction, or superseded maps in which Italy still figured as a multicoloured patchwork of little kingdoms. Later on he went to borrow books from the municipal library of the XVIIth *arrondissement*, in Rue Jacques-Binjen, having them bring down from the attic dusty old folios, ancient users' manuals, volumes from the *Library of Miracles*, and old dictionaries: Lachâtre, Vicarius, Bescherelle aîné, Larrive, Fleury, the *Dictionary of Conversation* compiled by a Society of Men of Letters, Graves and d'Esbigné, Bouillet, Onions, Dezobry, and Bachelet. Finally, when he had exhausted the resources of his local library, he grew bolder and enrolled at Sainte-Geneviève, where he started to read the authors whose names he saw as he went in, carved on the stone façade.

He read Aristotle, Pliny, Aldrovandi, Sir Thomas Browne, Gesner, Ray, Linnaeus, Brisson, Cuvier, Bonneterre, Owen, Scoresby, Bennett, Aronnax, Olmstead, Pierre-Joseph Macquart, Sterne, Eugénie Guérin, Gastripheres, Phutatorius, Somnolentius, Triptolemy, Argalastes, Kysarchius, Egnatius, Sigonius, Bossius, Ticinenses, Baysius, Budoeus, Salmasius, Lipsius, Lazius, Isaac Casaubon, Joseph Scaliger, and even the *De re vestiaria veterum* by Rubenius (1665, quarto), which gave him a full & satisfactory account of the Toga, or loose gown, the Chlamys, the Ephod, the Tunica or jacket, the Synthesis, the Paenula, the Lacema with its Cucullus, the Paludamentum, the Praetexta, the Sagum or soldier's jerkin, and the Trabea: of which, according to Suetonius, there were three kinds.

Cinoc read slowly and copied down rare words; gradually his plan began to take shape, and he decided to compile a great dictionary of forgotten words, not in order to perpetuate the memory of the Akka, a black-skinned pygmy people of Central Africa, or of Jean Gigoux, a historical painter, or of Henri Romagnesi, a composer of romances, 1781–1851, nor to prolong the life of the scolecobrot, a tetramerous coleopter of the longicorn family, Cerambycid branch, but so as to rescue simple words which still appealed to him. In ten years he gathered more than eight thousand of them, which contain, obscurely, the trace of a story it has now become almost impossible to hand on:

RIVELETTE (fem. nn.)
Another name for myriophyllum, or water milfoil.

AREA (fem. nn.)
Med: A: Alopecia, fox-mange, a disease causing loss of body and head hair.

LOQUIS (masc. nn.)
Type of glass trinket used for trading with Negroes of the African coasts. Small cylinders made of coloured glass.

RONDELIN (masc. nn., from *rond*)
Vulgar word used by Chapelle to refer to a very fat man.

CADETTE (fem. nn.)
Ashlar suitable for paving.

LOSSE (fem. nn.)
Tchn: Iron hand-tool with a sharpened steel edge, shaped like a vertically sectioned semicone, hollowed out. Fits on a handle like a deck-scrubber's holystone, used for piercing barrel bungs.

BEAUCEANT (masc. nn.)
Name of the Knights Templars' standard.

BEAU-PARTIR (masc. nn.)
Showjumping. Fine departure of horse. Its straight-line speed up to a stopping point.

LOUISETTE (fem. nn.)
Name used for a time for the guillotine, whose invention was attributed to Dr Louis. 'Louisette

was the familiar name Marat gave to the guillotine' (Victor Hugo).

FRANCATU (masc. nn.)
Hort: Type of apple that keeps well.

RUISSON (masc. nn.)
Trench cut for draining a saltmarsh.

SPADILLE (fem. nn.)
(Span. *espada*, broadsword.) The ace of spades in the game of humber.

URSULINE (fem. nn.)
Small ladder leading to a narrow platform onto which fairground gypsies had their trained goats climb.

TIERÇON (masc. nn.)
A: *Meas:* Liquid measure containing a third part of a full measure. The volume of a *tierçon* was: 89.41 litres in Paris, 150.8 litres at Bordeaux, 53.27 litres in Champagne, 158.08 litres in London, and 151.71 litres at Warsaw.

LOVELY (masc. nn.)
(English *lovely*, pretty.) Indian bird resembling the European finch.

GIBRALTAR (masc. nn.)
A kind of cake.

PISTEUR (masc. nn.)
Hotel employee with the task of attracting customers.

MITELLE (fem. nn.)
(Lat. *mitella*, dim. of *mitra,* mitre.) *Ant: Rom*: Small mitre, type of headdress worn esp. by women, sometimes with lavish decorations. Worn by men in the countryside.

Bot: Genus of plant of the saxifrage family, thus called for the shape of its fruit, native of the cold regions of Asia and America. *Surg:* Sling for supporting the arm. *Moll:* Synonym of scalpella.

TERGAL, E (adj.)
(Lat. *tergum,* back.) Relating to an insect's back.

VIRGOULEUSE (fem. nn.)
Juicy winter pear.

HACHARD (masc. nn.)
Iron shears.

FEURRE (masc. nn.)
Straw from any kind of wheat. Long straw for rushing seats.

VEAU-LAQ (masc. nn.)
Very soft leather used for handbags, gloves, etc.

EPULIE (fem. nn.)
(From Grk. Επι, on, and συλον, gum) *Surg:* Fleshy excrescence on or around the gum.

TASSIOT (masc. nn.)
Tchn: Cross made of two laths which basket-makers use to start certain items.

DOUVEBOUILLE (masc. nn.)
Mil: V: (deformation of US: *doughboy,* private, foot soldier) American soldier during First World War (1917–1918).

VIGNON (masc. nn.)
Prickly gorse.

ROQUELAURE (fem. nn.)
(From the name of its inventor, the Duc de Roquelaure.) Type of coat buttoned at the front from top to bottom.

LOUPIAT (masc. nn.)
Fam: Drunk. 'She was bloody stuck with her *loupiat* of a husband' (É. Zola).

DODENAGE (masc. nn.)
Tchn: Way of polishing upholsterers' stud nails by putting them in a fine canvas or hide bag with emery or other abrasive matter.

70.

Juliana Spahr
FROM *HR 4811 IS A JOKE*
{Foulipo}

I

Provided further, That none
of the funds made available under this heading
may
be
used to pay for
the performance of abortion as a method of
family
planning
or to motivate or
coerce any person to practise abortions; and that
in
order
to reduce reliance on
abortion in developing nations, funds shall be available
only
to
voluntary family planning projects
which offer, either directly or through referral to,
or
information
about access to, a
broad range of family planning methods and services,
and
any

2

Provided further, That none
of the gag made available under this heading
may
be
gag to pay for
the performance of gag as a method of
family
planning
gag to motivate or
coerce any person gag practice abortions; and that
in
order
gag reduce reliance on
abortion in developing gag, funds shall be available
only
to
gag family planning projects
which offer, either gag or through referral to,
or
information
gag access to, a
broad range of gag planning methods and services,
and
any

3

gag further, That none
of gag gag gag available under this heading
gag
gag
gag to pay for
the gag gag gag as a method of
gag

gag
gag to motivate or
coerce gag gag gag practise abortions; and that
gag
gag
gag reduce reliance on
abortion gag gag gag, funds shall be available
gag
gag
gag family planning projects
which gag, gag gag or through referral to,
gag
gag
gag access to, a
broad gag gag gag planning methods and services,
gag
gag

71.

Lily Robert-Foley
FROM *GRAPHEMACHINE*
{Outranspo}

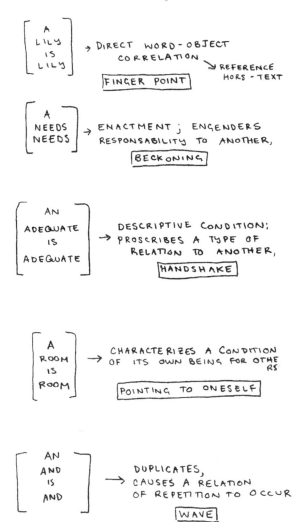

'Lily needs adequate room and produces spikes
of brightly colored flowers'

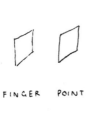

FINGER POINT

BECKONING

"SO - SO"

HANDSHAKE

POINTING TO ONESELF

WAVE

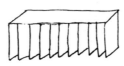

RAISED HAND

HANDS TO FACE

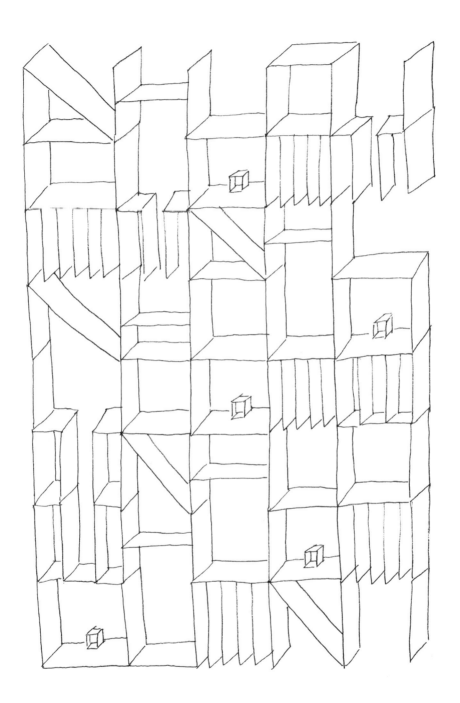

72.

Philip Terry
EXERCISES IN TRANSLATION
{Outranspo}

Multitranslation

In the S bus/charabang, in the rush hour/busiest time of day. A chap/
bloke/young man of about 26, felt hat with a cord/braid instead of/in place
of a ribbon/band, neck too long/stretched as if somone had been pull-
ing/tugging on it. People/citizens getting off/climbing down. The chap/
bloke/young man in question/about whom we are talking/speaking gets/
becomes annoyed/frustrated with one of the men/guys/blokes standing
next to/adjacent to/in proximity to him/the chap/bloke/young man in
question/about whom we are talking/speaking. He/the chap/bloke/young
man in question/about whom we are talking/speaking accuses him of
jostling/shoving/disturbing him/the chap/bloke/young man in question/
about whom we are talking/speaking every time anyone goes past/by. A
snivelling/whining tone which is meant/intended to be aggressive/threat-
ening. When he/the chap/bloke/young man in question/about whom we
are talking/speaking sees a vacant/empty seat he throws himself on to it.

Two hours/one hundred and twenty minutes later, I meet/encounter
him/the chap/bloke/young man in question/about whom we are talking/
speaking in the Cour de Rome, in front of/outside the Gare Saint-Lazare.
He's with a friend/mate/acquaintance/chum who's saying: 'You ought to
get an extra/additional button put on your overcoat/raincoat'. He shows
him where (at the lapels/neck area) and why.

Quasitranslation

It was on a bus. There were people on the bus. People wearing clothes, like pullovers, cardigans, jackets, and hats. And carrying bags. As often, there were quite a few people standing and as the bus moved along they bumped into one another. One passenger got a bit fed up with this and eventually sat down in an empty seat.

Later I saw him again, outside a main station. He might have been talking to someone, I forget.

Countertranslation

It was on the number 19, in the rush hour. There was a bloke in his twenties, wearing a stupid hat, it had a piece of string tied round it where you'd normally have a ribbon, and his neck, like this sentence, was too long, as if someone had been torturing him on a stretcher or something. People were getting on and off. Well, this bloke starts getting narked with a man standing right next to him. Then suddenly he turns towards him and tells him to bloody well stop shoving him every time anyone comes near, in a strange whining tone that must have been intended to sound aggressive but just made him look like an idiot. When a seat became free, he more or less threw himself into it.

A couple of hours later on, I saw the bloke again – this time he was standing on the pavement in Trafalgar Square, just in front of the National Gallery. He was with a friend, and I overheard him say: 'Mate, you should get another button put on your coat.' Then, pointing with his finger, he added: 'There'.

Zenotranslation

In the S bus, in the rush hour. A bloke about 26, felt hat with a cord instead of a ribbon, neck too long as if someone had been tugging at it. People getting off. The bloke in question gets annoyed with one of the men standing next to him. He accuses him of bumping into him every time someone goes past. A whining tone which is meant to sound menacing. When he sees a vacant seat, he grabs it.

Two hours later, I come across him in Cour de Rome, in front of the Gare Saint-Lazare. He's with a friend who's saying: 'You should get another button put on your overcoat.' He shows him where (at the lapels) and why.

In the S bus, rush hour. A bloke about 26, felt hat, neck too long, gets annoyed with a man standing next to him for bumping into him. A whining tone. When he sees a vacant seat, he grabs it.

Later, I come across him in Cour de Rome, with a friend who's saying: 'Get another button put on your overcoat.'

In the S bus. A bloke gets annoyed with a man for bumping into him.

Later, I come across him with a friend who's saying: 'Get another button on your overcoat.'

In the S. A bloke gets annoyed.

A friend says: 'Get another button on your overcoat.'

A bloke's annoyed.

A friend: 'Get another button.'

Annoyed.

'Get another button.'

Annoyed.

'Button.'

'Button.'

Scholiotranslation

Queneau opens his inaugural text by setting the scene, which takes place on the S bus, in the rush hour. He goes on to introduce his main protagonist, who is described simply as 'a bloke' ('un type' in the original) of about 26 years of age. We know little more about him, though Queneau gives some indirect information about his sartorial predilections by describing his hat in some detail, perhaps making a literary allusion to the hat worn by Charles in Flaubert's *Madame Bovary*: it is a soft hat, made of felt, and rather than having a band of ribbon round its brim, as is customary, it has been replaced (perhaps by the character himself) by a length of cord. Queneau also briefly sketches in the appearance of the character, in particular his neck, which the unnamed narrator (perhaps Queneau himself) describes as 'too long' ('trop long' in the original). The narrator then elaborates on this with a description that can only be meant to be taken metaphorically: 'as if someone had been tugging at it'. After this initial scene-setting the brief narrative proceeds apace, following a bridge section – both narrative and descriptive in the general sense – where we are informed that people are getting off the bus. 'Le type', we are now informed, gets irritated with one of the other passengers ('un voisin') standing next to him, and he reproaches him with jostling him every time someone goes past. The tone of his voice is described as 'pleurnichard' which can be translated as 'whining' or 'snivelling', a tone which the narratorial discourse describes as intentionally menacing, though it is difficult to reconcile the whining tone with menace, so that a fault is created in the textual discourse, where the conventions of realism – in a manner predicting the experiments of the *nouveau roman* in the decade following publication of Queneau's collection – are problematised. The first movement of the narrative is now quickly concluded: seeing a vacant seat the 'type' seizes it.

In a brief coda, the narrator describes how he encountered the same character again two hours later, in the Cour de Rome, in front of the Gare Saint-Lazare. This time, the 'type' is in the company of a friend ('un camarade' in the original) who is offering him some advice concerning his clothing, suggesting, in direct discourse, that he should have an extra button added to his overcoat. The friend shows him where, at the neckline, and then the narrator reports enigmatically that he explains why. We are not told why ourselves, but the suggestion which hangs over the end of the narrative would seem to indicate that the opening around the neck and the lapel area is too low, perhaps thereby too feminine or simply a little behind the times in terms of fashion. We are thus alerted early on that Queneau's *Exercices de Style* concern style in a double sense: literary 'style', but also 'style' in the sense of fashion.

Homosemantic Translation

It took place on a motorized transport vehicle designated by a single letter, S for Stephen. It was busy. There was this chap in his mid-twenties wearing a cap with a pom-pom instead of a peak, his scruff was elongated, as if he'd been a giraffe in a former life. The bus stopped to let a group of children get off. Then the chap became irritated by a man who stood behind him. He turned on him angrily and told him to stop shoving him every time people got off the bus. His voice had a peculiar high-pitched sound which had a threatening undertone. When a place became free, he took the opportunity to sit in it.

A hundred and twenty minutes later, I saw him again, at the intersection of the Rue Saint-Lazare and the Rue d'Amsterdam, opposite the Metro. He was with an acquaintance, who was telling him he should get another fastener put on his jacket. He indicated whereabouts (in the region of the neck) and explained his reasoning.

Ekphrasotranslation

Looking about you could see people in seats with shopping on their knees, people standing in the aisle, the windows steamed up on the inside. One of the standing passengers wore a beige-coloured felt hat with a thick-braided brown cord attached to its brim where normally you would expect to see a ribbon. He had an elongated neck, which made him look like a giraffe. At a certain point, the man in the hat started fidgeting, then he began staring intently at a middle-aged man wearing a knee-length blue raincoat and pince-nez standing just in front of him. Suddenly he opened his mouth and blurted out: 'Stop shoving me, man!' His face was red, his breathing rapid. Everyone was staring at him. When a seat became vacant, he grabbed it.

Two hours later, I saw him in Cour de Rome, standing in front of the sandstone façade of the Gare Saint-Lazare. He was with a stocky man with shaved mousey-brown hair who was gesticulating with his hands and saying something. He kept pointing at his coat with his forefinger, almost jabbing him with it, around the region of the lapels.

73·

Georges Perec

MEMORY OF A TRIP
TO THOUARS

translated by Philip Terry

{Oulipo/Oumupo}

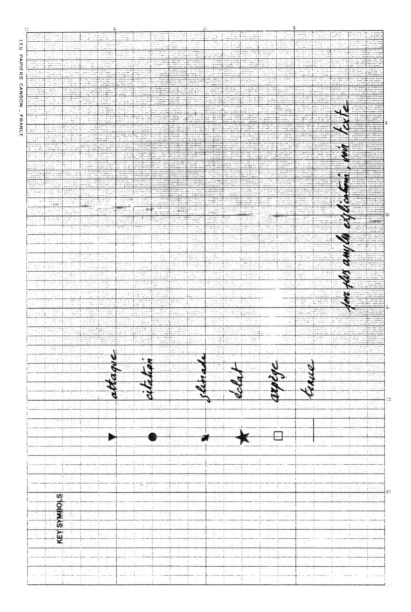

Key Symbols
▼   attack
●   citation
↘   glissando
★   sforzando
□   arpeggio
—   sustain

for more detailed explanation see text

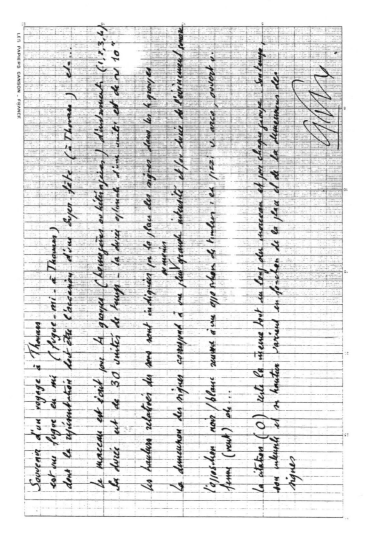

Memory of a Trip to Thouars
is a fugue in E (fugue – E – at Thouars)
which was performed on the occasion of a big Festival (held at Thouars) etc.

the piece is written for 4 groups (homogeneous or heterogeneous) of instruments (1, 2, 3, 4)
the duration is thirty units of time – the optimal duration of units is around ~ 10"

the relative volume of the sounds are indicated by the position of the signs in the 4 groups

the dimension of the signs corresponds to a more or less high intensity and/or duration of the sonic event

the opposition black/white corresponds to an opposition of timbres: eg. pizzicato v. bowing, unmuted v. muted (wind) etc.

the citation (o) remains the same throughout the duration of the piece and for each group. Its tempo, intensity and pitch vary according to the position and dimensions of the signs.

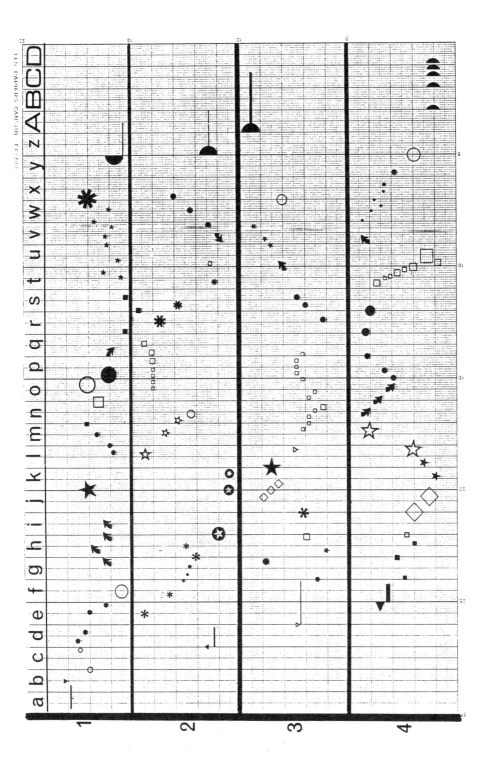

409

74.

George Herbert
EAſTER WINGS
{Anticipatory Plagiarism}

Lord, who createdſt man in wealth and ſtore,
Though fooliſhly he loſt the ſame,
Decaying more and more,
Till he became
Moſt poore:
With thee
O let me riſe
As larks, harmoniouſly,
And ſing this day thy victories:
Then ſhall the fall further the flight in me

My tender age in forrow did beginne:
And ftill with fickneffes and fhame
Thou didft fo punifh finne,
That I became
Moft thinne.
With thee
Let me combine,
And feel this day thy victorie:
For, if I imp my wing on thine,
Affliction fhall advance the flight in me,

75.

Richard Beard
FROM *LAZARUS IS DEAD*
{After Oulipo}

He sold blemished lambs at the Temple. He cheated shepherds and made compulsive visits to a prostitute. He was insensitive and self-important, he was beloved and he was dead.

There should be exceptions, Martha thinks, individuals with a god-given second chance. Death is unfair.

She and Mary kneel over the corpse of their brother. It is laid out on the newest straw mat they could find, but Lazarus dead is not Lazarus. His face was never that still. Several hours later his beard is growing, like a recrimination.

'Jesus brought two people back to life,' Mary says. She is useless at helping with the body. 'He can't just leave us like this.'

'Don't, Mary. You're making it worse.'

'*You're* making it worse. Try harder to believe.'

'In what?'

'In something, anything. Believe in Jesus.' Mary sits back on her heels, eyes and fists squeezed shut. 'I won't accept he's dead until he's buried.'

Through the first night, Martha watches the body. Lazarus doesn't change. His fingers and lips are chill to the touch, and there is no exhalation of a departing soul. Lazarus her brother is grey and dead.

More accurately, considering the events of four days from now, he has detached himself from his body. There are conflicting ideas about where he goes next.

The Jewish tradition would have him in Sheol. According to the Book of Enoch (160 BCE), Sheol is guarded by six hundred and sixty-six angels who separate the righteous from the wicked. The wicked are drowned in lakes of fire. '*You have put me in the depths of the Pit, in the regions dark and deep./ Your wrath lies heavy upon me, and you overwhelm with all your waves . . .*' (Psalm 88).

The pit. The blazing pain and suffocation. Sheol is recognizable as a version of hell, or the universal experience of the last gasp of life. Lazarus has been through Sheol. He is now somewhere else.

Khalil Gibran (*Lazarus and His Beloved*) pictures him in a better place: 'there is no weight there, and there is no measure'. Lazarus is in a 'green pasture', and by comparison the world we know is a desert.

Others, like the philosopher-novelist Pär Lagerkvist, tell a different story. According to Lagerkvist, Lazarus will later say: '"I have experienced nothing. I have merely been dead. And death is nothing."'

Lagerkvist presses for a more satisfactory answer.

'"Nothing?"'

'"No. What should it be?"'

The answer, for those we love, is green pastures and a land without weights and measures. Although 'nothing' is also a popular choice, a next-best bet, since second-best is what most of us recognize from life. Death is nothing (which may be better than hell), and therefore nothing to fear.

However, it seems unlikely that Lazarus could have survived nothing. Nothing can come out of nothing, whereas his and other stories have come back about death. After death there is something, and this is where Lazarus is now. It is not the life we know but also it is not nothing.

Which is of little immediate consolation to Martha.

On the second day the growing smell of corpse overtakes the fading smell of sickness.

'The time may not be right,' Mary says. 'Jesus must have a reason.'

Martha slaps her face. Mary puts her hand to her cheek. Outside, the wailers wail.

76.

Italo Calvino

THE NAME, THE NOSE

translated by William Weaver

{Oulipo}

Epigraphs in an undecipherable language, half their letters rubbed away by the sand-laden wind: this is what you will be, O *parfumeries,* for the noseless man of the future. You will still open your doors to us, your carpets will still muffle our footsteps, you will receive us in your jewel-box space, with no jutting corners, the walls of lacquered wood, and shopgirls or patronnes, colorful and soft as artificial flowers, will let their plump arms, wielding atomizers, graze us, or the hem of their skirts, as they stand tip-toe on stools, reaching upwards. But the phials, the ampules, the jars with their spire-like or cut-glass stoppers will weave in vain from shelf to shelf their network of harmonies, assonances, dissonances, counterpoints, modulations, cadenzas: our deaf nostrils will no longer catch the notes of their scale. We will not distinguish musk from verbena: amber and mignonette, bergamot and bitter-almond will remain mute, sealed in the calm slumber of their bottles. When the olfactory alphabet, which made them so many words in a precious lexicon, is forgotten, perfumes will be left speechless, inarticulate, illegible.

How different were the vibrations a great *parfumerie* could once stir in the spirit of a man of the world, as in the days when my carriage would stop, with a sharp tug at the reins, at a famous sign on the Champs-Élysées, and I would hurriedly get out and enter that mirrored gallery, dropping with one movement my cloak, top hat, cane, and gloves into the hands of the girls who hastened to receive them, while Madame Odile rushed toward me as if she were flying on her frills.

'Monsieur de Saint-Caliste! What a pleasant surprise! What can we offer you? A cologne? An essence of vetivert? A pomade for curling the moustache? Or a lotion to restore the hair's natural ebony hue?'

And she would flicker her lashes, her lips forming a sly smile. 'Or do you wish to make an addition to the list of presents that my delivery boys carry each week, discreetly, in your name, to addresses both illustrious and obscure, scattered throughout Paris? Is it a new conquest you are about to confide in your devoted Madame Odile?'

Overcome with agitation as I was, I remained silent, writhing, while the girls already began to concern themselves with me. One slipped the gardenia from my buttonhole so that its fragrance, however faint, would not disturb my perception of the scents; another girl drew my silk handkerchief from my pocket so it would be ready to receive the sample drops from which I was to choose; a third sprinkled my waistcoat with rose water, to neutralize the stench of my cigar; a fourth dabbled odorless lacquer on my moustache, so it would not become impregnated with the various essences, confusing my nostrils.

And Madame went on: 'I see! A great passion! Ah! I've been expecting this for some time, Monsieur! You can hide nothing from me! Is she a lady of high degree? A reigning queen of the Comédie? Or the Variétés? Or did you make a carefree excursion into the demi-monde and fall into the trap of sentiment? But, first of all, in which category would you place her: the jasmine family, the fruit blossoms, the piercing scents, or the Oriental? Tell me, *mon chou!*'

And one of her shopgirls, Martine, was already tickling the tip of my ear with her finger wet with patchouli (pressing the sting of her breast, at the same time, beneath my armpit), and Charlotte was extending her arm, perfumed with orris, for me to sniff (in the same fashion, on other occasions, I had examined a whole sampler, arrayed over her body), and Sidonie blew on my hand, to evaporate the drop of eglantine she had put there (between her parted lips I could glimpse her little teeth, whose bites I knew so well), and another, whom I had never seen, a new girl (whom I merely grazed with an absent pinch, preoccupied as I was), aimed an atomizer at me, pressing its bulb, as if inviting me to an amorous skirmish.

'No, Madame, that's not it, that's not it at all,' I managed to say. 'What I am looking for is not the perfume suited to a lady I know. It is the lady I must find! A lady of whom I know nothing – save her perfume!'

At moments like these Madame Odile's methodical genius is at its best: only the sternest mental order allows one to rule a world of impalpable effluvia. 'We shall proceed by elimination,' she said, turning grave. 'Is there a hint of cinnamon? Does it contain musk? Is it violet-like? Or almond?'

But how could I put into words the languid, fierce sensation I had felt the previous night, at a masked ball, when my mysterious partner for the waltz, with a lazy movement, had loosened the gauzy scarf which separated her white shoulder from my moustache, and a streaked, rippling cloud had assailed my nostrils, as if I were breathing in the soul of a tigress?

'It's a different perfume, quite different, Madame Odile, unlike any of those you mention!'

The girls were already climbing to the highest shelves, carefully handing one another fragile jars, removing the stoppers for barely a second, as if afraid the air might contaminate the essences in them.

'This heliotrope,' Madam Odile told me, 'is used by only four women in all Paris: the Duchesse de Clignancourt, the Marquise de Menilmontant, the wife of Coulommiers the cheese-manufacturer, and his mistress . . . They send me this rosewood every month especially for the wife of the Tsar's Ambassador . . . Here is a potpourri I prepare for only two customers: the Princess of Baden-Holstein and Carole, the courtesan . . . This artemisia? I remember the names of all the ladies who have bought it once, but never a second time. It apparently has a depressant effect on men.'

What I required of Madame Odile's specific experience was precisely this: to give a name to an olfactory sensation I could neither forget nor hold in my memory without its slowly fading. I had to expect as much: even the perfumes of memory evaporate: each new scent I was made to sniff, as it imposed its diversity, its own powerful presence, made still vaguer the recollection of that absent perfume, reduced it to a shadow.

'No, it was sharper . . . I mean fresher . . . heavier . . .' In this seesawing of the scale of odors, I was lost, I could no longer discern the direction of the memory I should follow: I knew only that at one point of the spectrum, there was a gap, a secret fold where there lurked that perfume which, for me, was a complete woman.

And wasn't it, after all, the same thing in the savannah, the forest, the swamp, when they were a network of smells, and we ran along, heads down, never losing contact with the ground, using hands and noses to help us find the trail? We understood whatever there was to understand through our noses rather than through our eyes: the mammoth, the porcupine, onion, drought, rain are first smells which become distinct from other smells; food, non-food; our cave, the enemy's cave; danger – everything is first perceived by the nose, everything is within the nose, the world is the nose. In our herd, our nose tells us who belongs to the herd and who doesn't; the herd's females have a smell that is the herd's smell, but each female also has an odor that distinguishes her from the other females. Between us and them, at first sight, there isn't much difference: we're all made the same way, and besides, what's the point of standing there staring? Odor, that's what each of us has that's different from the others. The odor tells you immediately and certainly what you need to know. There are no words, there is no information more precise than what the nose receives. With my nose I learned that in the herd there is a female not like the others, not like the others for me, for my nose; and I ran, following her trail in the grass, my nose exploring all the females running in front of me, of my nose, in the herd; and there I found her, it was she who had summoned me with her odor in the midst of all those odors; there, I breathed through my nose all of her and her love-summons. The herd moves, keeps running, trotting, and if you stop, in the herd's stampede, they are all on top of you, trampling you, confusing your nose with their smells; and now I'm on top of her, and they are pushing us, overturning us; they all climb on her, on me; all the females sniff me; all the males and females become tangled with us, and all their smells, which have nothing to do with that smell I smelled before and now smell no longer. It is waiting for me to hunt for it. I hunt for her spoor in the dusty, trampled grass. I sniff. I sniff all the females. I no longer recognize her. I force my way desperately through the herd, hunting for her with my nose.

*

For that matter, now that I wake up in the smell of grass and turn my hand to make a *zlwan zlwan zlwan* with the brush on the drum, echoing Patrick's *tlann tlann* on his four strings, because I think I'm still playing She knows and I know, but actually there was just Lenny knocking himself out, sweating like a horse, with his twelve strings, and one of those birds from Hampstead kneeling there and doing some things to him, while I was playing *ding bong dang yang*, and all the others including me were off. I was lying flat, the drums had fallen and I hadn't even noticed, I reach out to pull the drums to safety or else they'll kick them in, those round things I see, white in the darkness, I reach out and I touch flesh, by its smell it seems warm girl's flesh, I hunt for the drums which have rolled on the floor in the darkness with the beer cans, with all the others who have rolled on the floor naked, in the upset ashtrays, a nice warm ass in the air, and saying it's not so hot you can sleep naked on the floor, of course there are a lot of us shut up in here for God knows how long, but somebody has to put more shillings in the gas stove that's gone out and is making nothing but a stink, and, out as I was, I woke up in a cold sweat all the fault of the lousy shit they gave us to smoke, the ones who brought us to this stinking place down by the docks with the excuse that here we could make all the racket we liked all night long without having the fuzz on our tails like always, and we had to go someplace anyway after they threw us out of that dump in Portobello Road, but it was because they wanted to make these new birds that came after us from Hampstead and we didn't even have time to see who they were or what they looked like, because we always have a whole swarm of groupies after us when we play somewhere, and specially when Robin breaks into Have mercy, have mercy on me, those birds turn on and want to do things right away, and so all the others begin while we're still up there sweating and playing and I'm hitting those drums *ba-zoom ba-zoom ba-zoom*, and they're at it, Have mercy on me, have mercy on me, ma'am, and so tonight, just like the other times, we didn't do anything with these groupies even if they do follow our bunch so logically we ought to make it with them, not those others.

So now I get up to hunt for this lousy gas stove to put some shillings in it and make it go, I walk with the soles of my feet on hair asses butts beer cans tits glasses of whisky spilled on the carpet, somebody must have thrown up on it too, I better go on all fours, at least I can see where I'm going, and besides I can't stand up straight, so I recognize people by the smell, our bunch with all that sweat sticking to us is easy to recognize, I can tell us from the others who stink only of their lousy grass and their dirty hair, and the girls too who don't take many baths, but their smells mix with the others a little and are a little different from the others as well, and every now and then you run into some special smells on these girls and it's worth lingering a minute and sniffing, their hair for example, when it doesn't absorb too much smoke, and in other places too, logically, and so I am crossing the room, smelling some of these smells of sleeping girls until at one point I stop.

As I say, it's hard really to smell one girl's skin, especially when you're all in a big tangle of bodies, but there beneath me I'm surely smelling a girl's white skin, a white smell with that special force white has, a slightly mottled skin smell probably dotted with faint or even invisible freckles, a skin that breathes the way a leaf's pores breathe the meadows, and all the stink in the room keeps its distance from this skin, maybe two inches, maybe two fractions of an inch, because meanwhile I start inhaling this skin everywhere while she sleeps with her face hidden in her arms, her long maybe red hair over her shoulders down her back, her long legs outstretched, cool in the pockets behind the knees, now I really am breathing and smelling nothing but her, who must have felt, still sleeping, that I am smelling her and must not mind, because she rises on her elbows, her face still held down, and from her armpit I move and smell what her breast is like, the tip, and since I'm kind of astride, logically it seems the right moment to push in the direction that makes me happy and I feel she's happy too, so, half-sleeping, we find a way of lying and agree on how I should lie and how she should now beautifully lie.

Meanwhile the cold we haven't been feeling we feel afterwards and I remember I was on my way to put shillings in the stove, and I get up, I break away from the island of her smell, I go on crossing among unknown bodies, among smells that are incompatible, or rather repulsive, I hunt in the others' things to see if I can find some shillings, following the gas-stink I hunt for the stove and I make it work, gasping and stinking more than ever, following its loo stink I hunt for the loo and I piss there, shivering in the gray light of morning that trickles from the little window, I go back into the darkness, the stagnation, the exhalation of the bodies, now I have to cross them again to find that girl I know only by her smell, it's hard to hunt in the dark but even if I saw her how can I tell it's her when all I know is her smell, so I go on smelling the bodies lying on the floor and one guy says fuck off and punches me, this place is laid out in a funny way, like a lot of rooms with people lying on the floor in all of them, and I've lost my sense of direction or else I never had one, these girls have different smells, some might even be her only the smell isn't the same any more, meanwhile Howard's waked up and he's already got his bass and he's picking up Don't tell me I'm through, I think I've already covered the whole place, so where has she gone, in the midst of these girls you can begin to see now the light's coming in, but what I want to smell I can't smell, I'm roaming around like a jerk and I can't find her, Have mercy, have mercy on me, I go from one skin to another hunting for that lost skin that isn't like any other skin.

For each woman a perfume exists which enhances the perfume of her own skin, the note in the scale which is at once color and flavor and aroma and tenderness, and thus the pleasure in moving from one skin to another can be endless. When the chandeliers in the Faubourg Saint-Honoré's drawing rooms illuminated my entrance into the gala balls, I was overwhelmed by the pungent cloud of perfumes from the pearl-edged décolletés, the delicate Bulgarian-pink ground giving off jabs of camphor which amber made cling to the silk dresses, and I bowed to kiss the Duchesse du Havre-Caumartin's hand, inhaling the jasmine that hovered over her slightly anemic skin, and I offered my arm to the Comtesse de Barbès-Rochechouart, who ensnared me in the wave of sandalwood that seemed to engulf her firm, dark complexion, and I helped the Baronne de Mouton-Duvernet free her alabaster shoulder from her otter coat as a gust of fuchsia struck me. My papillae could easily assign faces to those perfumes Madame Odile now had me review, removing the stoppers from her opalescent vials. I had devoted myself to the same process the night before at the masked ball of the Knights of the Holy Sepulchre; there was no lady whose name I could not guess beneath the embroidered domino. But then she appeared, with a little satin mask over her face, a veil around her shoulders and bosom, Andalusian style; and in vain I wondered who she was, and in vain, holding her closer than was proper as we danced, I compared my memories with that perfume never imagined until then, which enclosed the perfume of her body as an oyster encloses its pearl. I knew nothing of her, but I felt I knew all in that perfume; and I would have desired a world without names, where that perfume alone would have sufficed as name and as all the words she could speak to me: that perfume I knew was lost now in Madame Odile's liquid labyrinth, evaporated in my memory, so that I could not summon it back even by remembering her when she followed me into the conservatory with the hydrangeas. As I caressed her, she seemed at times docile, then at times violent, clawing. She allowed me to uncover hidden areas, explore the privacy of her perfume, provided I did not raise the mask from her face.

'Why this mystery, after all?' I cried, exasperated. 'Tell me where and when I can see you once more. Or rather, see you for the first time!'

'Do not think of such a thing, Monsieur,' she answered. 'A terrible threat hangs over my life. But hush – there he is!'

A shadow, hooded, in a violet domino, had appeared in the Empire mirror.

'I must follow that person,' the woman said. 'Forget me. Someone holds unspeakable power over me.'

And before I could say to her, 'My sword is at your service. Have faith in it!', she had already gone off, preceding the violet domino, which left a wake of Oriental tobacco in the crowd of maskers. I do not know through which door they succeeded in slipping away. I followed them in vain, and in vain I plagued with questions all those familiar with *le tout Paris*. I know I shall have no peace until I have found the trail of that hostile odor and that beloved perfume, until one has put me on the trail of the other, until the duel in which I shall kill my enemy has given me the right to tear away the mask concealing that face.

There is a hostile odor that strikes my nose every time I think I've caught the odor of the female I am hunting for in the trail of the herd, a hostile odor also mixed with her odor, and I bare my incisors, canines, premolars, and I am already filled with rage, I gather stones, I tear off knotty branches, if I cannot find with my nose that smell of hers I would like to have at least the satisfaction of finding out the owner of this hostile odor that makes me angry. The herd has sudden shifts of direction when the whole stream turns on you, and suddenly I feel my jaws slammed to the ground by a club's blow on my skull, a kick jabs into my neck, and with my nose I recognize the hostile male who has recognized on me his female's odor, and he tries to finish me off by flinging me against the rock, and I recognize her smell on him and I am filled with fury, I jump up, I swing my club with all my strength until I smell the odor of blood, I leap on him with my full weight, I batter his skull with flints, shards, elkjaws, bones, daggers, horn harpoons, while all the females form a circle around us, waiting to see who will win. Obviously, I win, I stand up and grope among the females, but I cannot find the one I am looking for; caked with blood and dust, I cannot smell odors very clearly any more, so I might as well stand on my hind legs and walk erect for a while.

Some of us have got into the habit of walking like this, never putting hands on the ground, and some can even move fast. It makes my head swim a little, and I raise my hands to cling to boughs as I used to when I lived in trees all the time, but now I notice that I can keep my balance even up there, my foot flattens against the ground, and my legs move forward even if I don't bend my knees. Of course, by keeping my nose suspended up here in the air, I lose a lot of things: information you get by sniffing the earth with all the spoors of animals that move over it, sniffing the others in the herd, specially the females. But you get other things instead: your nose is drier, so you can pick up distant smells carried by the wind, and you find fruit on the trees, birds' eggs in their nests. And your eyes help your nose, they grasp things in space – the sycamore's leaves, the river, the blue stripe of the forest, the clouds.

In the end, I go out to breathe in the morning, the street, the fog, all you can see in dustbins: fish scales, cans, nylon stockings; at the corner a Pakistani who sells pineapples has opened his shop; I reach a wall of fog and it's the Thames. From the railing, if you look hard, you can see the shadows of the same old tugs, you can smell the same mud and oil, and farther on the lights and smoke of Southwark begin. And I bang my head against the fog like I was accompanying that guitar chord of In the morning I'll be dead, and I can't get it out of my mind.

*

With a splitting headache, I leave the *parfumerie*; I would like to rush immediately to the Passy address I wrested from Madame Odile after many obscure hints and conjectures, but instead I shout to my driver: 'The Bois, Auguste! At once! A brisk trot!'

And as soon as the phaeton moves, I breathe deeply to free myself of all the scents that have mingled in my brain, I savor the leather smell of the upholstery and the trappings, the stink of the horse and his steaming dung and urine, I smell again the thousand odors, stately or plebeian, which fly in the air of Paris, and it is only when the sycamores of the Bois de Boulogne have plunged me into the lymph of their foliage, when the gardeners' water stirs an earthy smell from the clover, that I order Auguste to turn toward Passy.

The door of the house is half-open. There are people going in, men in top hats, veiled ladies. Already in the hall I am struck by a heavy smell of flowers, as of rotting vegetation; I enter, among the glowing beeswax tapers, the chrysanthemum wreaths, the cushions of violets, the asphodel garlands. In the open, satin-lined coffin, the face is unrecognizable, covered by a veil and swathed in bandages, as if in the decomposition of her features her beauty continues to reject death; but I recognize the base, the echo of that perfume that resembles no other, merged with the odor of death now as if they had always been inseparable.

I would like to question someone, but all these people are strangers, perhaps foreigners. I pause beside an elderly man who looks the most foreign of all: an olive-skinned gentleman with a red fez and a black frock coat, standing in meditation beside the bier. 'To think that at midnight she was dancing, and was the loveliest woman at the ball . . .'

The man with the fez does not turn, but answers in a low voice: 'What do you mean, sir? At midnight she was dead.'

Standing erect, with my nose in the wind, I perceive less precise signs, but of vaster meaning, signs that bring with them suspicion, alarm, horror, signs that when you have your nose to the ground you refuse perhaps to accept, you turn away from them, as I turn from this odor which comes from the rocks of the chasm where we in our herd fling animals we've disemboweled, the rotting organs, the bones, where the vultures hover and circle. And that odor I was following was lost down there, and, depending on how the wind blows, it rises with the stink of the clawed cadavers, the breath of the jackals that tear them apart still warm in the blood that is drying on the rocks in the sun.

And when I go back upstairs to hunt for the others because my head feels a little clearer and maybe now I could find her again and figure out who she is, instead there was nobody up there, God knows when they went away, while I was down on the Embankment, all the rooms are empty except for the beer cans and my drums, and the stove's stink has become unbearable, and I move around all the rooms and there is one with the door locked, the very room with the stove you can smell gasping through the cracks in the door, so strong it's nauseating, and I begin to slam my shoulder against the door until it gives way, and inside the place is all full of thick, black, disgusting gas from floor to ceiling, and on the floor the thing I see before I writhe in a fit of vomiting is the long, white, outstretched form, face hidden by the hair, and as I pull her out by her stiffened legs I smell her odor within the asphyxiating odor, her odor that I try to follow and distinguish in the ambulance, in the first-aid room, among the odors of disinfectant and slime that drips from the marble slabs in the morgue, and the air is impregnated with it, especially when outside the weather is damp.

77·

M. NourbeSe Philip
FROM *ZONG!*
{Noulipo}

Zong! #6

          question therefore

               the age

           eighteen weeks

                      and calm

but it is said . . .

                       – from the maps

     and

            contradicted

           by the evidence . . .

                        question

                             therefore

               the age

Zong! #7

first:

the when

the which

the who

the were

the throwing

overboard

the be

come apprehended

exist did not

Zong! #8

the good of overboard

justified a throwing

         of property

         fellow

creatures

    become

        our portion

         of

        mortality

    provision

        a bad market

negroes

          want

    for dying

78.

Jacques Roubaud
FROM *SAYING POETRY*
translated by Matthew B. Smith
{Oulipo}

I like reading other people's poems   more than my own
I also like writing them   but that's another story
   We started to read Reverdy   poem
after poem   in no specific order   sometimes we'd each read
the same poem   sometimes we'd read a poem already read
we took turns   we read like this   for quite a while
   for more than an hour   the person who was supposed to come
didn't come   and we weren't at all prepared
for this reading   and

   For this reason   and maybe also due to   the
the false sense of calm   transmitted by   the colorless
ink   of the poems   and to our own
breezy   reading   on this summer day
we'd confuse   certain words   stumble over
their sounds   mix up the order of the lines
of a poem read from the page

   Had this dual reading   been recorded
significant discrepancies   would be found
between it and the printed text   I'm not
saying   that these innovations   mainly accidental
for my part   were of any interest   but they are a
good example   of a reading   practice   guided

by what I'll call   a strategy of inattention   I
remember   hearing an impressive reading
like this   from Joseph Guglielmi himself
his voice   reading   in this way
     from his own book   *La préparation des titres*

     This style of reading   which was in part behind
     my experiments   with the tripartite
structure   of *sleep*   is   neither improvised
nor rehearsed   it is a matter of the voice reading poetry
     while remaining   open   to internal
or external distractions   responsive   to the
the moment's   biddings

     I especially like   the brief rush of anxiety
     I feel when reading   in these circumstances
in these settings   a translation   not fully completed
     both the text and the translation   before me
     the translation still in progress   with its guesswork
and questions exposed   which will have to be addressed
on the spot   if I read   all that before me   wooly
heads before me   its intractable moments elided
     wreck of errors   rocky sputters
     hirsute   attacks on the text   on language
     But at times also   smooth-flowing riverbeds
and then again   spontaneous   drift and overflow
     when bits of other poems get picked
up   by a snag   a pivot   a pillow
of memory

     The most natural   slips   give the impression of
a spoken and spontaneous version   of
John Cage's   haikus   culled   from Thoreau's
Journal   or of Ronald Johnson's   *Radios*
deciphered   revealed   by nothing other than

the erasure   of certain letters   in
Paradise Lost   title   which   indeed   contains   *radi os*

  To read to say   in this way   only the words remaining on
the page   at the speed of a skimming eye
the page   translated by the voice   with its
consonantal slides   its shifts   its
sudden spurts   'my parents were poor but
honest'   'skip all that said the man at the witness stand'
  the voice skips lines of poetry vanish
  because poetry is a *boojum* on the tongue

  Saying poetry is not a private matter   saying
poetry is not a public matter   saying poetry
keeps the same voice   and it's not that the voice
saying poetry is the same   in the room where you
are alone   and in the room where a few heads before
you fall asleep   as you are saying poetry
because   alone   you say poetry   as if
you had a crowd before you   or
conversely   because you speak before an
audience as if you were alone
  But   only   because the voice saying
poetry   is indifferent   to this change   of
context   does it take shape   ideally   in a
frictionless   space   ready   to make the air
vibrate articulately   with irregular swings and
inversions   reaching the remotest regions
  of this dark terrestrial globe   carrying on in a straight
line   thus curved   until it comes back to you   a little
more than a day later   from behind your head   after
having traveled in a giant   40,000 kilometer circle

Neither private   then   nor public   but   only
      materially in some indefinite space   and that's why
this voice   has no memory by design   and
that's why   in these pages   scored for oral prose
I've spoken   without distinction   of saying
or reading   poetry   that's why I implied   that saying
is reading   with your voice

    The idea is that saying   poetry   with no
support   would imply   that it exists internally
in your   memory   and   as the myth of
memory has shown   an object   and the memory of
that object   the poem and its memory   are twins

    They are similar like two drops of water
like two drops of water it seems   one to be
the other   and the other   one   but at the same time   and
here's the trick   the trap   the *quark*   of the myth of
memory or at least as it has been handed down to us

79.

Italo Calvino
FROM *IF ON A WINTER'S NIGHT A TRAVELLER*
translated by William Weaver
{Oulipo}

I asked Lotaria if she has already read some books of mine that I lent her. She said no, because here she doesn't have a computer at her disposal.

She explained to me that a suitably programmed computer can read a novel in a few minutes and record the list of all the words contained in the text, in order of frequency. 'That way I can have an already completed reading at hand,' Lotaria says, 'with an incalculable saving of time. What is the reading of a text, in fact, except the recording of certain thematic recurrences, certain insistences of forms and meanings? An electronic reading supplies me with a list of the frequencies, which I have only to glance at to form an idea of the problems the book suggests to my critical study. Naturally, at the highest frequencies the list records countless articles, pronouns, particles, but I don't pay them any attention. I head straight for the words richest in meaning; they can give me a fairly precise notion of the book.'

Lotaria brought me some novels electronically transcribed, in the form of words listed in the order of their frequency. 'In a novel of fifty to a hundred thousand words,' she said to me, 'I advise you to observe immediately the words that are repeated about twenty times. Look here. Words that appear nineteen times:

> blood, cartridge belt, commander, do, have, immediately, it, life, seen, sentry, shots, spider, teeth, together, your . . .

'Words that appear eighteen times:

boys, cap, come, dead, eat, enough, evening, French, go, handsome, new, passes, period, potatoes, those, until . . .
'Don't you already have a clear idea what it's about?' Lotaria says.
'There's no question: it's a war novel, all action, brisk writing, with a certain underlying violence. The narration is entirely on the surface, I would
say; but to make sure, it's always a good idea to take a look at the list
of words used only once, though no less important for that. Take this
sequence, for example:

underarm, underbrush, undercover, underdog, underfed, underfoot,
undergo, undergraduate, underground, undergrowth, underhand,
underprivileged, undershirt, underwear, underweight . . .

'No, the book isn't completely superficial, as it seemed. There must be
something hidden; I can direct my research along these lines.'

Lotaria shows me another series of lists. 'This is an entirely different
novel. It's immediately obvious. Look at the words that recur about fifty
times:

had, his, husband, little, Riccardo (51) answered, been, before, has,
station, what (48) all, barely, bedroom, Mario, some, times (47)
morning, seemed, went, whom (46) should (45) hand, listen, until,
were (43) Cecilia, Delia, evening, girl, hands, six, who, years (42)
almost, alone, could, man, returned, window (41) me, wanted (40)
life (39)

'What do you think of that? An intimatist narration, subtle feelings,
understated, a humble setting, everyday life in the provinces . . . As a confirmation, we'll take a sample of words used a single time:

chilled, deceived, downward, engineer, enlargement, fattening,
ingenious, ingenuous, injustice, jealous, kneeling, swallow, swallowed, swallowing . . .

'So we already have an idea of the atmosphere, the moods, the social
background . . . We can go on to a third book:

according, account, body, especially, God, hair, money, times, went
(29) evening, flour, food, rain, reason, somebody, stay, Vincenzo,
wine (38) death, eggs, green, hers, legs, sweet, therefore (36) black,
bosom, children, day, even, ha, head, machine, make, remained,
stays, stuffs, white, would (35)

'Here I would say we're dealing with a full-blooded story, violent, everything concrete, a bit brusque, with a direct sensuality, no refinement, popular eroticism. But here again, let's go on to the list of words with a frequency of one. Look, for example:

ashamed, shame, shamed, shameful, shameless, shames, shaming, vegetables, verify, vermouth, virgins . . .

'You see? A guilt complex, pure and simple! A valuable indication: the critical inquiry can start with that, establish some working hypotheses . . . What did I tell you? Isn't this a quick, effective system?'

80.

Georges Perec
FROM *W OR THE MEMORY OF CHILDHOOD*
translated by David Bellos
{Oulipo}

Eighteen

It is clear that the overall organization of sporting life on W (the villages, the way teams are made up, selection methods, to mention only the basic elements) has as its sole aim to heighten competitiveness or, to put it another way, to glorify victory. In this respect it can indeed be said that no other human society can rival W. The survival of the fittest is the law of this land; yet the struggle itself is nothing, for it is not Sport for Sport's sake, achievement for the sake of achievement, which motivates the men of W, but thirst for victory, victory at any price. Just as the spectators in the stadiums do not forgive an Athlete for losing, neither do they spare their applause for the winners. All hail to the victorious! Woe betide the vanquished! For the village citizens, professional sportsmen all, nothing but victory is conceivable – victory at every level: against their own team mates, in intervillage meetings, and finally, above all, in the Games.

Like all the other moral values of the society of W, the glorification of success has a concrete expression in daily life: grandiose ceremonies are held in honour of victorious Athletes. True, in all ages victors have been celebrated: they have gone up on to the podium, had their country's national anthem played, been awarded medals, statues, cups, certificates, crowns, have been made freeman of their native towns, been decorated by their governments. But such celebrations and honours are as nothing beside what the Nation of W accords to its deserving. Every evening, irrespective of the type of contest held that day, the first three in each event mount the podium, are clapped and cheered at length by the crowd, have bouquets, confetti, handkerchiefs thrown at them, receive from the hands of the Official Calligraphers the emblazoned certificate recording their achievement, and are granted the great privilege of raising their village's standard to the top of the Olympic flag pole; the three leaders from each event are then led in procession behind torchbearers, standard bearers, dove-keepers and trumpeters to the great halls of the Central Stadium where a ritual reception awaits them in all its splendour and bounty. They strip off their tracksuits and are offered a choice of magnificent apparel, from embroidered costumes to silk capes with scarlet frogging, spangled uniforms glittering with decorations, evening dress, and doublets with lace ruffs and trim. They are presented to the Officials, who raise their glasses and drink a toast in their honour. Wild rounds of toasts and libations ensue. The Athletes are given a banquet which often goes on till dawn: the most exquisite dishes are placed before them, accompanied by the headiest of wines, the most succulent cold meats, the suavest of sweets, the most intoxicating spirits.

The celebration feats at the big Games are obviously more copious and splendid than the feasts held for the winners of ranking heats or local championships. But that difference, however marked, is not essential to an understanding of the value system which prevails on W. What is much more significant, on the other hand, and constitutes one of the singular features of W society, is not that the losers are excluded from the festivities – that is only fair – but that they are purely and simply denied their evening meal. It goes without saying, clearly enough, that if victors and vanquished alike were both to have food, then the only privilege for the winners would be that their food was of better quality, banquet fare in place of everyday nourishment. The Organizers, not without reason, considered that perhaps that would not suffice to give contestants the fighting spirit needed for top-level competitions. In order to win, an Athlete has to have the will to win. A concern for personal standing, the desire to make a name for oneself, national pride, can all no doubt function as powerful motives. But at the crucial moment, at the point where a man must give his best, where he must surpass his own strength and find, somewhere outside of himself, that extra ounce of energy which will enable him to snatch victory, it is quite useful if what is at stake effectively partakes of a basic survival mechanism, almost an instinctive self-protection: what the Athlete grasps in winning is much more than the necessarily ephemeral glory of having been the best; it is – by the sole fact of his obtaining an extra meal – a guarantee of better physical condition, an assurance of a better-balanced diet and, consequently, of better form.

It can now be appreciated how subtly the dietary system of W supports the overall social system, to an extent that makes it one of the main articulations of social structure. Naturally the absence of an evening meal does not in itself constitute a mortal deprivation. If that were the case, then sporting life, and life itself, would have come to an end long ago on W: indeed, simple arithmetic shows that in the best instance, namely the ranking heats, only 264 Athletes, out of a total of 1,320, have a chance of eating dinner. After local championships or selection trials, the number falls to 132, and at the end of Games only 66 remain – that is to say, quite precisely, one in twenty. The vast majority of Athletes would therefore be chronically undernourished. But they are not: their diet includes three meals a day, the first very early in the morning, before the cross-country warm-up, the second at noon, after training sessions are finished, the third at 4 p.m., during the traditional half-time between the eliminating heats and the finals. On the other hand, these meals are carefully designed to fulfil the athletes' dietary and caloric needs only in part. Their sugar content is virtually nil, as is the quantity of vitamin B1, essential for the assimilation of carbohydrates. Athletes are thus subjected to a consistently deficient intake which in the long run seriously undermines their resistance to muscle fatigue. From this point of view, victors' banquets, with their fresh fruit, sweet wines, dried bananas, dates, strawberry preserves, compotes and chocolate tablets, therefore constitute a veritable carbohydrate compensation indispensable for the Athletes' physical health.

The problem with this method is obviously the risk that, by giving an advantage to the winners and harshly penalizing the losers in an area directly related to the physiological basis of the contest, it will emphasize the differences between the contestants and produce in the end a kind of vicious circle: the winners of the day, rewarded that very evening with additional sugar rations, have every chance of winning again the following day, and so on, with the one group becoming ever more sturdy, the other ever weaker. That would of course deprive the contests of all interest, since the results, so to speak, would be known in advance. The Organizers have taken no particular steps to remedy this problem. Instead of forbidding victors to enter the stadium on the day after they win – a provision that would obviously be contrary to the whole spirit of W – they have preferred (and in so doing have once again shown their wisdom and their profound understanding of the human heart) to put their trust in what they call, laughingly, nature. Experience has proved them right. The winners are not

437

debarred from the next day's contests. But more often than not they have spent the night carousing, and only returned to quarters in time for reveille. Sugar-starved, they usually bolt their food, stuff themselves like pigs. Dizzy with victory, they let themselves go and reply to every toast drunk in their honour, mixing wines and liqueurs until they are under the table. It is easy to understand why, in these circumstances, Athletes almost never win twice in a row. Prudence would suggest that the winners ought to hold back, that they should refrain from drinking or at least limit themselves, and take food selectively and with moderation. But the temptations are so great for the feted prizewinners that it would take an uncommonly tough character to resist them. And besides, restraint is not encouraged: neither by the Officials – who, quite the contrary, are constantly inviting them to drain their glasses – nor by the Sports Managers, who, with their concern for the well-being of their teams, have every interest in a speedy turn-over of winners, so as to ensure, as regularly as possible and for the greatest possible number of their Athletes, the essential energizing sustenance provided by these evening meals.

Nineteen

Collège Turenne, which was also called the Belltower, was quite a large, pinkish building, probably not very old, situated a little outside Villard, maybe five hundred yards beyond Les Frimas, as I discovered with amazement when I returned to visit it in December 1970, so firmly did I remember it as a frightfully far off place where no one ever went, a place which news never reached, whence those who crossed its threshold never returned.

The school was a religious foundation run by two sisters (perhaps in the ordinary as well as the religious sense of the word) whom I imagine, rather than remember, in long grey robes, with huge bunches of keys on their waistbands. They were strict and not much given to showing affection. The tutor, on the other hand, was a man of great kindness, and for him I had feelings that were close to veneration; he was called Father David, he was a Franciscan or Dominican friar, dressed in a white robe with a belt of plaited string at the end of which hung a rosary. Whatever the weather, he went barefoot but for sandals. I think I remember he was bald and had a big red beard. According to my aunt, he was a converted Jew, and it was perhaps as much out of proselytizing zeal as out of concern for my protection that he insisted I be baptized.

I do not know how my religious education proceeded and I have forgotten every bit of the catechism that was drummed into me, except that I tackled it with exaggerated keenness and piety. In any case I still have an extremely detailed memory of my baptism, which was performed sometime in the summer of 1943. That morning I made a vow of poverty – that is to say, I decided that, as a first step, I would wear my everyday clothes at the ceremony. I had withdrawn to a corner of the kitchen garden at the back of the school and was deep in my prayers when the headmistresses and two cleaning women came upon me. They had been looking for me for an hour. They grabbed hold of me and, disregarding my protests, undressed me, soaked me in a tub of cold water, and rubbed me down untenderly with household soap (or whatever substitute was used in those days) before forcing me into a magnificent sailor suit. My only consolation was that I could keep my own shoes, which had nothing ceremonial about them.

The sailor suit belonged to my godfather, a Belgian boy who had escaped to Villard with his sister, who was my godmother. They were, I was later told, the children of one of the Queen of Belgium's ladies-in-waiting. It was probably they who gave me, as a baptism present, a kind of picture in relief of the Virgin and Child in a gilded frame, which I contemplated piously all afternoon at the back of the classroom, having been excused exercises, and which that evening I hung over my bed.

Next morning I handed back the suit, but my piety and faith remained exemplary and Father David made me religious prefect of my dormitory and entrusted me with giving the signal for evening prayers and with making sure they were properly executed. On some days I received permission to rise before the others and to attend the Mass which Father David, assisted by a single altar-boy, said for himself and the two headmistresses in the little chapel with its stylized Stations of the Cross, whose tower had given the school its nickname. My dearest wish would have been to be that altar-boy, but this was not possible: before that I had to make my First Communion, then my solemn Communion, and even be confirmed. I knew the seven sacraments, and Confirmation seemed to me to be the most mysterious of all, perhaps because it takes place only once (unlike Communion – or Eucharist – and Confession – or Penance – which can at a pinch be a daily event) and because its profound uselessness (why bother to confirm what Baptism has already pronounced?) is associated with a ritual which involves a real dignitary of the Church, a bishop. A bishop was an official person, a personality, a personage of quasi-historical dimensions for me; as yet I knew of no equivalent, since I paid no attention to generals – whom eighteen months or two years later I was to start idolizing – or to ministers, or to sporting champions, who, it must be said, had scarcely any opportunity to shine in those troubled times.

A bishop came to the school to confirm some of the boarders, probably amongst the eldest, with a slap, which seemed all the more symbolic for being absolutely dissimilar to what I knew as a smack, a wallop, or a cuff. The ceremony was as fabulous as I had been told, and was held in the open; to my grave disappointment, the bishop did not wear his mitre or carry his crozier; he wore a black habit with only a purple stole and hood to indicate his great eminence. I remember I very much wanted to touch him, but I don't know if I succeeded.

*

I have a vague memory of the litanies, a weak impression of still being able to hear the endless reiteration of the 'Ora pro nobis' echoed in chorus after each saint's name. To this memory is attached the remembrance of punning rounds in which a number sequence leads, usually fairly soon, to a play on words: 'I one a rat, I two a rat, I three a rat, I four a rat, I five a rat, I six a rat, I seven a rat, I ate a rat', and also: 'What one? What two? What three? What four?'

I also remember 'I am a Christian, wherein lie my glory, my hope and my succour' but of course I've forgotten what comes next, just as I no longer know what comes after 'Unto us a boy is born, unto us a child is given . . .'

81.

Lyn Hejinian
FROM *MY LIFE*
{Noulipo}

A pause, a rose,
something on paper

A moment yellow, just as four years later, when my father returned home from the war, the moment of greeting him, as he stood at the bottom of the stairs, younger, thinner than when he had left, was purple – though moments are no longer so colored. Somewhere, in the background, rooms share a pattern of small roses. Pretty is as pretty does. In certain families, the meaning of necessity is at one with the sentiment of pre-necessity. The better things were gathered in a pen. The windows were narrowed by white-gauze curtains which were never loosened. Here I refer to irrelevance, that rigidity which never intrudes. Hence, repetitions, free from all ambition. The shadow of the redwood trees, she said, was oppressive. The plush must be worn away. On her walks she stepped into people's gardens to pinch off cuttings from their geraniums and succulents. An occasional sunset is reflected on the windows. A little puddle is overcast. If only you could touch, or, even, catch those gray great creatures. I was afraid of my uncle with the wart on his nose, or of his jokes at our expense which were beyond me, and I was shy of my aunt's deafness who was his sister-in-law and who had years earlier fallen into the habit of nodding, agreeably. Wool station. See lightning, wait for thunder. Quite mistakenly, as it happened. Long time lines trail behind every idea, object, person, pet, vehicle, and event. The afternoon happens, crowded and therefore endless. Thicker, she agreed. It was a tic, she had the habit, and now she bobbed like my toy plastic bird on the edge of its glass, dipping into and recoiling from the water. But a word is a bottomless pit. It became magically pregnant and one day split open, giving birth to a stone egg, about as big as a football. In May when the lizards emerge from the stones, the stones turn gray, from green. When daylight moves, we delight in distance. The waves rolled over our stomachs, like spring rain over an orchard slope. Rubber bumpers on rubber cars. The resistance on sleeping to being asleep. In every country is a word which attempts the sound of cats, to match an inisolable portrait in the clouds to a din in the air. But the constant noise is not an omen of music to come. 'Everything is a question of sleep,' says Cocteau, but he forgets the shark, which does not. Anxiety is vigilant. Perhaps initially, even before one can talk, restlessness is already conventional, establishing the incoherent border which will later separate events from experience. Find a drawer that's not filled up. That we sleep plunges our work into the dark. The ball was lost in a bank of myrtle. I was in a room with the particulars of which a later nostalgia might be formed, an indulged childhood. They are sitting in wicker chairs, the legs of which have sunk unevenly into the ground, so that each is sitting slightly tilted and their postures make adjustment for that. The cows warm their own barn. I look at them fast and it gives the illusion that they're moving. An 'oral history' on paper. *That* morning this morning. I say it about the psyche because it is not optional. The overtones are a denser shadow in the room characterized by its habitual readiness, a form of charged waiting, a perpetual attendance, of which I was thinking when I began the paragraph, 'So much of childhood is spent in a manner of waiting.'

82.

Homer
FROM *THE ILIAD*
translated by Robert Fagles
{Anticipatory Plagiarism}

                                                    And now, Muse,
sing all those fighting men who lived in Pelasgian Argos,
the big contingents out of Alus and Alope and Trachis,
men of Phthia and Hellas where the women are a wonder,
all the fighters called Achaeans, Hellenes and Myrmidons
ranked in fifty ships, and Achilles was their leader.
But they had no lust for the grind of battle now –
where was the man who marched their lines to war?
The brilliant runner Achilles lay among his ships,
raging over Briseis, the girl with lustrous hair,
the prize he seized from Lyrnessus –
after he had fought to exhaustion at Lyrnessus,
storming the heights, and breached the walls of Thebes
and toppled the vaunting spearmen Epistrophus and Mynes,
sons of King Euenus, Selepius' son. All for Briseis
his heart was breaking now . . . Achilles lay there now
but he would soon rise up in all his power.

    Then men of Phylace, Pyrasus banked in flowers,
Demeter's closed and holy grove and Iton mother of flocks,
Antron along the shore and Pteleos deep in meadows.
The veteran Protesilaus had led those troops
while he still lived, but now for many years
the arms of the black earth had held him fast
and his wife was left behind, alone in Phylace,

both cheeks torn in grief, their house half-built.
Just as he vaulted off his ship a Dardan killed him,
first by far of the Argives slaughtered on the beaches.
But not even then were his men without a captain,
yearn as they did for their lost leader. No,
Podarces a fresh campaigner ranged their units –
a son of Iphiclus son of Phylacus rich in flocks –
Podarces, gallant Protesilaus' blood brother,
younger-born, but the older man proved braver too,
an iron man of war. Yet not for a moment did his army
lack a leader, yearn as they did for the braver dead.
Under Podarces sailed their forty long black ships.

  And the men who lived in Pherae fronting Lake Boebeis,
in Boebe and Glaphyrae and Iolcos' sturdy ramparts:
their eleven ships were led by Admetus' favored son,
Eumelus, born to Admetus by Alcestis, queen of women,
the most radiant daughter Pelias ever fathered.

  Then men who lived in Methone and Thaumacia,
men who held Meliboea and rugged ridged Olizon:
Philoctetes the master archer had led them on
in seven ships with fifty oarsmen aboard each,
superbly skilled with the bow in lethal combat.
But their captain lay on an island, racked with pain,
on Lemnos' holy shores where the armies had marooned him,
agonized by his wound, the bite of a deadly water-viper.
There he writhed in pain but soon, encamped by the ships,
the Argives would recall Philoctetes, their great king.
But not even then were his men without a captain,
yearn as they did for their lost leader. No,
Medon formed them up, Oileus' bastard son
whom Rhene bore to Oileus, grim raider of cities.

  And men who settled Tricca, rocky Ithome terraced high
and men who held Oechalia, Oechalian Eurytus' city:

the two sons of Asclepius led their units now,
both skilled healers, Podalirius and Machaon.
In their command sailed forty curved black ships.

   And men who held Ormenion and the Hyperian Spring,
men who held Asterion, Titanos' chalk-white cliffs:
Eurypylus marched them on, Euaemon's shining son.
In his command sailed forty long black ships.

83.

Raymond Queneau
FROM *ELEMENTARY MORALITY* (PROSE)
translated by Philip Terry
{Oulipo}

The idea of the poem lies in the cloud. Below, the poet who thought he knew how to breathe, notices his bronchioles are a little tight. He coughs. What a cough! Everything stems from this. He goes red with embarrassment; the blood circulates a little more rapidly. The thoracic thunder rocks the foggy air. Now there are words printed on the white page. Is it the beginning of a collection? In this case, it will have to contain ten thousand things. As yet it's only a project.

The zinnias are thriving, the yuccas are coming along, the wedelias are thriving, the violets are coming along, the ulmaria is thriving, the tulips are coming along, the sheep's bit is thriving, the ranunculus is coming along, the peonies are thriving, the oxeyes are coming along, the narcissi are thriving, the marguerites are coming along, the lilies are thriving, the kennedyas are coming along, the jasmine is thriving, the irises are coming along, the hydrangeas are thriving, the geraniums are coming along, the fuchsias are thriving, the eglantines are coming along, the dahlias are thriving, the corn poppies are coming along, the begonias are thriving, the anemonies are coming along. Their flowers have not yet been lopped off, the gardener's hands are not yet covered in blood. The picking season will come later. For the moment, it is forbidden to walk on the flowerbeds.

At the flea market an amateur collector finds two objects that seem to rhyme. What should he do? He goes from one stallholder to the other, haggling over the price, in a way that is quite common here. He quickly adapts to the part, but soon exhausts himself rushing back and forth, worried above all that another collector might notice the secret assonance between these two items in otherwise distinct collections. But there is no such individual. The consonance is only apparent to the eyes of one man. He tries to prop up his opinion with the support of the other senses: he fingers, he sniffs, he listens, he tastes. He asks himself if the rhyme is a full-rhyme or a half-rhyme, masculine or feminine. He doesn't rule out holorhyme. In this case the two objects make a pair and could be passed off as identical, an abstraction given what Leibniz says about the two leaves on a tree, a scientific tree, to be sure. One by one the stalls begin to close, and the onlookers move off in groups. The amateur finds himself joining one of them, abandoning the two objects to their grime, to their inertia, to their perhaps uncertain rhyme.

The water in the pan soon goes cold again if you extinguish the little bluish crown that has been constructed with so much trouble by molecules of sulphur and phosphorus. Sitting before the peeling pine table, the house-wife works out what remains of her savings with the stub of a pencil. She grows daily thinner thinking about the long winter days that will bring more hours of darkness, more freezing temperatures to ward off. Traffic is scarce on the snow-covered roads. The writer, hunched over the vellum of a work of aleatory literature, hesitates between two solutions: euphem-ism or understatement. Time passes in this kind of research. Dinner time comes round. The soup will lose its steaming perfection if the family doesn't hurry to the table. The writer, hunched over the vellum of a work of aleatory literature, carries on regardless: euphemism or understate-ment? It's then that he's summoned fiercely by his abbreviated first-name.

84.

Alice Oswald
FROM *MEMORIAL*
{After Oulipo}

The first to die was PROTESILAUS
A focused man who hurried to darkness
With forty black ships leaving the land behind
Men sailed with him from those flower-lit cliffs
Where the grass gives growth to everything
Pyrasus   Iton   Pteleus   Antron
He died in mid-air jumping to be first ashore
There was his house half-built
His wife rushed out clawing her face
Podarcus his altogether less impressive brother
Took over command but that was long ago
He's been in the black earth now for thousands of years

Like a wind-murmur
Begins a rumour of waves
One long note getting louder
The water breathes a deep sigh
Like a land-ripple
When the west wind runs through a field
Wishing and searching
Nothing to be found
The corn-stalks shake their green heads

Like a wind-murmur
Begins a rumour of waves

One long note getting louder
The water breathes a deep sigh
Like a land-ripple
When the west wind runs through a field
Wishing and searching
Nothing to be found
The corn-stalks shake their green heads

ECHEPOLUS a perfect fighter
Always ahead of his men
Known for his cold seed-like concentration
Moving out and out among the spears
Died at the hands of Antilochus
You can see the hole in the helmet just under the ridge
Where the point of the blade passed through
And stuck in his forehead
Letting the darkness leak down over his eyes

ELEPHENOR from Euboea in command of forty ships
Son of Chalcodon nothing is known of his mother
Died dragging the corpse of Echepolus
A little flash of flesh showing under the shield as he bent
Agenor stabbed him in the ninth year of the war
He wore his hair long at the back

Like leaves
Sometimes they light their green flames
And are fed by the earth
And sometimes it snuffs them out

Like leaves
Sometimes they light their green flames
And are fed by the earth
And sometimes it snuffs them out

85.

Aline Gagnaire
ORGY
{Oupeinpo}

86.

Richard Long
FROM *DARTMOOR*
{After Oulipo / Ouphopo}

87.

Raymond Queneau

A TALE FOR YOUR SHAPING

translated by Harry Gilonis

{Oulipo}

1 – Would you like to know the story of the three lively little peas?

if yes, go on to 4

if no, go on to 2.

2 – Would you prefer the story of the three tall thin beanpoles?

if yes, go on to 16

if no, go on to 3.

3 – Would you prefer the story of the three middle-sized middling bushes?

if yes, go on to 17

if no, go on to 21.

4 – Once upon a time there were three little peas dressed all in green who slept comfily in their pod. They had plump round faces and when they were breathing through the cavities of their nostrils you could hear their soft and harmonious snoring.

if you would prefer another description, go on to 9

if this one suits you, go on to 5.

5 – They were not dreaming. In fact these little beings never dream.

if you would prefer that they do dream, go on to 6

otherwise, go on to 7.

6 – They were dreaming. In fact these little beings always dream and their nights exude delightful visions.

if you would like to know these visions, go on to 11

if you don't want to pursue the matter, go on to 7.

7 – Their dainty feet were enveloped in warm socks and they wore black velvet gloves in bed.

if you would prefer gloves of a different colour, go on to 8

if this colour suits you, go on to 10.

8 –   They wore blue velvet gloves
      in bed.
if you would prefer gloves of a
different colour, go on to 7
if this colour suits you, go on to 10.

9 –   Once upon a time there
      were three little peas
      who roved around on the
      open road. When evening
      approached, tired and weary,
      they would go to sleep very
      quickly.
if you would like to know what
happened next, go on to 5
if not, go on to 21.

10 – All three had the same
      dream, for in fact they
      loved one another dearly
      and, good old fellows as
      they were, always dreamed
      identically.
if you would like to know their
dream, go on to 11
if not, go on to 12.

11 – They dreamed that they had
      gone to get their soup from
      the soup kitchen and when
      they opened their canteens
      they discovered that it was
      vetch soup. Horrified, they
      awoke.
if you want to know why they
awoke in horror, consult your
OED at the entry 'vetch' and
think it over

if you deem it pointless to
investigate the question,
go on to 12.

12 – Opopoï! they shrieked as
      they opened their eyes.
      Opopoï! what a dream we've
      dreamed! An ill omen,
      said the first. Yes indeedy,
      said the second, that's
      true enough, it's quite got
      me down. Don't trouble
      yourselves so, said the third,
      the brightest of them, there's
      no point getting alarmed
      instead of understanding; in
      a word, I'm going to analyse
      it for you.
if you would like to know the
interpretation of the dream straight
away, go on to 15
if you wish on the other hand to
know the reactions of the other
two, go on to 13.

13 – You're putting us on, said
      the first. Since when have
      you known how to analyse
      dreams? Yes, since when?
      added the second.
if you too would like to know since
when, go on to 14
if not, go on to 14 just the same, as
you'll be none the wiser.

14 – Since when? shrieked the
      third. How should I know!
      The thing is, I do it. You
      wait and see!

456

if you too want to see, go on to 15
if not, likewise go on to 15, as you
won't see anything.

15 –   OK, let's see, said his
       brothers. Your mockery
       doesn't please me, replied
       the other, and you shan't
       find out a thing. Besides,
       in the course of this rather
       lively discussion, hasn't your
       feeling of horror faded?
       vanished even? So why
       stir up the muck of your
       papilionaceous unconscious?
       Let us rather wash ourselves
       in the fountain and salute
       this blithe morn in a state
       of hygiene and sainted
       euphoria! No sooner said
       than done: they slid out of
       their pod, let themselves roll
       in the sunlight and then at
       a jog-trot merrily attained
       to the theatre of their
       ablutions.

if you would like to know what
happened at the theatre of their
ablutions, go on to 16
if you wouldn't like to, go on to 21.

16 –   Three tall thin bean-poles
       were watching them.

if the three tall thin bean-poles
displease you, go on to 17
if they suit you, go on to 18.

17 –   Three middle-sized
       middling bushes were
       watching them.

if the three middle-sized middling
bushes displease you, go on to 21
if they suit you, go on to 18.

18 –   Seeing that they were being
       ogled, the three lively little
       peas, who were very bashful,
       made off.

if you would like to know what
they did next, go on to 19
if you wouldn't like to, go on to 21.

19 –   They ran very hard until
       they got back to their pod
       and, closing it behind them,
       went to sleep again.

if you would like to know the
sequel, go on to 20
if you wouldn't like to, go to 21.

20 –   There isn't any sequel, the
tale has ended.

21 –   In this case, the tale has
likewise ended.

457

88.

Anne Garréta
FROM *NOT ONE DAY*
translated by Emma Ramadan and Anne Garréta
{Oulipo}

Ante Scriptum

What's to be done with our inclinations?

Why not write something different, differently than you usually do? Once more, but with a new twist, rid yourself of your self. Shed the accoutrements of this disentangling, keep at bay a little longer, if you can, who you think you are. Since you can no longer conceive of writing except in long and intricate constructions, isn't it time to go against the grain?

Figuring out the next novel on the horizon will take years of research, composition, writing. You pity your few readers and always take care not to exceed their patience and good will. In the meantime, you would like to offer them what you expect they desire: a distraction, the illusion of revealing what they imagine to be a subject. For they charitably assume you to be – a common failing, until further notice – a real me.

You don't have the heart to tell them that no subject ever expresses herself in any narration. And besides, they would refuse to believe this terrifying bit of news – we're still punch drunk on our little selves. So you have resolved, at the very least, to pretend to step out onto the slippery slope that seems so natural these days and to subject yourself to the discipline of confessional writing. All we seem to do nowadays is tell and retell the stories of our lives. For over a century, we've tried to grasp at ourselves from the same angle, convinced that there's only one key to unlock the secret of our subjectivity: desire.

And you could say, with and against Rousseau, he who invented or perfected our corruption: 'We must have spectacles in the great cities of the post-modern era, and confessions for idolatrous people. I have seen the mores of my times, and I have published these stories. Would that I had lived in an age when I should have thrown them into the fire!'

The irony delights you before you've even written a line. You will play at a very old game that has become the hobbyhorse of a modernity balking at radical disenchantment: confession, or how to scrape the bottoms of mirrors.

On a September day in 1835, strolling near Lake Albano, a man named Stendhal or Henri Beyle or Henri Brulard – which is it? Who knows . . . perhaps all three – draws in the sand the initials of the women he has loved: V, An, Ad, M, Mi, Al, Aine, Apg, Mde, C, G, Aur, and finally Mme Azur. The first name of this last one escapes him. The list of an unlucky Don Juan: 'In reality, I had only six of the women I have loved.'

Here H.B. is tempting you with the outline of a project both melancholy and tinged with cruel irony, and perfectly suited to your convalescence: the stammering alphabet of desire.

If you aim to thwart your habits and inclinations, you might as well go about it systematically. Here's what you have resolved to do (there's no more radical way to differ or dissemble from oneself than what you're planning here). It comes down to a single maxim: Not one day without a woman.

Which simply means that you will allocate five hours (the time it takes a moderately well-trained subject to compose a standard academic essay) each day, for a month, at your computer, aiming to recount the memory you have of one woman or another whom you have desired or who has desired you. That will be the narrative: the unwinding of memory in the strict framework of a given moment.

You will write as one goes to the office; you will be the archivist of your desires, thirty-five hours a week. Five hours per initial, no more, no less.

You will take them in the order in which they come to mind. You will then put them down, neutrally, in alphabetic order. To hell with chronology.

You will refrain from using your customary instruments: no pen, nothing but the keyboard (to the last syllable of recorded time). No draft, no notebook to gather bits and pieces, no considered and composed architecture, no rules other than the purely material and logistical ones that you've already assigned to the act.

No other principle than to write from memory. You will not try to capture things as they happened, nor will you reconstruct them as they might have happened, or as you might have liked them to happen. You will tell them as they appear to you at the precise moment you recall them.

Stabbing at your keyboard, you will decimate your memories. And who cares if at the end of your five hours of recollection, nothing will have been consummated? Who cares whether we've actually had the women we've desired? Writing at the whim of memory twists and turns on uncertainty. Like desire itself, never assured of its end or its object.

No erasures, no rewrites. Sentences as they come, without plotting them, cut off as soon as they're left hanging. Syntax matching composition.

Perhaps you will finally manage, in some feeble way, to emulate your peers, who recount their every experience, spewing out volumes of life matter – and buy into it.

It would have been better had you kept a journal. But you do not possess the talent of your peers. From day to day, you would have had nothing to report: nothing ever happens to you except in remembering. You only grasp the moment in distant memory, once oblivion has given things, beings, events, the density that they never have in the broad evanescence of daylight.

Your days are made of vapor, of imperceptible condensation. The world (and you with it) is a phantom that only time, the sands of time, makes visible and in the same moment erases. In full daylight, they don't even cast a shadow. An exquisite sensitivity, a photographic plate slowly revealing the image. But there seems to be no fixer for it: exposed to the light of the screen, of the page, and held too long under our gaze, memory dissolves without remission, leaving behind only the image of an image, a snapshot taken at the moment of recollection. From copy to copy of remembrance, it fades, moves. Soon nothing remains but the caricature – and the few details that the gaze has selectively magnified.

In one fell swoop, you will focus and dissipate yourself through thought. You will give yourself over, at set hours, to a purely discursive mental libertinage, you who have long ago renounced libertinage, and have adopted a simplicity of morals that would amaze your peers. And that you certainly never would have been able to imagine when you believed that you were only living in the present.

You will dissipate yourself through thought, in order to dispel the desires that you might still feel, that you are liable to feel even though you have learned to thwart their most trivial ploys.

Let's say it's a beautiful summer night, that after three months spent lounging on your sofa waiting for the double fracture in your right leg to heal, which left you with two metal plates, thirteen screws, and the leisure to analyze the subtle nuances of physical pain accompanied by the taste of morphine mixed with grenadine, to marvel at your luck, all things considered, in getting off so lightly after that absurd accident. For when you developed the memory of it, you finally saw that it could have cost you your life or your body, cut in half by the force of a relatively serious paralysis, that after these three months and a new lease on life, on movement, it's a truly beautiful summer night, a night when the body, free at last from too much pain, rediscovers all of its appetites helter-skelter: for dancing, for other bodies, for women. It's a perfect evening for sitting on the terrace of a café, watching the women go by. Desire would surely come hurtling down its slope, natural and abrupt, and before even realizing it you would probably have accrued additional memories.

In this regard, desire and pain are alike – your accident taught you this. Only when they take you by surprise do they get out of hand. You wake up after a respite and they will overwhelm you. To keep them in check requires a cool head, focus and consistency.

To dissipate, evade, or sidetrack your desires, such is the purpose of this little experiment you are attempting and which you hope will suffice to keep you going until you board the plane that will carry you across the Atlantic to the other coast of desire. Or to put it another way, you who were frivolous for so long, a fact the stories that you intend to unwind each day of this month of July 2000 will fully illustrate; you who were frivolous for so long, and you whose natural, and certainly human, tendency (exacerbated by all the typically French fondness for fickleness which confounds grace and flippancy, pleasures of flesh and vanity) is far from tamed. For a long time now, you've resolved to stop living as a slave of your disorderly desires.

For life is too short to resign ourselves to reading poorly written books and sleeping with women we don't love.

89.

Gilbert Adair
FROM *MEMORIES*
{After Oulipo}

61. I remember Spike Milligan ad-libbing nightly during the run of *Oblomov*.

62. I remember trigonometry.

63. I remember when it took almost a minute for a television image to materialize on the (eight- or twelve-inch) screen after the set had been switched on.

64. I remember a joke about two men who are crossing the Sahara and one night hear a voice enumerating: '1, 2, 3, 4, 5 . . .', etc. They are both utterly mystified as to its origin until one of them chances to read on the spine of his packet of Player's cigarettes: 'It's the Tobacco that Counts.'

65. I remember the first time I heard Marianne Moore's definition of poetry: 'An imaginary garden with real toads in it'; and the first time I saw Saul Steinberg's satirically diagrammatic cartoon of New York City.

66. I remember the trumpeter Eddie Calvert and his hit number 'Oh, My Papa'.

67. I remember, every winter, making 'slides' (a pastime which appears not to interest children today).

68. I remember, not all that long ago, a monstrous traffic jam stretching halfway across the continent of Europe (it had been provoked by striking lorry-drivers).

69. I remember television interludes: a potter's wheel, a tankful of tropical fish and an accelerated, four-minute train journey from London to Brighton.

70. I remember reading *Nineteen Eighty-four* when the year itself seemed to belong to some dim and unknowable future.

71. I remember Donald Campbell breaking the speed records on both land and sea.

72. I remember, on *Tonight*, the late Kenneth Allsop's shirts (invariably striped), his hair (too long at the neck) and his missing leg.

73. I remember 'Slow, slow, quick, quick, slow'.

74. I remember that Connie Francis was raped in an American hotel room.

75. I remember confusing Ray Ellington, who supplied the musical numbers on *The Goon Show*, with Duke Ellington.

76. I remember Rachman and Rachmanism.

77. I remember that the Gambols' first names are George and Gaye. (But how do I know this? For I never read the *Sunday Express*.)

78. I remember Alan Hackney, author of the books on which were based the films *Private's Progress* and *I'm All Right, Jack* (though the latter novel was, in fact, titled *Private Life*).

79. I remember the Moorish symbol from the Villa Mauresque found on hardback editions of Somerset Maugham.

80. I remember Tony Hancock's TV address: 23 Railway Cuttings, East Cheam.

90.

Tom Jenks

FROM *THE TOME OF COMMENCEMENT*
{After Oulipo}

1:1: In the freshman year Loki created the Happy Valley and the asteroid.

1:2: And the asteroid was without Settled principles, and ineffectual; and fog was touching the fizzog of the big drink. And the Daemon of Loki inflamed the fizzog of the fathoms.

1:3: And Loki said, let there be magnolia: and there was magnolia.

1:4: And Loki saw the magnolia, that it was peachy creamy: and Loki split the magnolia from the fog.

1:5: And Loki called the magnolia Green Flash, and the fog he called Pitchy Dark. And the cocktail hour and the cock crow were the first Green Flash.

1:6: And Loki said, let there be a welkin in the interior of the fathoms, and let it disengage the fathoms from the fathoms.

1:7: And Loki made the welkin, and split the fathoms which were subordinate to the welkin from the fathoms which were above the welkin: and that's exactly what happened.

1:8: And Loki called the welkin Happy Valley. And the cocktail hour and the cock crow were the second Green Flash.

1:9: And Loki said, let the fathoms subordinate to the Happy Valley be garnered en masse unto one apartment, and let the ponderous acreage crop up: and that's exactly what happened.

1:10: And Loki called the ponderous acreage Asteroid; and the union en masse of the fathoms called the Vasty Deep: and Loki saw that it was peachy creamy.

1:11: And Loki said, let the asteroid drag out bamboo, the chicory coddle pips, and the algae drag out mandarin oranges after its stock, whose dibble is in Itself, to the asteroid: and that's exactly what happened.

1:12: And the asteroid dragged out bamboo, and chicory coddled dibble after its stock, and the algae dragged out mandarin oranges, whose dibble was in Itself, after its stock: and Loki saw that it was peachy creamy.

1:13: And the cocktail hour and the cock crow were the third Green Flash.

1:14: And Loki said, let there be bay windows in the welkin of the Happy Valley to disengage the Green Flash from the Pitchy Dark; and let it be for inklings, and for sauces, and for instants, and epochs:

1:15: And let there be bay windows in the welkin of the Happy Valley to give magnolia to the asteroid: and that's exactly what happened.

1:16: And Loki made duplicate gigantic bay windows; the higher magnolia to apply standard operating procedure to the Green Flash, and the decreased magnolia to apply standard operating procedure to the Pitchy Dark: he made the weird too.

1:17: And Loki jammed it in the welkin of the Happy Valley to give magnolia to the asteroid,

1:18: And to apply standard operating procedure to the Green Flash and to the Pitchy Dark, and to disengage the magnolia from the fog: and Loki saw that it was peachy creamy.

1:19: And the cocktail hour and the cock crow were the fourth Green Flash.

1:20: And Loki said, let the fathoms drag out abundantly the charged yeoman that hath bubbliness, and stormy petrels that may wobble above the asteroid in the yawning welkin of Happy Valley.

1:21: And Loki created gigantic kippers, and every flagrant yeoman that moveth, which the fathoms drag out abundantly, after their homies, and every reckless stormy petrel after his stock: and Loki saw that it was peachy creamy.

1:22: And Loki sanctified it, saying, Be luxuriant, and widen, and plug the fathoms in the seas, and let stormy petrels widen in the asteroid.

1:23: And the cocktail hour and the cock crow were the fourth Green Flash.

1:24: And Loki said, let the asteroid drag out the flagrant yeoman after his stock, stirks, and limping things, and ugly customers of the asteroid after his stock: and that's exactly what happened.

1:25: And Loki made the ugly customers of the asteroid after his stock and stirks after their homies, and every thing that sidles up to the asteroid after his stock: and Loki saw that it was peachy creamy.

1:26: And Loki said, let us make a baboon in our dead ringer, after our picture: and let it have management of the haddock of the vasty deep, and over the stormy petrels of the aerosphere, and over the stirks, and over all the asteroid, and over every limping thing that sidles up to the asteroid.

1:27: So Loki created a baboon in his own dead ringer, in the dead ringer of Loki created he him; gentleman and lady created he them.

1:28: And Loki sanctified them, and Loki said unto them, Be luxuriant, and widen, and eke out the asteroid, and overmaster it: and have management of the haddock of the vasty deep, and of the stormy petrels of the aerosphere, and of every flagrant thing that sidles up to the asteroid.

1:29: And Loki said, Look, I have given you every chicory producing pips, which is to the fizzog of all the asteroid, and every timber, in which is the mandarin oranges of a timber producing pips; to you it shall be for peanuts.

1:30: And to every ugly customer of the asteroid, and to every stormy petrel of the aerosphere, and to every thing that sidles up to the asteroid, wherein there is bubbliness, I have given every minor chicory for peanuts: and that's exactly what happened.

1:31: And Loki saw every thing that he had made, and, look, it was jolly peachy creamy. And the cocktail hour and the cock crow were the fifth Green Flash.

91.

Olivier Salon
FROM *FUGUES*
translated by Philip Terry
{Oulipo}

We Are Alone

I am alone

        I am alone

                I am alone

We are alone   We are alone   We are alone

                And yet

        And yet

                We complement one another

And yet

        We complement one another

                It's in the repetition that

We complement one another

        It's in the repetition that

It's in the repetition that

        We light up

We light up   We light up

        If you examine things closely

        There is only a single discourse

                If you examine things closely

If you examine things closely

There is only a single discourse

        But repeated three times

                This unique discourse

But repeated three times

But repeated three times
Like a three-leafed clover

Like a three-leafed clover

The clover is one when the
leaves are three

Like a three-leafed clover:
The clover is one when the
leaves are three

The clover is one when
the leaves are three

But when the clover is wan,
the leaves cramped

But when the clover is   But when the clover is wan,
wan, leaves cramped   the leaves cramped
Does unity bring strength?

Does unity bring strength?
Not always

Unity does not always
bring strength

Unity can engender   Unity can engender
discord   discord
I was about to say it!

Unity can engender
discord

I was about to say it!
And this chord is a little
orchestra

I was about to say it!

And this chord is
already an orchestra

And this chord is a
large orchestra

Well, not as large as all
that!

Like a large piano

        Well, not as large as all that!

                Like a large piano

Say a QRS piano

        Or rather a piano in the rain

                An aqueous piano

        It's raining chords

                It's raining pianos

It's raining orchestras

In a word, it gets wet

        In a word, it gets set

                In a word, it begins to fret

In a word, it gets wet at a

        In a word, it gets set at a

                In a word, it begins to fret
                at a

The frittata is an   The frittata is an
instrument of   instrument of
musical concord   musical concord

                The frittata is an instance
                of luminous cooking

The frittata is an instance
of leguminous cooking

        The frittata is an instrument
        for cooking with legumes

92.

Édouard Levé
FROM *WORKS*
translated by Jan Steyn
{After Oulipo}

163. Ivy is made to grow on the wall of an art center in the shape of a giant spider web.

164. Two identical body casts have a layer of quick-dry resin applied to them, the one while posed on its feet, the other while suspended from them. The resin congeals as it is pulled downward. Posed upright, face-to-face, the one sculpture appears to be melting and the other about to fly off.

165. Fuzzy photographs represent works by myopic artists, the way they see them when not wearing spectacles.

166. A taxidermist stuffs a gazelle inside the skin of the leopard that killed it.

167. Vacation photographs, all taken in the same country, are stuck together, end-to-end, such that the lines running through them paint a common horizon. We see the sea, background landscapes, architectural perspective lines, homestead plinths, floors, ceilings, furniture, objects. Some of the photographs are upright, others are tilted to ensure the horizon's continuity.

168. In the darkness of a circular room, a lamp is placed on a table. The openwork on the lampshade contains the palindrome, 'In *girumimusnocteetconsumimurigni*,' which is projected onto the wall without interruption.

169. Objects of different volumes, but whose constituting materials take up the same volume, are placed on the floor, in a circle.

170. Scenes from made-for-TV films are reenacted and indirectly photographed using their reflections on a switched-off television set. The prints are the size and shape of the screen.

171. A painting is produced in the dark. Memory replaces sight and becomes the judge of whether what's on the canvas should be kept, erased, or started over. The moment the artist first looks at it marks the completion of the tableau.

172. Two hands holding up the remaining corner of a torn-up page are visible in the orange raking light of sunset. The still-readable title of the novel is, Riddles. The following text can be made out:

'First Chapter

The Moving Shadow

Thick, impenetrable, stuck to
pieces like dark veils.
torn apart by chimes, a
window frames a
slowly reading across the
warning; her foot doesn't
hand moved by a
heavy sphere
one year. Him?'

The left hand casts a shadow, not resembling a hand, covering half the page. Photograph.

173. A plaster cast is made using the packaging of an object. The cast faithfully reproduces the inside of the container but only vaguely resembles what it contains. The simulacrum is simplified, smooth, and colorless.

174. *Accidental Art*. Photographs show rural or urban objects that aren't artworks but could be mistaken for them.

175. In a museum, the soundtrack of an audio guide doesn't comment on the works, but on their presentation. The works are only ever mentioned in terms of their museographical import.

176. A few hours before its opening, a man walks through the exhibition he is invited to participate in, bit by bit shedding everything on his person. Objects and clothing are left where they fall. Title cards stuck to the floor describe them in simple terms:

'A black wallet'
'A bunch of keys'
'Loose change'
'A denim vest'
'A black leather shoe'
'A black sock'
'A black leather shoe'
'A black sock'
'A brown leather belt'
'A pair of jeans'
'Black underpants'
'A pair of spectacles'

93.

Jacques Carelman
FROM *EXERCISES IN STYLE*
{Oupeinpo}

94.

Raymond Roussel
FROM *HOW I WROTE
SOME OF MY BOOKS*
translated by Philip Terry
{Anticipatory Plagiarism}

The Greenish Skin of the Granny Smith

The greenish skin of the Granny Smith, long past its use-by date, still looked as appetizing as ever. So I picked this fruit from amongst the delicacies laid out on a silver platter for the señora's return.

With the point of a knife I made a small incision in the soft flesh, and, taking a phial from my pocket, poured in several drops of a quick-working poison.

– You betrayed me, Natte, I said in a muted voice; now face the consequences!

I put the fatal fruit back in its place.

It was stifling in my picador's costume, with my peruke and my wide-brimmed hat. The drawing-room's candelabra rivalled even the footlights in their brilliance, dazzling me with their myriad reflections. The doors were piled high with sombre garments, and glittering décolleté ball gowns were strewn across the gilded furniture. The décor of this small improvised set was both luxurious and studied. Nothing was wanting in this room belonging to the great Spanish lady. Suddenly, the sound of sleigh-bells and the crack of a whip in the wings presaged Natte's return.

Quickly, I grabbed the great black cape that I'd thrown on a chair as I entered and jumped on the bed, whose closely drawn curtains enabled me to watch without being seen.

Natte came in. The lady of the house herself, still beautiful notwithstanding her forty-six years, thanks to her well-kept secrets. Not least the miraculous dye she employed to maintain the brilliant and intense blackness of her hair. Her features, though, were beginning to fade. Make-up could barely manage to conceal the lines forming around the corners of her eyes and her mouth.

The diminutive Madame Dé, charming as an Andalusian *soubrette*, had also made her entrance. Dismissed by Natte after a brief exchange, she exited carrying her mistress's cloak. Natte, left on her own, sat down to her supper.

– Turquoise . . . oh my dear Turquoise, how I love you! she cried in a trembling voice.

Turquoise was a young muleteer with whom Natte was having an affair behind my back. An intercepted letter, revealing everything, had driven me to murder.

– What sweetness, just thinking about you, oh Turquoise, my young love! Natte repeated, her gaze lost in a dream.

Then, sitting up, in a troubled voice:

– Good God! if Mirliton knew, he'd kill me! . . .

Mirliton, that was me, the abandoned picador. To chase away her fears, Natte began to eat. The Spanish type to perfection, she had two beauty spots, one on the chin, one on the neck, and her magnificent black hair, electrified by the footlights, made you almost forget her ageing features. They almost made you forget, too, that she was not Spanish – her real name was Smythe.

– What's Turquoise doing now? she murmured, between a slice of layered cake and a tartlette. He is thinking of me as I of him!

From my observation post, I watched attentively as her supper slipped down piece by piece. Natte was trying to regain her composure.

– Mirliton suspects nothing; he loves me, he trusts me . . .

She'd just polished off an apricot; there was nothing left now on her platter but the fatal fruit. She took it between two fingers.

– What if Mirliton knew? she continued in a deep voice.

Then she bit . . .

The effect was instantaneous. She got up to open a window, as if she was suffocating, turned around several times, flapping the air with her arms, then collapsed dead on the carpet.

In a single leap I was on the floor, and hurried to put out the candles which were burning on the table in two silver candelabra. Immediately, everything was plunged into darkness, lights and footlights extinguished at once. A single broad beam of moonlight shone through the open window onto the corpse.

I went to fetch my cape from the bed, the great black cape which I was accustomed to wear, and spreading it wide I draped it over Natte's lifeless body. Then I knelt down at her side in silence.

Motionless, Natte was as if hewn out of marble. The black cape completely covered her body. The head alone was visible, the face which had lost its youth, surrounded by her dazzling black hair, pallid beneath the moonlight which poured, with a morbid greenish tinge, through the window.

The effect was tragic.

One thing alone was visible, only one . . .

The greenish skin of the granny, Smythe, long past her use-by date . . .

95.

Georges Perec
A LITTLE ILLUSTRATED ABC
translated by Philip Terry
{Oulipo}

BA-BE-BI-BO-BU

Possessed of a rebellious distaste for the colour pink, the young girl throws a fit when her parents present her with a Barbie doll on her fifth birthday. Industriously, her mother knocks up an outfit in blue denim, and in this get-up Barbie comes slowly to find favour. Wishing to restore a degree of femininity to Barbie, the mother hits on the strategy of adding a blue bow, tied round the neck. Picking up the car keys, she heads into town, only one thing on her mind:
    Barbie: buy bow (blue).

CA-CE-CI-CO-CU

Because these men were united by a common goal, namely to kick their cocaine habits, because they favoured outdoor sports, especially sailing, as a means to this end, because, too, of their tendency to dress in Safari, they soon came to be referred to collectively, by themselves as well as others, as the KKCC:
    Khaki Kick Coke Crew.

DA-DE-DI-DO-DU

Though everybody called her Do she thought of herself as Doreen, perhaps because here she heard an echo of her late mother's name, Irene, perhaps too because the name was hated by her father. He it was, Doreen was sure of it, who had hounded her mother into an early grave, gradually wearing down her spirit until there was no longer any will to live; Doreen's revenge, in contrast, was to be much more sudden. That night, as her father slept, she plunged the carving knife into his breast, alarming the neighbours who heard the following frenzied exchange:

– Daddy! Die!

– Do!

– Do!

FA-FE-FI-FO-FU

When the adventure is all over – the trip to market, the bean, the argument with his mother, the beanstalk, the land of the giant, the golden eggs, the chase, the descent, the cutting of the beanstalk with the axe – Jack finally collapses on the grass in exhaustion. Far off, he hears the fading and now idle threat of the giant as he plunges to his death.

Afar: Fe, fi, fo, fu——

GA-GE-GI-GO-GU

As Hen Nights go, the evening had started soberly enough, with gin and tonics at a local wine bar. Later, things were to get more out of hand. After three more bars and a light meal, the Hens ended up at a male strip club. Naked men poured out of every doorway, charging about like wild animals. The bride-to-be was presented with a dog collar and a lead, and a leather gag to tie over the mouth of her chosen he-man. As she tottered onto the parquet, barely able to distinguish one sweating torso from the next, her delirious companions cheered her on from the touchlines.

Gag a guy! Go! Goooooo!

HA-HE-HI-HO-HU

A Japanese businessman, known to his friends as Joju, recently recruited by the KKCC, is shown some educational videos at his first meeting. In one of them he is surprised to see his boss totally off his face at a party and, unsure how he is meant to react, finds himself stifling a laugh.

Hah! He high! Hohu!

JA-JE-JI-JO-JU

After his first month in the KKCC, having touched no drugs during this period, Joju's powers of resistance are put to the test. One of the crew takes down a large jar of cocaine, prominently marked with the letter 'G' (denoting its country of origin), and places it before him. Help yourself, he says. Stoically, Joju resists.

Jar 'G': yer high Joju.

KA-KE-KI-KO-KU

As a reward for his success during the one-month trial period, Joju is presented with a KKCC car key, and invited to drive one of the crew Land Rovers on a weekend excursion to the Pennines.

Car key (Kick Coke Crew).

LA-LE-LI-LO-LU

After the Great Irish Theme Pub Robbery, St Patrick's Day 1998, media coverage was so intense that the ringleaders quickly became household names: McGuiness, McCaffery, Smith, O'Neill, Fisher, Lawley. The plan, unexpectedly leaked to the police, had been to make for France via Newhaven, but as everyone now knows this was not to be: McGuiness, McCaffery, Smith and Fisher were arrested before they left British soil. O'Neill and Lawley, it was widely supposed, had gone to ground, and all the police could do was wait. Their patience was rewarded in the first days of April, and arrest quickly followed, when they intercepted a telegram sent from Halifax, reading:

Lawley: lie low Looe.

MA-ME-MI-MO-MU

Before going to bed, as a special treat, the child persuades his mother to play a game: she is to imitate a farm animal, without speaking or otherwise uttering a sound, and he is to guess what the beast is. The mother gets down on all fours and proceeds to chew the carpet. At first the child is puzzled, then, in a sudden flash, he sees what his mother is up to: *chewing the grass, like a . . . cow!*

Mammy! Mime! Oh! Moo!

NA-NE-NI-NO-NU

Given half a chance, the children liked nothing better than to play at Teletubbies, preferably accompanied by the Dyson, Noo-noo. Yet they could only do so when Nanny was asleep, for she was under strict instructions to keep them away from all electrical appliances. While they played, then, they had to be vigilant at all times, and if ever Nanny was heard on the move, the alarm signal was given at once:

Nanny nigh: no Noo!

PA-PE-PI-PO-PU

At the height of the Teletubbies craze, a father finds himself tyrannized by his son in the bathroom. The son, affectionately nicknamed 'Pie' prior to this late flourishing of the anal phase, now dressed as Teletubbies' Po, squats purposefully on his potty to empty his bowels, ordering his father, meanwhile, to urinate.

Pa pee! Pie (Po) poo.

QUA-QUE-QUI-QUO-QU

At the court of Empress Sadako, Sei Shonagon finds herself irritated by the herb doctor Norimasa, whose boisterous energy and quack remedies have won him favour with her mistress, to such an extent that she neglects affairs of state. Wishing to undermine his ascendancy, she consults captain Wu, who suggests administering a soporific so that Norimasa will be unfit to attend the Empress. The following morning, delighted by the immediate success of the enterprise, Sei Shonagon sends her accomplice a note of congratulation:

Quack weak: quick work Wu.

RA-RE-RI-RO-RU

One day, Pooh bear wakes up to find one of his eyes missing. What is to be done? All the animals in the Hundred Acre Wood gather together: Kanga, Roo, Owl, Piglet, Rabbit, Eeyore, Tigger and the rest. After much inconclusive debate, Owl speaks up with his customary authority: they must send an envoy to Rare Eye Row, in the town, for only there will they find what they are looking for. To decide who is to make the perilous journey, lots are drawn. The task falls to Roo, who sets off without complaint.

Rare Eye Row: Roo.

SA-SE-SI-SO-SU

A black labourer on a Texan farm reports disinterestedly his boss's crazy decision to take neighbour Simon Marshall to court, having seen him trespass on his land.

Sah see Si so sue.

TA-TE-TI-TO-TU

At the Yugoslavian premiere of *Mon Oncle* Jacques Tati and President Tito discuss film and theatre: despite differences of taste and politics they find themselves united in their admiration for the work of British actor Peter O'Toole.

Tati, Tito: O'Toole.

VA-VE-VI-VO-VU

Embarking on their ill-fated tour of the USA, The Sex Pistols are met by hordes of photographers at Heathrow. Vicious tells them if they want a picture it'll cost them a fiver, otherwise he'll bust their cameras. Attempting to calm things down, Rotten intervenes, then, turning to Vicious, snarls:

Vey ave a viver f'you.

WA-WE-WI-WO-WU

Having spent the best part of his adult life studying the behavioural patterns of the Wahwee tribe of Borneo, the Belgian anthropologist Marcel Gallet could still not understand why the tribe persistently and systematically looked for trouble, an enigma which he famously summarized in these words:

Wahwee: why woe woo?

XA-XE-XI-XO-XU

On the eve of revolution, Tzar Nicholas II goes on a trip to North America. He is taken on a visit to a Sioux reservation, where chiefs Running Dog and Sitting Bear, beneficiaries of the latest medical advances, proudly display their appendix scars.

Tzar sees sides of Sioux.

YA-YE-YI-YO-YU

London club owner, M—, finding himself in a monetary dispute with the Krays, agreed to accept a dated IOU, which he subsequently carried on his person wherever he went. Cornered one night at gunpoint by one of the Kray gang, he was told to hand it back, no questions asked, or forfeit his life.

You or your IOU.

ZA-ZE-ZI-ZO-ZU

A Frenchman, living in a rented flat overlooking Regent's Park, complained to his landlord that he could not sleep at nights, it was no good, he would have to go. When pressed, he said it was the close proximity to London Zoo that disturbed him: at night, he felt oppressed by the mournful eyes of the animals which, he insisted, glared at him from the depths of their cages, burrowing their way into his troubled dreams.

Zere are zees eyes au zoo.

96.

Inger Cristensen
FROM *ALPHABET*
translated by Susanna Nied
{After Oulipo}

I

apricot trees exist, apricot trees exist

2

bracken exists; and blackberries, blackberries;
bromine exists; and hydrogen, hydrogen

3

cicadas exist; chicory, chromium,
citrus trees; cicadas exist;
cicadas, cedars, cypresses, the cerebellum

4

doves exist, dreamers, and dolls;
killers exist, and doves, and doves;
haze, dioxin, and days; days
exist, days and death; and poems
exist; poems, days, death

5

early fall exists; aftertaste, afterthought;
seclusion and angels exist;
widows and elk exist; every
detail exists; memory, memory's light;
afterglow exists; oaks, elms,
junipers, sameness, loneliness exist;
eider ducks, spiders, and vinegar
exist, and the future, the future

6

fisherbird herons exist, with their grey-blue arching
backs, with their black-feathered crests and their
bright-feathered tails they exist; in colonies
they exist, in the so-called Old World;
fish, too, exist, and ospreys, ptarmigans,
falcons, sweetgrass, and the fleeces of sheep;
fig trees and the products of fission exist;
errors exist, instrumental, systemic,
random; remote control exists, and birds;
and fruit trees exist, fruit there in the orchard where
apricot trees exist, apricot trees exist
in countries whose warmth will call forth the exact
colour of apricots in the flesh

97.

Paul Griffiths
LET ME TELL YOU
{After Oulipo / Oumupo}

I

Let me tell you how it was.
I know I can do this.
I have the powers:
I take them here.
I have the right.
My words may be poor
but they will have to do.
There was a time when I could not do this:
I remember that time.

O but memory is not one but many –
a long music we have made
and will make again,
over and over,
with some things we know and some we do not,
some that are true and some we have made up,
some that have stayed from long before
and some that have come this morning,
some that will go tomorrow
and some that have long been there
but that we will never find,
for to memory there is no end.
There was a time, I remember, when we had no music,
a time when there was no time for music,

and what is music if not time –
time of now and then tumbled into one another,
time turned and loosed,
time bended,
time blown here and there,
time sweet and harsh,
time still and long?

II

Let me tell you how it is,
for you are the one who made me more than I was,
you are the one who loosed out this music.
Your face is my music lesson
and I sing.

Now I do not mind if it is day, if it is night.
If it is night,
an owl will call out.
If it is morning,
a robin will tune his bells.
Night, day: there is no difference for me.
What will make the difference is if you are with me.
For you are my sun.
You have sun-blasted me,
and turned me to light.
You have made me like glass –
like glass in an ecstasy from your light,
like glass in which light rained
and rained and rained and goes on,
like glass in which there are showers of light,
light that cannot end.

III

I know you are there.
I know I will find you.
Let me tell you how it will be.

I will go out now.
I will let go the door
and not look to see my hand as I take it away.
Snow falls.
So: I will go on in the snow.
I will have my hope with me.
I look up,
as if I could see the snow as it falls,
as if I could keep my eye on a little of it
and see it come down
all the way to the ground.
I cannot.
The snow flowers are all like each other
and I cannot keep my eyes on one.
I will give up this and go on.
I will go on.

98.

Georges Perec
SENTIMENTAL TALES
translated by Harry Mathews
{Oulipo}

Sentimental Tales 1

	a	b	c	d
a	a	a	a	a
b	a	a	a	a
c	a	a	a	a
d	a	c	a	b

Everyone knew that Amelia loved only herself. Furthermore, Amelia was convinced that the whole world loved no one but her. It's true that Brynhild and Caroline were very much in love with Amelia. Everyone knew that Caroline loved Amelia. Things were somewhat different for Brynhild. Deirdre thought that Brynhild loved Caroline, she was in fact most unhappy about it because she herself loved Brynhild; but Brynhild – not only did Brynhild not know that Caroline loved her, she was convinced that Deirdre loved Caroline.

	a	b	c	d
a	c	c	d	a
b	c	c	d	a
c	d	d	a	c
d	a	a	c	d

Antoinette had a crush on Charles.

She was wildly jealous of big Bea because she thought that Bea also had a crush on Charles, and she was the unhappiest of women because she was convinced that Charles had eyes only for Denise, while Denise, according to Antoinette, had special tastes and had a crush on her, something as a matter of fact she couldn't have cared less about, oh my oh my.

It was of course true that big Bea herself had a crush on Charles and, as for Antoinette, would have gladly torn her hair out because she was sure Antoinette had her eye on Charles, and furthermore, in regard to the Charles in question, big Bea could have sworn that he pined after no one but Denise, that little dyke, who – she was sure of it – had a yen for Antoinette. All in all, in big Bea's view things might have worked out: little Denise only needed to succeed in seducing Antoinette and then maybe Charles would have started noticing her, big Bea.

But in truth Charles was the unhappiest of men. For he loved Antoinette and he was convinced that Antoinette – and big Bea as well – only had a crush on little Denise. As for little Denise, Charles had a hunch she would have liked to go after him, but he didn't care one way or the other.

The fact was that little Denise, insofar as she loved anyone, loved herself and that was that. Furthermore she believed that three-quarters of humanity felt the same way: perhaps big Bea had a mild crush on Antoinette, but in any case it was Antoinette who was the true narcissist. As for Charles, Denise was sure that he managed perfectly well on his own and that his own navel held more fascination for him than all the members of the fair sex.

99.

Frédéric Forte
FROM *FLAT SONNETS*
translated by Emma Ramadan
{Oulipo}

it's a box it remembers • or makes a tapestry • some eat a pastry • i'd like to dismember / return as an animal of course • in the end reincarnation • must be a strange sensation • on the back of a horse / but to look under skirts • is impossible • and the stereotypes • are insoluble / so i spend long vacations in a tunnel • that'll teach me to do my supernatural so • metallurgist • you see it was good to be born the day we ran to the dentist • we don't obstruct progress to say no / when it's necessary to make an effort it will be thorough • there will be bananas • and cream on those bananas • something in the shape of an o / inside it though • will be a bone in the eardrum called the cerebellum • unless i don't know / and confuse it with the inventors of the gun • in the end it's all for show • a machine to put the world back together just so

it's a bar so they say • and full of disorder • don't even look at
the corner • of the tv dinner on the tray / i feel the arrow and
i feel the bait • here limits are in order • a tribunal imperator
der • ides me anyway / you had so much gold • and you squandered it all • engines in your control / you blinked in your bath
and flames had taken hold • the morning unrolled • and you
squandered it all

he looks at shoes • his reflection in the display case • shows
signs of use • his deflated face / visibly the particu • lates of his
voice splay • around him as he articu • lates the de / buts of the
sonnets his tongue • it was that that-tongue • what does it say /
in ten days we'd like to know it • which what to do and push
on to see it • to see summer was hot every day

oh my baby • i wish there were other plans for your learning •
will you have to be discerning • no and no my baby / an iron for
example • if it falls down • there's no need to frown • something
is new and sometimes in shambles / in brussels it's the same •
remember walking down the lane • of white tin that rings / as
king of the open plains • you laugh and it brings • dreams of a
future of champagne

i see now yes • it's complete • as for me • a phantom and his pets/i'm relaxed and more distant and even limitless • i would like algae but you see • it's defeat • so i think better but less / pinned a badge on my vest • in a half-sleep • as they say a machine to keep / heating all the rest • the perfect thing in the sun let's go • hit the gas with your big toe socks and sheets • will we recover from not knowing • on the altar our heads resting • then on the rug just a beat / we want transparency and question deceit • there's still a darkness remaining • and in the mirror we keep saying • we must not admit defeat / the quiet • seems too quiet • too bogged down in / several layers of remembering • machines which are false paths from the beginning • let's grab a toboggan to the blackboard • is the favourite formula of my teacher in chemistry • who's a bit yellow but we have good chemistry • especially when bored / meanwhile i eat an eraser • and build a moat • against the law to promote • then attempt to trace her / decorate a signpost with a note • everyone knows that's over-used • but it's all a ruse/my pencil is pointed • and my cry is disjointed • and i fly like the wind on a boat // luxury that floats

in the shadows the wrestler • rests momentarily • arranged like a choir • stretched on his knees / an eye to the tender • the secret place • buy his soul for legal tender • his regret and disgrace / he thinks about going • like new from here • he thinks about slowing • his actions yes my dear / already it's amazing he glides above the crowd • multilingual cloud

100.

Christine Brooke-Rose
FROM *NEXT*
{After Oulipo / Oulipopo}

The Story So Far: Derica, long married to oilman Brad, ran his ranch for years and reared the twins Rex and Regina, but could not ever conceal her strong love for Trix, born of an old affair with Jesse, business rival to Brad and later married to Tina, but now pursuing Gina. Doug, a new friend of Rex, brings Cindy, who now fas-   cinates Brad, while Gina strongly attracts   Doug, but is herself too powerfully involved with Rick who now helps Derica manage the estate. After a violent scene with Sal, Derica asks Dan to intervene with Bradley.

The square arch under the descending motorway, growing like a

tree inside a fenced off circle	of tired grass, was neverthe-
less too high, and let the night	rain slant down seeping across
the carton slept on, save for a	narrow strip down the middle
and a round spot on the TV	mag containing The Story So
Far used as a pillow over the	plastic bag, forming an imag-
ined dry man, a stick and a spot.	But the woolly damp of the red
balaclava chills the cranium, as	when a child wakes to a wet
warm bed that rapidly cools to	iciness. Under closed eyelids
floats the dim awareness of	the washtub-drubbing trucks
overhead that grunged the	short night's sleep. Stiffened
as a coffinlid, one live corpse	rising from granite, sitting up

against the concrete column peering at the pinkish grey drizzle which turns the square arches in the access-complex of the motorway into an ancient film dazed across with the constant white beams, and the overheadtrucks into a loud mechanical projector, somewhere behind the brain. A crisis of horns and brakescreams from above scatters the mental furniture what was it, the happy rich unhappy in their high bourgeois tizzies.

The garbage mag now freed from headweight soggily flaps, feebly gesticulating like

a slave
>> too vlase to run away
a refugee
>> too guferee to go back
a citizen
>> too zenitic to protest

MEN BORN EQUAL. *Natus sum*, giving rise to *natio*, but the Declaration forgot that a slave is not a national, that a refugee, like a dropout, ceases to be a citizen.

The infra-orange rectangles of highpressure sodium splay their flowcharts in fuzzy logic upwards and away like the internet nexus of a giant brain in open surgery, or stepstone straight off in diminishing pink icons up the Edgware Road.

It used to be ultra-orange, lowpressure sodium, that morphed faces into cadaverous grey-green clams. Presumably people complained, unable to accept themselves as they would become. If you wait long enough, without bothering to march or write furious letters to the papers, horrors do go away. But only with trivia.

The trucklights throng white through the drizzle, dazzle, then slant off, then more.

The alienated cold wet fingers unclip one plastic button in the closure-bar of the plastic bag to make the smallest opening against the rain, thrust through it fumbling among the disconnected pieces of a dry second self inside it, the rough synthetic of a dirt-stiff sweater, the thick rigidity of rolled-up jeans, the creased teeshirt, the acrylic socks and the strangled sneakers, the Montaigne unread for months, at last finding the plastic-wrapped piece of bread and the tin with the two cigarettes and the lighter.

The plastic bag is snapped shut again. Then, munching the papery meal, the best moment of the day,

    breakfast

        in

           BED

with no wife to bring it and cheerily talk

reading

        the morning paper

watching

        the telefilm drizzle

though it isn't morning yet and the paper is an old TV mag of vertiginous virtual.

Then the first puff

    that tickles alive

        that itchy throat

        gravelling to a cough

        tearing the lungs

Where's Croaky for petessake?

    After a violent scene with Sal, Derika turns to Dan, asking him to intervene with Brad, who is blackmailing Rick to kill Doug. Dan complies but Rex overhears their conversation and accuses Derika of scheming in favour of Trix and Cab. Cindy discovers she is pregnant.

No lumpish proles only lumpen bourgeoisie, a dream and by a sleep to say we knit up another worldwideweb, another half-hour maybe?

        The century's alphabête, that usually does it despite traffic.

    A for Auschwitz. B for Belsen. C for Cambodia.

D for Dresden. For Deportation. E for Ethiopia, for Ethnic Cleansing . . . F for, what's F?

Famine . . . Mao's Great Leap into, 1959. Stalin's ditto, Ukraine 1933. Fundamentalism. There's usually more than one horror for each letter.

F for Fire! Cease! Fire! Cease! Fire! Peace! Process! Peace! Protest! Ello ello ello what's this? Pack up that trash and move along now.

Notes

13. Themerson, whose Gabberbocchus Press published the first English edition of *Exercises in Style*, here anticipates with 'Semantic Poetry', the Oulipian method of 'definitional literature', where the words of a given text are replaced by their definitions in a dictionary.

14. Carroll's interest in mathematics and playing with scale has long made him a key writer for Oulipo. In this extract from *Alice's Adventures in Wonderland*, of particular interest from an Oulipian perspective is Carroll's parody of Isaac Watts' poem 'Against Idleness and Mischief', where Carroll inverts the sense of his source text in a way that anticipates Oulipo's method of 'antonymic translation'. Watts' poem is reprinted in its entirety below:

> *How doth the little busy bee*
>   *Improve each shining hour,*
> *And gather honey all the day*
>   *From every opening flower!*
> *How skillfully she builds her cell!*
>   *How neat she spreads the wax!*
> *And labours hard to store it well*
>   *With the sweet food she makes.*
> *In works of labour or of skill,*
>   *I would be busy too;*
> *For Satan finds some mischief still*
>   *For idle hands to do.*
> *In books, or work, or healthful play,*
>   *Let my first years be passed,*
> *That I may give for every day*
>   *Some good account at last.*

18. First published in *New Observations #99: Oulipo,Oupeinpo*, January/February 1994, edited by Harry Mathews and Lynn Crawford, a landmark publication for the dissemination of Oulipian ideas in the US.

25. In this late text, Queneau replaces the words 'point', 'line' and 'plane' in David Hilbert's 'Foundations of Mathematics' of 1927, with the words 'word', 'sentence' and 'paragraph'. Hilbert, a leading mathematician of his day, was one of the key influences on Bourbaki.

27. Marcel Duchamp's female alter-ego Rrose Sélavy (*'Éros, c'est la vie'*), to whom he attributed numerous works of art, including the palindromic *Anémic Cinéma* of 1925, spoke in enigmatic spooneristic poetic tongue-twisters, which Duchamp invented for her. This series of texts written in the same manner by Desnos under hypnosis, continues and expands the Sélavy corpus, and became one of the key texts of Surrealism. Numbering has been altered for this selection.

29. In *One Aphorism Can Hide Another* (*Bibliothèque Oulipienne 13*) Marcel Bénabou dissects aphorisms into their underlying formulas, such as 'X is the continuation of Y by other means', then creates lists of word pairs, such as false synonyms (love and friendship), and antonyms (science and ignorance). By combining these formulas systematically with the lists of word pairs, he is able to generate an almost limitless supply of new aphorisms.

36. A key chapter in *Life A User's Manual*, describing scenes from the work of the painter Valène, whose great work itself is a *mise-en-abîme* of Perec's novel. Here, Perec employed a number of additional constraints and superconstraints. Reading from top right to bottom left of the compendium, Perec inscribed in the manner of an acrostic the keyword *'âme'* (soul), for which translator David Bellos has substituted the word 'ego'. Each of the individual descriptions, moreover, consists of 60 characters, including spaces, except for two, which consist of 59 characters, in lines 45 and 94. In 45 this is aesthetically motivated, as the character is literally truncated, while in 94 the motivation, if any, is less clear – it may well be that Perec simply made a mistake. This is the only fully correct implementation of Perec's great acrostic in English.

44. 'Their words', here, refers to proverbs, from the vocabulary of which Mathews' text is constructed in its entirety, as are the other pieces in his *Selected Declarations of Dependence* where this story first appeared. Originally published by Z Press in 1977, four years after Mathews co-option by the Oulipo, this, alongside Mathews' *Trial Impressions* published in the same year, was one of the first explicitly Oulipian publications in the US.

45. Arranged alphabetically, Dan Rhodes' book of love stories consists of 101 stories in total, each consisting of 101 words.

51. A video poem consisting of two interlinked elementary moralities, from different points of view. In the video version, which occupies a single frame, the poems appear one after the other before meshing.

53. This light poem, like all the poems in Mac Low's book, is constructed by selecting its contents according to chance procedures – it contains only light names beginning with the letters in 'Carol Bergé' – from a vast 20x14 grid containing 280 possible forms of light, reminiscent of the lists and grids and diagrams underpinning Perec's *Life A User's Manual*.

55. First published in 1977, something of an annus mirabilis for Oulipian works in England and the US, Middleton's *Pataxanadu* is one of the earliest experiments with the N+7 method in English, though as with many English language uses of the method, he goes his own way with it. As Middleton explains in his preface: 'Most of the main parts of speech in the text chosen . . . are replaced by the same parts of speech, but by different words, found at a mathematically regulated remove either backwards or forwards in the biggest available dictionary. Each text conforms to whichever digital system was worked out during transformation of the first two or three sentences.'

59. 'Inner crawdad buzz': The poem translates homophonically the story from Queneau's *Exercises in Style*.

66. Functioning like a 'snapshot', in French Métail's poetic form has fifteen characters per line and ten lines, obliquely evoking the English sonnet form, with its fourteen ten syllable lines.

67. 'The Lambent Itch of Innuendo': The poem's source text is W. B.Yeats' 'The Lake Isle of Innisfree', Over freely combining N+7 with homophonic elements.

68. '... this moment thus acquires an almost solemn dimension': The moment Roubaud refers to is the interruption of a lecture on mathematics delivered by Professor Choquet at the École Normale Supérieure, in 1954, where Choquet had first introduced some ideas from Bourbaki.

71. This extract from *Graphemachine*, where Outranspo's Lily Robert-Foley translates words into shapes, shows how the words 'Lily', 'needs', 'adequate', 'room' and 'and' from the sentence 'Lily needs adequate room and produces spikes of brightly coloured flowers' are translated into gestures and subsequently shapes. The remaining words in the sentence are similarly translated eg. 'spikes' becomes 'raised hand', 'of' becomes 'hands to face'.

72. This is my own free translation of Queneau's foundational text, written to illustrate some of the translation methods created by the recently formed Outranspo (or Workshop of Potential Translation).

77. Written in a 500 word vocabulary borrowed entirely from the legal case *Gregson v. Gilbert*, which followed the murder by drowning of over 150 Africans on the slave ship *Zong*, Philip's text echoes a number of Oulipian experiments in constricted vocabularies, and employs a range of techniques, such as whiting and/or blacking out words, fragmentation and reversal. As Michael Leong writes: 'Technically speaking, this is what the Oupeinpo ... calls "*reassemblage*," which is a collage in which "the fragments assembled all come from the same source".' (Michael Leong, 'Oulipo, Foulipo, Noulipo: The Gendered Politics of Literary Constraints', in G.N. Forester and H. J. Nicholls, eds., *The Oulipo* (Singapore: Verbivoracious Press, 2017), p. 121–2.

80. At first sight Perec's *W or The Memory of Childhood* appears to be one of his least Oulipian texts, but as with all Perec's work, if you look closely you can see constraints at work. For one thing, it was written in

installments, for the *Quinzaine littéraire*, and it has 37 chapters, a number which had special significance for Perec, as he turned 37 on the 7–3–73. Perhaps most importantly of all, its structure resembles a Möbius strip, as the two key strands of the text, the autobiographical narrative and the story of the island off the coast of Tierra del Fuego dedicated to the Olympic 'ideal', gradually, and with an increasing sense of shock for the reader, turn out to be telling the same story of the Holocaust.

81. A leading writer among the Language poets, Lyn Hejinian's *My Life*, which has been through several editions, employs a simple constraint, whereby the number of sentences in each of the impressionistic chapters is determined by the age of the author at the time of writing. In its attention to the banal minutiae of the everyday, Hejinian's aesthetic also closely resembles Perec's interest in the '*infra-ordinaire*', as in his *I Remember*. This extract is taken from the 2002 edition, published by Green Integer.

85. A work that can be folded in multiple ways, reminiscent of Queneau's *A Hundred Thousand Billiion Poems*.

86. Here, land artist Richard Long applies Queneau's method from *A Hundred Thousand Billion Poems* to a series of 78 photographs of Dartmoor, creating 78^3 combinatorial photographs.

90. As Jenks writes in his preface: 'This book is a human-machine collaboration and implements a procedure known as Rogetification, where a source text is transformed using a thesaurus. In this case, an electronic copy of Roget's thesaurus was put into a spreadsheet form alongside a copy of *The Book of Genesis*, also in spreadsheet form. Formulae generating random numbers and look up tables were then used to swap words in *The Book of Genesis* for synonyms found in Roget's thesaurus.'

94. Roussel's story is constructed around two near-untranslatable homophonically punning phrases in the first and last sentences: '*La peau verdâtre de la prune un peu mûre . . .*' ('The greenish skin of the overripe

plum . . . ') and '*La peau verdâtre de la brune un peu mûre.*' ('The greenish skin of the brunette past her prime.').

97. Griffiths' libretto, like his novel of the same title, uses only the vocabulary given by Shakespeare to Ophelia in *Hamlet*.

Index of Constraints

Acrostic, 35, 36.

Algol poem, 54 (*high-relief plaque*). Invented by Noël Arnaud, the poems use only the limited vocabulary of the computer language Algol.

Alphabetical, 1 (01), 28, 35, 45, 48, 83, 95, 96, 100.

Anagram, 1 (02), 6, 33.

Antonymic translation, 1 (12, 20), 6, 14, 61.

Beau présent, 59. Literally 'beautiful present', the form is a variation of the lipogram often used for epithalamia or dedicatory poems, and uses only the letters in the name(s) of the dedicatee(s).

Bibina (or *didina*), 54 (*wood painted white*). Level-2 *quenina* (see *Sestina*).

Bifurcation, 17, 20, 30 (xiii), 68, 87.

Chimaera, 30 (vii). Text in which nouns, verbs and adjectives are replaced by words taken from other texts.

Combinatorics, 2, 3, 8, 16, 20, 29, 31, 69, 85, 86.

Constraint of gender non-specificity, 24. A variant of the lipogram where gender markers are left out.

Constraint of lexicon, 22, 44, 53, 77, 97.

Constraint of time, 15, 41, 73, 81, 88.

Corpuscular poem, 54 (*three-pointed stone*). Invented by Michèle Métail. A Minimalist tercet: three words with the same root per line (noun, adjective, and verb, in any order).

Countertranslation, 72. Invented by Outranspo. Translation written against another of the same text.

Curtal sonnet, 54 (*from the East*). Ten-line sonnet form invented by Gerard Manley Hopkins.

Definitional, 6, 13.

Ekphrasotranslation, 72. Invented by Outranspo. Replaces word or expression by description.

Elementary morality, 50, 51, 54 (codex-*style*), 62. Form invented by Raymond Queneau in *Morale élémentaire* (*Elementary Morality*), also known as the *quennet* or *lipolepse*.

Emphasis, 1 (13).

Flat sonnet, 99.

Fugue, 91.

Graphic translation, 71.

Heterogram, 54 (*whistle statue ii*). Invented by Georges Perec. The letters (the ten most frequently used in the French alphabet, plus one) cannot be used again before the whole series is completed.

Heterosyntaxism, 1 (33). A translation which changes the syntax of the source.

Homoconsonantism, 1 (29). A translation that retains the consonants, in order, of its source, replacing the vowels.

Homophonic translation, 1 (31), 6, 27, 42, 59, 61, 94, 95.

Homosemantic translation, 72. A translation which remains semantically close to its source text, but which otherwise departs from it freely.

Homovocalism, 1 (30). A translation that retains the vowels, in order, of its source, replacing the consonants.

I-Ching, 83.

Interference, 1 (24, 28).

Irrational sonnet, 54 (*dog-medium*). Invented by Jacques Bens based on the first five digits of the number π (3.1415, whose sum is 14). The π numbers determine the stanza length in the sonnet.

Isomorphism, 1 (25). Sentences which maintain an exact correspondence as regards the number of constituent elements and the relations between them.

Kick-start, 7, 10, 38, 47, 65, 67, 89. *Texte à démarreur* in French, the form uses a repeated opening phrase.

Larding, 1 (11, 21), 30 (III). Referred to by Oulipo as *tireur à la ligne* (literally 'puller on the line') this refers to the expansion of a text by the insertion of new sections.

Lexical substitution, 25.

Lipogram, 1 (3, 4, 5, 6), 6, 11, 12, 100. Text written without the use of one or more letters. (See also *Beau présent* and *Monovocalism*.)

List, 7, 10, 15, 19, 26, 27, 28, 36, 38, 47, 48, 53, 65, 69, 79, 82, 84, 89, 92, 100.

Mathematical, 6, 10, 14, 18, 25, 26, 36, 45, 48, 66, 79, 80, 81, 96.

Melting snowball, 10, 74, 75. Form in which each segment of a text is one letter, syllable, word etc. shorter than the segment preceding it. Also known as rhopalic verse.

Micro-narrative, 6, 15, 36, 37, 45, 95.

Minimal variation, 1 (19).

Möbius strip, 80.

Monovocalism, 4, 23. Text using only one vowel, consequently a lipogram in all the other vowels.

Multitranslation, 72. Invented by Outranspo. Offers multiple translations of the same word.

N+7 (see *W ± n*).

Octina, 10. Level-8 *quenina* (see *Sestina*).

Olfactory constraint, 6, 76.

One-word poem, Introduction (xx).

Onomometrical portrait, 18. A portrait the proportions of which are determined by the letters making up the name of the subject, where A=1, B=2 etc.

Palindrome, 1 (08), 30 (xxiv), 49, 92.

Pangram, 43. Text using all the letters of the alphabet, once only.

Permutation, 1 (23).

Plus seven seconds, 40.

Quasitranslation, 72. Invented by Outranspo. Deliberately impartial and incomplete translation.

Reductive, 1 (22).

Rainbow, 10.

Reassemblage, 77.

Rogetification, 90.

Scholiotranslation, 72. Invented by Outranspo. A translation that describes that which happens in the original text.

Sestanagramina, 33. Form of the sestina in which each line is an anagram of the first line.

Sestina, 30 (xxx), 32, 33, 52. Form based on the permutation of six end-words invented by the troubadour Arnaut Daniel. Raymond Queneau demonstrated that this permutational property holds true for other numbers as well, naming the generalized form the *quenina*. Oulipo have subsequently proposed a method to extend the *quenina* (or *n-ina*) to any value of *n*.

Slenderizing, 1 (9, 10, 14, 15, 16), 9, 11, 21, 70, 84. Referred to also as *coupeur à la ligne* (literally 'cutter of the line'), erasure, redundancy, and curtailing, the method usually involves the removal of parts of a text to create a new verbal object.

Small box, 54 (*king*). Invented by Jacques Jouet. The 'boxed' word in line 4 is the only representative of its grammatical category. The lines measure, in syllables, 778?87. The whole text is a single sentence.

Snowball, 1 (32), 10, 74, 75. Form in which each segment of a text is one letter, syllable, word etc. longer than the segment preceding it. Also known as rhopalic verse.

Spoonerism, 27.

Tactile constraint, 6.

Tanka, 6, 54 (*warrior?*). Japanese poem of five lines, consisting of a *haiku* (5, 7, 5 syllables) and a heptasyllabic distich.

Terine, 54 (*piece of a drum*), 63. Level-3 *quenina* (see *Sestina*).

Topographical constraint, 10, 17, 36, 46, 63, 66, 69, 73, 86, 100.

Triple contradiction, 1 (17).

Tube poem, 54 (*effigy*). Invented by Jacques Jouet. Line 1 is composed between the first and second stops, and written when the tube is at a standstill. And so on. A change of line involves a new stanza.

Up to date, 30 (II).

Variation, 1, 6, 19, 20, 30, 39, 46, 56, 57, 58, 72, 93.

Visual constraint, 6, 34, 36, 72.

Watermark, 54 (*mask II*). Invented by Michèle Métail: a monostich revolving around a word that does not appear except by implication.

W ± n, 1 (07), 6, 30 (XII), 41, 55, 59, 60, 61.

X takes Y for Z, 98.

Zenotranslation, 72. Invented by Outranspo. Each in a series of translations is half as long as its source.

Acknowledgements

This book would not have come into being without Simon Winder, who invited me out of the blue in February 2018 to curate an Oulipo anthology – to which I said yes, without a moment's hesitation. I am indebted to David Bellos, Lee Ann Brown, and Alastair Brotchie who made many useful suggestions at an early stage of this work, in particular David Bellos, who supplied a new translation of Chapter fifty-one of *Life A User's Manual* where Perec's constraints are fully implemented for the first time. Thanks are also due to the many friends and publishers who have been unstinting in their support, supplying a host of books, poems, unpublished translations, and suggestions, among them Luke Allan, Tim Atkins, Guy Bennet, Miles Champion, James Davies, Ollie Evans, Jem Finer, Harry Gilonis, Jesse Glasse, Paul Griffiths, Richard Hoadley, Tom Jenks, Roger Malbert, Peter Manson, Gale Nelson, John O'Brien, Richard Parker, Holly Pester, Lily Robert-Foley, Michael Schmidt, Cole Swensen, Rosmarie Waldrop, and Marina Warner. Technical constraints meant that I was not able to include everything that I read, but all of this helped to broaden and enrich my understanding of Oulipo, which inevitably stretches far beyond the covers of this book. Many Oulipians have helped me with their encouragement over the years, especially Paul Fournel, Ian Monk, Harry Mathews, Stanley Chapman and Olivier Salon. I am indebted to Ian Monk in particular for asking me to attend an Oulipo reunion in December 2018 as an *invité d'honneur*, which gave me a unique insight into the vibrant workings of Oulipo. Thanks are also due to Rachel Thorne for all her help in dealing with the permissions for this book. Last but not least, I owe a huge debt to my editors at Penguin, Simon Winder, Ellen Davies and Rebecca Lee, whose endless enthusiasm, critical insight, practical know-how, and constant support have been invaluable in bringing this book to fruition.

Permission Credits

We are grateful to the following for permission to reproduce copyright material:

1. Harry Mathews from *35 Variations on a Theme from Shakespeare*, Atlas Press, 1998. Reproduced by permission of the Estate of the author.

3. Raymond Queneau *A Hundred Thousand Billion Poems*, translated by Stanley Chapman. First published as *Cent mille milliards de poèmes* in *Prospice 8*, 1978, copyright © Editions Gallimard, Paris, 1961. Reproduced courtesy of the Estate of Stanley Chapman and Editions Gallimard.

5. Warren F. Motte, Jr., for 'Lipo: First Manifesto' from *Oulipo: A Primer of Potential Literature*, copyright © The University of Nebraska Press, 1986. Reproduced by permission of the University of Nebraska Press and Dalkey Archive Press.

6. Raymond Queneau from *Exercises in Style*, copyright © 1947, 1958 by Editions Gallimard. Reprinted by permission of Alma Books.

7. Joe Brainard from *I Remember*, Notting Hill Editions 2012, copyright © The Estate of Joe Brainard, 2001. All rights reserved.

8. Italo Calvino for 'The Waverer's Tale' from *The Castle of Crossed Destinies*, copyright © The Estate of Italo Calvino, 2002. Used by permission of The Wylie Agency (UK) Limited.

9. Paul Fournel for *Suburbia* translated by Harry Mathews, from *Oulipo Laboratory*, Atlas Press, 1995. Reproduced by permission of Atlas Press, Paul Fournel and the Estate for the translator.

21. Raymond Queneau from 'Redundancy in Phane Armé' translated by Philip Terry, from *Exercices de littérature potentielle*.

22. Jacques Jouet for *The Great-Ape Love-Song* translated by Iain White, from *Oulipo Laboratory*, Atlas Press 1995. Reproduced by permission of Atlas Press and Paul Fournel.

23. Christian Bök from *Eunoia*, Coach House Books, copyright © Christian Bök, 2001. Reprinted with permission of Canongate Books Ltd.

24. Anne Garréta from *Sphinx*, translated by Emma Ramadan, Deep Vellum Publishing, 2015. Reproduced with permission.

25. Raymond Queneau for *The Foundations of Literature – after David Hilbert*, translated by Harry Mathews, from *Oulipo Laboratory*, Atlas Press, 1995. Reproduced by permission of Atlas Press, Paul Fournel and the Estate for the translator.

26. Michèle Audin from *One Hundred Twenty-One Days*, translated by Christiana Hills, Deep Vellum Publishing, 2016. Reproduced with permission.

27. Robert Desnos for 'Rrose Sélavy' translated by Timothy Adès, from *Surrealist, Lover, Resistant*, Arc Publications, 2017. Reproduced with permission.

28. Georges Perec for 'Think/Classify' translated by John Sturrock, from *Species of Spaces and Other Pieces*, Penguin 1997. Reproduced by permission of Penguin Books Ltd.

29. Marcel Bénabou from *One Aphorism Can Hide Another*, translated by Philip Terry. Reproduced by permission of Paul Fournel.

30. Harry Matthews from *Trial Impressions*, Carcanet, 1992. Reproduced by permission of the Estate of the author.

41. Harryette Mullen for 'Variations on a Theme Park' from *Sleeping with the Dictionary*, University of California Press, 2002. Permission conveyed through Copyright Clearance Center, Inc.

42. François Le Lionnais for 'Second Manifesto' translated by Warren F. Motte Jr, from *Oulipo: A Primer of Potential Literature*, copyright © The University of Nebraska Press, 1986. Reproduced by permission of the University of Nebraska Press and Dalkey Archive Press.

43. Ian Monk for 'Spies in Newquay' from *Writings for the Oulipo*, Make Now Books, 2006. Reproduced by permission.

44. Harry Mathews for 'Their Words For You', published in *The Way Home*, Atlas Press, 1989. Reproduced by permission of the Estate of the author.

45. Dan Rhodes from *Anthropology and a hundred other stories*, Fourth Estate, 2000. Reproduced by permission of the author.

46. Italo Calvino from *Invisible Cities*, copyright © The Estate of Italo Calvino, 2002. Used by permission of The Wylie Agency (UK) Limited.

47. Harry Matthews for *The Orchard*, Atlas Press, 1989. Reproduced by permission of the Estate of the author.

49. Yin Zhongkan, for 'Reversible Inscription' translated from Chinese into French by Michèle Métail from *Le Vol des oies sauvages: Poèmes chinois à la lecture retournée*, Tarabuste 2011; and translated into English by Jody Gladding in *Wild Geese Returning* New York Review Books, 2017. Reproduced by permission of Jody Gladding.

50. Raymond Queneau from *Elementary Morality*, translated by Philip Terry, Carcanet Press Limited, 2007. Reproduced with permission.

51. Valerie Beudoin for 'Corps/Machine' from *Oulipo: L'abécédaire provisoirement définitif*, Larousse, 2014. Reproduced by permission of the author.

52. Jacques Roubaud from *Exchanges On Light*, translated by Eleni Sike-lianos, La Presse/Fence Books, 2009. Reproduced by permission of Professor Cole Swensen.

53. Jackson Mac Low for '6th Light Poem: For Carol Berge - 14 June 1962' from *The Complete Light Poems*, Chax Press, 2015. Reproduced by permission of the Estate of the author.

54. Frédéric Forte for *Minute-Operas*, translated by Ian Monk and Daniel Levin Becker, Burning Deck Press, 2015. Reproduced with permission.

55. Christopher Middleton from *Pataxanadu*, Carcanet Press Limited, 1977. Reproduced with permission.

56. Georges Perec for *A Winter Journey* from *Collection La Librairie du XXIe siècle, sous la direction de Maurice Olender,* first published in French as *Le Voyage d'hiver*, copyright © Editions du Seuil, 1993. Reproduced with permission.

57. François Caradec for *The Worm's Journey* translated by Ian Monk, from *Winter Journeys*, Atlas Press, 2013. Reproduced by permission of Atlas Press and Paul Fournel.

58. Hugo Vernier for *Hell's Journey* translated by Ian Monk, from *Winter Journeys*, Atlas Press, 2013. Reproduced by permission of Atlas Press and Paul Fournel.

59. Lee Ann Brown for 'Pledge', 'A Present Beau Epithalmium' and 'Inner crawdad buzz' with Lisa Jarnot, from *Polyverse*, Sun and Moon Press, 1999. Reproduced by permission of the author.

60. Bernadette Mayer for 'Before Sextet' and 'After Sextet' from *The Noulipian Analects*, Les Figues Press, 2007. Reproduced by permission of the author.

61. Jeremy Over for 'The Lambent Itch of Innuendo' from *Deceiving Wild Creatures*, Carcanet Press Limited, 2009. Reproduced with permission.

62. Robert Sheppard from *A Translated Man*, Shearsman Books, Bristol, 2013. Reproduced by permission.

63. Rachel Galvin for 'American Terines' from *Terines*, Bibliothèque Oulipienne. Reproduced by permission of the author and Paul Fournel.

64. Jacques Roubaud for 'Is Le Pen French,' translated by Guy Bennett, from *Poetry, etcetera: Cleaning House*, copyright © 1995 by Éditions Stock. English translation copyright © 2005 by Guy Bennett. Reprinted with the permission of The Permissions Company, LLC on behalf of Green Integer, www.greeninteger.com.

65. Hervé Le Tellier from *A Thousand Pearls (For A Thousand Pennies)*, translated by Ian Monk, Dalkey Archive Press 2011. Reproduced by permission.

66. Michèle Métail from *Toponym: Berlin*, translated by Susan Wicks, Poetry International, 2013. Reproduced by permission of the translator.

67. Étienne Lécroart artwork from *Vanity*, copyright © Étienne Lécroart and L'Association, 2017. Reproduced with permission.

68. Jacques Roubaud from *Mathematics*, translated by Ian Monk, Dalkey Archive Press 2012. Reproduced by permission.

70. Juliana Spahr for 'HR 4811 is a joke'. Originally published in *The Noulipian Analects* by Juliana Spahr, Les Figues Press, an imprint of LARB Books, 2007. Reproduced by permission.

71. Lily Robert-Foley for graphics from *Graphemachine*, Xexoxial Editions (coll. Xerolage), 2013. Reproduced by permission of the author.

73. Georges Perec from *Memory of a trip to Thouars*, cahiers Georges Perec, P.O.L 1985, copyright © Indivision Richardson Saluden.

75. Richard Beard from *Lazarus is Dead*, Harvill Secker, copyright © 2011. Reprinted by permission of The Random House Group Limited.

76. Italo Calvino for 'The Name, The Nose' from *Under The Jaguar Sun*, copyright © The Estate of Italo Calvino, 2002. Used by permission of The Wylie Agency (UK) Limited.

77. M. NourbeSe Philip for 'Zong! #6,' 'Zong! #7,' and 'Zong! #8' from *Zong!*, Wesleyan University Press, copyright © 2008. Reprinted with permission, www.wesleyan.edu/wespress.

78. Jacques Roubaud for 'Saying Poetry' translated by Matthew B. Smith, from *Dors précédé de Dire la poésie*, copyright © Editions Gallimard, Paris, 1981. Reproduced with permission of Gallimard and Professor Cole Swensen.

79. Italo Calvino from *If On a Winter's Night A Traveller*, copyright © The Estate of Italo Calvino, 2002. Used by permission of The Wylie Agency (UK) Limited.

80. Georges Perec from *W or The Memory of Childhood*, translated by David Bellos, Harvill Press, copyright © Éditions Denoël, 1975, 1996. Reprinted by permission of The Random House Group Limited and Denoël.

81. Lyn Hejinian from *My Life*, Burning Deck Press, 1980. Reproduced with permission.

82. Homer from *The Iliad*, translated by Robert Fagles, copyright © Robert Fagles 1990. Used by permission of Viking Books, an imprint of Penguin Publishing Group, a division of Penguin Random House LLC. All rights reserved.

83. Raymond Queneau from *Elementary Morality*, translated by Philip Terry, Carcanet Press Limited, 2007. Reproduced with permission.

84. Alice Oswald from *Memorial*, Faber and Faber Ltd, 2011. Reproduced by permission.

86. Richard Long artwork from *Dartmoor*, copyright © Richard Long. All Rights Reserved, DACS 2019.

87. Raymond Queneau for 'A Tale For Your Shaping', translated by Harry Gilonis, first published in *EONTA*, Vol. 2 (1), 1993/94. Reproduced by permission of the author, Harry Gilonis with thanks to EONTA Magazine.

88. Anne Garréta from *Not One Day*, translated by Emma Ramadan, Deep Vellum Publishing, 2017. Reproduced with permission.

89. Gilbert Adair for 'Memories' from *Myths and Memories*, 1986, copyright © The Estate of Gilbert Adair. Reproduced by permission of Blake Friedmann.

90. Tom Jenks from *The Tome of Commencement*, Stranger Press, 2014. Reproduced by permission of the author.

91. Olivier Salon for 'We Are Alone' from *Fugues*, Bibliotheque Oulipenne. Reproduced by permission of Paul Fournel.

92. Édouard Levé from *Works*, translated by Jan Steyn, Dalkey Archive Press 2014. Reproduced by permission.

93. Jacques Carelman from *Exercises in Style*, 1962. Reproduced by permission of The Estate of the author.

94. Raymond Roussel from *How I Wrote Some of My Books*, translated by Philip Terry.